THE MOTHER LOAD

# THE MAD BATHROOM COMPANION

## THE MOTHER LOAD

**By "The Usual Gang of Idiots"**

Edited by John Ficarra and Nick Meglin

Introductions by
Trey Parker, Gene Shalit, and Gilbert Gottfried

FALL
RIVER
PRESS

This 2004 edition published by Fall River Press, by arrangement with *MAD* Books.

Cover art by Mark Fredrickson
Cover design by *MAD* Magazine

Fall River Press
122 Fifth Avenue
New York, NY 10011

ISBN: 978-0-7607-6345-2

Printed and bound in the United States of America

First Edition

20  19  18  17  16  15  14  13  12  11  10  9  8

Visit *MAD* online at: www.madmag.com

Though Alfred E. Neuman wasn't the first to say, "A fool and his money are soon
parted," here's your chance to prove the old adage right—subscribe to *MAD*!
Simply call 1-800-4-MADMAG and mention code 5MBC9. Operators are standing by
(the water cooler).

# THE MAD BATHROOM COMPANION

## By "The Usual Gang of Idiots"

**Edited by Nick Meglin & John Ficarra**

**Introduction by Trey Parker**

# Introduction

I was thrilled when *MAD* Magazine, one of the most important magazines of the twentieth century, asked me to write the introduction to their Bathroom Companion. It seems like more and more that when people think of poo, they think of me.

I started reading *MAD* when I was eight years old. I was an impressionable child, with a mind that was pure like morning snow. I had dreams of growing up to be an astronaut or a scientist. Reading *MAD* changed all that, however, and now I make cartoons with anal probes and Barbra Streisand monsters.

What I learned from *MAD*, is that anything that becomes too "cool" or too popular in our culture must be destroyed. Usually while everyone was singing something's praises, *MAD* was knocking it down. When I was a kid and everyone loved *Star Wars*, they made fun of *Star Wars*. When everyone started liking Jordache jeans, they made fun of that too. Anything that become cool in the country's eye was an open target for *MAD* Magazine, and that's what made it so great then—and what still makes it so great today. Why, I even opened a *MAD* Magazine last year and saw that they were making fun of *South Park*. But this, of course, was not great; it was juvenile, thoughtless, mindless crap, and if the *MAD* people ever do it again I will kick all their asses.

But enough about *MAD*, and enough about me. It is time to focus on your task at hand.

This book was meant to be used as a companion to pooping, and if you are using this book as it was intended, you are now seated on the toilet, as you have been countless other times. But did you know that right now, as you are pooping, an estimated *2.3 million* people around the world are pooping too? That's right, from Japan to Germany, Israel to Canada, people of all races and ethnicities are doing *exactly* what you're doing right now. Isn't that beautiful? Pooping is the common bond that unites us all; it is what makes us one.

Even more wonderful than the fact that people all around the world poop, is the fact that nobody can go without pooping. No matter how rich somebody is, or how famous or how sexy or beautiful, everyone has to put in time on the porcelain. Even Jennifer Lopez poops. Think about that. Go on, visualize Jennifer Lopez pooping for one second. That's it... Good.

What still puzzles me, though, is that if pooping is such a world-uniting, culture-crossing, and wonderful thing, why is it still so shrouded in silence and embarrassment? Why don't people talk more freely about their various bathroom habits and pleasures?

For example, most women do not realize that men often like to pretend they are giving birth when they poop. That's right. The truth is, we men are somewhat jealous that we can't have babies, and our potty time is the only time for us to fantasize. Men will try to deny it, but the fact remains that almost all men, at some point in their lives, have sat on the toilet doing breathing exercises, and waiting for the joyous moment to arrive so they can shout, *"It's a girl!"* and then name her something cute before flushing her away forever.

And most men would be surprised to know that women usually like to play a game called Bombs Away in the bathroom. They fill the toilet bowl with small cardboard ships that they have spent hours beforehand creating. Then, instead of sitting on the toilet, they stand on the rim, and the fun begins as they see how many Japanese D-42s they can sink.

Pooping is not about nastiness or vulgarity; pooping is about fun. Toilet time is precious time, not only for birthing fantasies and war games, but also for reading fine books like this one, or for reflecting on memories past, or even...for pondering our own reality and deep metaphysical inner self. And so, as you dive deeper into this eloquent collection, and continue with your toilet time, do not ask yourself what the nutritionist would ask: "What am I pooping?" Ask yourself the question the Zen Buddhist would ask: "What is it that is pooping?"

Howdy Ho!

**—Trey Park**

# ONE FAIRLY NICE DAY DOWNTOWN

### RULE # 1

Be helpful despite one's own problems

# MAD'S 14
# GOOD B

ARTIST: PAUL COKER

### RULE # 3

Show regard for the possessions of others.

### RULE # 4

Bolster the spirits of the ailing.

### RULE # 5

Give comfort to those facing hardship.

### RULE # 9

Be sensitive to the sad and downhearted.

### RULE # 10

Give helpful advice to the troubled.

### RULE # 11

Be tolerant of the mistakes of others.

# RULES OF EHAVIOR

WRITER: FRANK JACOBS

### RULE # 6
Maintain a positive outlook in times of crisis.

### RULE # 7
Be gracious in victory...

### RULE # 8
...and also in defeat.

### RULE # 12
Be courteous in times of stress.

### RULE # 13
Display good manners on all occasions.

### RULE # 14
Show compassion for the less fortunate.

What with the recent drug scandals rocking the baseball world, it's time to revise that grand old song, "Take Me Out to the Ball Game." So sing along, sports fans, as Mad presents...

# ZONK ME OUT AT THE BALL GAME

ARTIST: AL JAFFEE    WRITER: FRANK JACOBS
IDEA BY: JOHN AMBROSIO

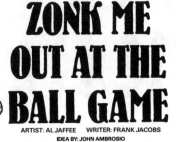

Zonk me out at the ball-game—
Zonk me out with co-caine!
I've got a gram in my catch-er's mitt—
Grab...a...straw and we'll all take a hit!
So let's toot, toot, toot in the club-house—
If you're...not high, that's a shame!
For it's one, two, three snorts—
    Get stoned!
**It's a new...ball...game!**

Zonk me out at the ball-game—
Zonk me out of my skull!
I've got a dealer who treats...me nice—
Highs...cost...high, but it's sure worth the price!
So let's toot, toot, toot in the bull-pen—
Hell, win...or lose, it's the same!
For it's one, two, three snorts—
    You're hooked!
**It's a new...ball...game!**

Zonk me out at the ball-game—
Zonk me till we get caught!
I'll tell the league that my nose...is clean,
Help...them...clean up the whole rotten scene,
'Cause I'll rat, rat, rat on my team-mates!
Who cares...if they get the blame!
For it's one, two, three snorts—
    Sell out!
**It's a new...ball...game!**

Coke is it!

Jaffee

# DRAMA ON PAGE 15

WRITER AND ARTIST: JOHN CALDWELL

## Q-TIP HAT PIN

Keep your hat on and your ears clean! Stainless steel hat pin is the perfect addition to any wardrobe. Head of pin is covered with hand-spun cotton to safely clean your ears, cassette heads or navel!

## SHOELACE DENTAL FLOSS

Got something stuck between your teeth? Just pull out one of the strands of dental floss entwined in your shoe laces and get rid of the disgusting food particle! Approved by the American Dental Association!

## CAR DOOR LOCK-LIFTER EARRINGS

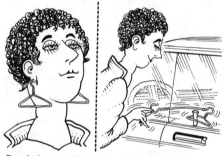

Ever lock yourself out of your car and not have an extra key? Simply attach the two telescoping metal earrings together and pop yourself back into the car!

Everything in this article serves a dual purpose, except this intro, which serves no purpose at all! If

# MAD'S DUA
# CLOT
# ACCES

ARTIST: AL JAFFEE

## SOMBRERO ORANGE JUICER

Hats off to this invention! What better way to keep the sun out of your eyes and vitamin "C" in your body! Just squeeze oranges on hardened steel top to make as many screwdrivers as needed on hot days!

## TOUPEE TEA COZY

Hot tea all day! This grooming accessory will keep your teapot steaming! Uniquely designed from human hair, fits most standard tea pots. Available in blonde, brunette, and silver blue for older folks.

## NAPKIN TIES

Tie stained? No problem! Just rip off another sheet and you're ready for a night on the town or that big meeting. Also handy if you run out of toilet paper!

## PEARL NECKLACE BIRTH CONTROL PILLS

Don't leave home without them! Convenient! Practical! Great for those mornings when you left the house in a rush! Also available: Diaphragm earmuffs.

you don't understand what this article is about just from the title, then you probably don't need...

# L PURPOSE
# HING
# SORIES

WRITER: MARK A. DRESSLER

## SUBWAY TOKEN CUFFLINKS

A must for any city dweller! With these decorative cufflinks you can get mugged and still take a subway home! Also available: matching token tie clip!

## CORN-ON-THE-COB FALSE FINGERNAIL SPEARS

Enjoy corn-on-the-cob without all the fuss and mess! Index fingernails have sharpened elongated tip to spear corn for carefree eating. Also great for cocktail parties when there aren't any toothpicks left!

## UNDERWIRE BRA ANTENNA

This sexy sporting accessory is really a powerful FM Antenna! Simply plug your Walkman into this specialized piece of underwear and you're all set! The bigger the cup size, the better the reception! Men—get the all-new Underwire Athletic Supporter!

# WRESTLING

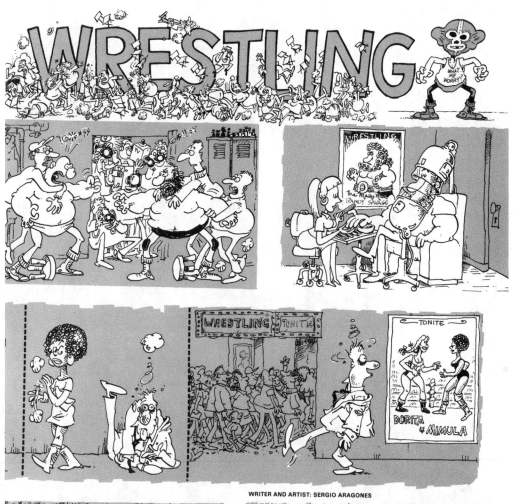

WRITER AND ARTIST: SERGIO ARAGONES

# IN THE OPERATING RO

# OM with DON MARTIN

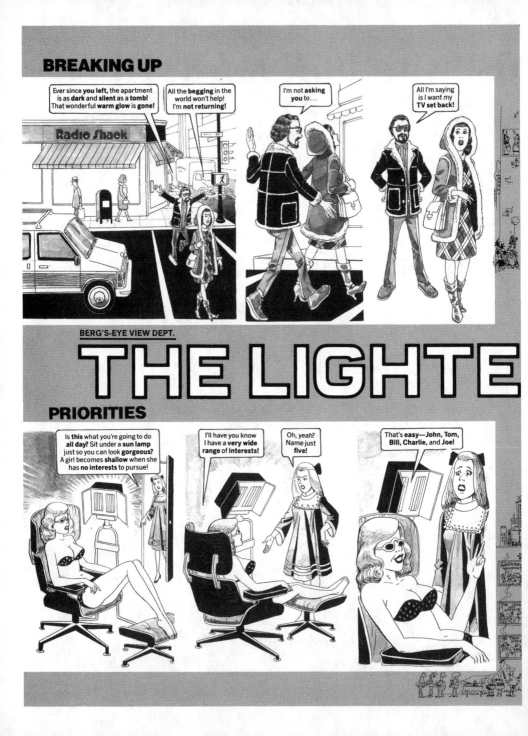

# R SIDE OF...

ARTIST & WRITER:
DAVE BERG

## TECHNOLOGY

It's an ugly world out there, what with wars and terrorists and muggers and all the rest. And it's time we prepared the kiddies by giving them the message as early as possible. Well, what better way to introduce them to the hard realities of life, than with Mad's...

## VIOLENT MOTHER GOOSE

ARTIST: JACK DAVIS        WRITER: FRANK JACOBS

## JACK SPRAT

Jack Sprat
Can swing his bat;
His wife can spray her mace;
He'll smack her hard
When she's off-guard;
She'll spritz him in the face.

Jack Sprat
Is knocked out flat,
His wife the worst of sights;
Though bitter foes,
At least it shows
They're into equal rights.

# THIS IS THE FILM THAT JACK MADE

This is the film that Jack made.

This is the girl who's blown away
who's in the film that Jack made.

This is the creep who stalks his prey,
Who blasts the girl who's blown away,
Who's in the film that Jack made.

This is the ax that splits the head
That's swung by the creep who stalks his prey,
Who blasts the girl who's blown away,
Who's in the film that Jack made.

This is the dude who winds up dead
From getting the ax that splits his head
That's swung by the creep who stalks his prey,
Who blasts the girl who's blown away,
Who's in the film that Jack made.

This is the salesman from Omaha,
Who calls on the dude who winds up dead
From getting the ax that splits his head
That's swung by the creep who blasts the
    girl who's in the film that Jack made.

This is the handy electric saw
That slices the salesman from Omaha,
Who calls on the dude who winds up dead
From getting the ax that splits his head
That's swung by the creep who blasts the
    girl who's in the film that Jack made.

This is the carnage of blood and gore
That's made by the handy electric saw
That slices the salesman from Omaha,
Who calls on the dude who gets the ax
    that's swung by the creep who blasts
    the girl who's in the film that Jack made.

These are the profits of bucks galore
That come from the carnage of blood and gore
That's made by the handy electric saw
That slices the salesman from Omaha,
Who follows the dude who gets the ax
    that's swung by the creep who blasts
    the girl who's in the film that Jack made.

# SING A SONG OF VIOLENCE

Sing a song of violence,
 Of punks and goons and thugs,
Of homicides and gang wars,
 Of corpses full of slugs.

If such atrocious doings
 Are not your cup of tea,
Well, tough, that's all you're getting
 Tonight on your TV.

# JACK BE NIMBLE

Jack be nimble;
 Jack be slick;
Jack meet mugger;
 Jack give kick.

Jack show quickness;
 Jack show skill;
Jack learn bullet
 Quicker still.

# OMAR HAD A LITTLE BOMB

Omar had a little bomb;
 He found it filled a need
For getting rid of all those folks
 With whom he disagreed.

Omar let his bomb go off
 Without the proper care;
And now we're finding little bits
 Of Omar ev'rywhere.

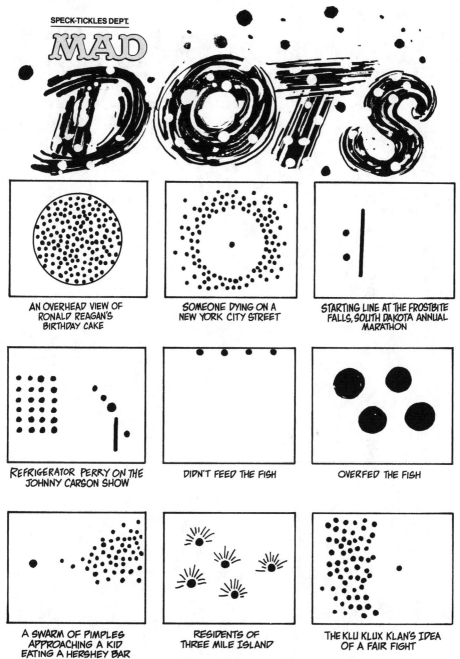

# MAD DOTS

AN OVERHEAD VIEW OF RONALD REAGAN'S BIRTHDAY CAKE

SOMEONE DYING ON A NEW YORK CITY STREET

STARTING LINE AT THE FROSTBITE FALLS, SOUTH DAKOTA ANNUAL MARATHON

REFRIGERATOR PERRY ON THE JOHNNY CARSON SHOW

DIDN'T FEED THE FISH

OVERFED THE FISH

A SWARM OF PIMPLES APPROACHING A KID EATING A HERSHEY BAR

RESIDENTS OF THREE MILE ISLAND

THE KLU KLUX KLAN'S IDEA OF A FAIR FIGHT

WRITER: MAT JACOBS

# AT THE BEDSIDE, *PART I*

ARTIST: HARRY NORTH   WRITER: CHARLIE KADAU

*In most states, renewing your driver's license is as easy as signing your name and enclosing a check. Simple, but what this procedure doesn't do is weed out unsafe drivers—motorists who have long since forgotten everything they had to learn in order to get their first license! How about you? Are your driving skills up to par? Or have you too become sloppy and careless behind the wheel! Spend a few minutes with this quiz and see:*

# are you a GOOD DRIVER ?

**BEGIN with the national speed limit of 55 miles per hour. ANSWER each question and add or subtract miles accordingly.**

## PART I—DRIVING HISTORY

**1)** If the statue of St. Christopher on your dashboard is on crutches, ADD 1 mile.

**2)** If you've ever received kickbacks from chiropractors for all the whiplash victims you send them, ADD 2 miles.

**3)** If Lee Iacocca has ever offered you a rebate *not* to buy a car, ADD 3 miles.

**4)** For each of the following that has been named in your honor, ADD accordingly:

   **a)** A tow truck, ADD 1 mile.

   **b)** A local demolition derby race track, ADD 2 miles.

   **c)** A national auto insurance company's "Extra High Risk Category," ADD 5 miles.

**5)** On the back of your driver's license where recent traffic violations are listed, if the words "See Attached Sheets" appear, ADD 2 miles.

**DRIVING HISTORY SUBTOTAL** . . . . . . . . . . . . . . . . . . . . . . . . . . . . . . _____

## PART II—ON THE ROAD

**1)** If you start each morning by pledging allegiance to a checkered flag, ADD 1 mile.

**2)** If your second car is an ambulance, ADD 2 miles.

**3)** If, while stopped at an intersection waiting for a red light to change, you...

   **a)** Rev your engine to intimidate those around you, ADD 1 mile.

   **b)** Place both hands on the horn, ready to blare it at senior citizens who might still be crossing when the light turns green, ADD 2 miles.

   **c)** Pick your nose, SUBTRACT 4 miles.

   **NOTE: If the above question does not apply to you because you never brake for a red light, ADD 5 miles.**

ARTIST: PAUL COKER

WRITER: JOHN PRETE

**4)** For every time you've looked in your rear-view mirror and seen a body lying in the street, ADD 2 miles. (If you've *never* looked in your rear-view mirror, ADD 4 miles.)

**5)** For each of the following bumper stickers that can be found on your car, ADD 1 mile:

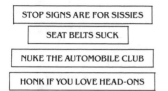

| |
|---|
| STOP SIGNS ARE FOR SISSIES |
| SEAT BELTS SUCK |
| NUKE THE AUTOMOBILE CLUB |
| HONK IF YOU LOVE HEAD-ONS |

**NOTE: If the message on your bumper sticker is incomprehensible because of blood splatterings and caked hair, TACK ON an additional 6 miles.**

**ON THE ROAD SUBTOTAL** ........................ _____

## PART III—HYPOTHETICAL SITUATIONS

**1)** It is a warm, sunny Sunday afternoon. You decide to jump in the car and visit your ailing Aunt Alba in the suburbs. Turning onto Aunt Alba's street, you pass a home for the blind, a "Deer Crossing" sign and a group of small children playing in the street. Which of the following comes closest in length to the skid marks you'll make as you pull up to Aunt Alba's?

   **a)** A standard 30-foot garden hose, ADD 2 miles.

   **b)** An unravelled wool sweater, ADD 5 miles.

   **c)** A computer printout of Joan Collins' ex-lovers, ADD 9 miles.

**2)** You're sitting over at a friend's home in a semi-conscious state after hours of heavy drinking. Suddenly, your friend announces "Everybody out!" Which of the following best describes what you would do in this situation?

   **a)** Stumble out to your car, spend 15 stupid minutes trying to insert your keys into the ignition, then finally peel out in a screeching blaze of glory, ADD 3 miles.

   **b)** Same as "a," except that you would take the time to throw up in your friend's driveway before you peel out, ADD 4 miles.

   **c)** If the question does not apply because you would have been involved in a drunk driving accident on your way *to* the party, ADD 7 miles.

**HYPOTHETICAL QUESTIONS SUBTOTAL** ........ _____

**GRAND TOTAL** ................................... _____

| S C O R I N G | **51—60** | **61—70** | **71 or Above** |
|---|---|---|---|
| | *Your driving skills are like those of a recent graduate of a high school Driver's Ed class. In other words, you have none! You are a threat to all life.* | *You have the driving skills of a deaf, dumb and blind man! Walk everywhere!!* | *You have a great future ahead of you as a New York City cab driver! Apply at once!* |

Back in MAD #234, we gave guys hints on "How To Pick Up Girls." Our mail response showed that liberated women of today want equal time when it comes to learning pick-up lines guaranteed to impress great hunks. So, ladies (and, ahem, certain gentlemen) we now present the following batch of ice-breakers, Your guide to...

# HOW TO PICK UP GUYS

## AT A FAST FOOD HANGOUT

Excuse me, can I take a bite out of your bun?

*OR*

Forget that silly contest card. Why don't you rub me with the edge of a quarter?

*OR*

"Have it your way" is my slogan, too!

TRY OUR HEIMLICH MEAT LOAF

CHUCK YEAGER SANDWICH

## AT A FOOTBALL GAME

That's me they're talking about in the huddle!

*OR*

Hi, my panties are made of Astroturf!

*OR*

I keep having this reoccuring dream that an entire football team tackles and lands on top of me. I wonder what it means?

I HATE FOOTBALL POSTERS MADE CHEAP

HOO U.

HI TECH

## AT A SKI RESORT

I forgot my gloves. is there anyplace I can put my hands to keep them warm?

*OR*

These stretch pants are something, aren't they? I often wonder if two people could get into one pair?

*OR*

Skiing all day is fun but what's to do all night?

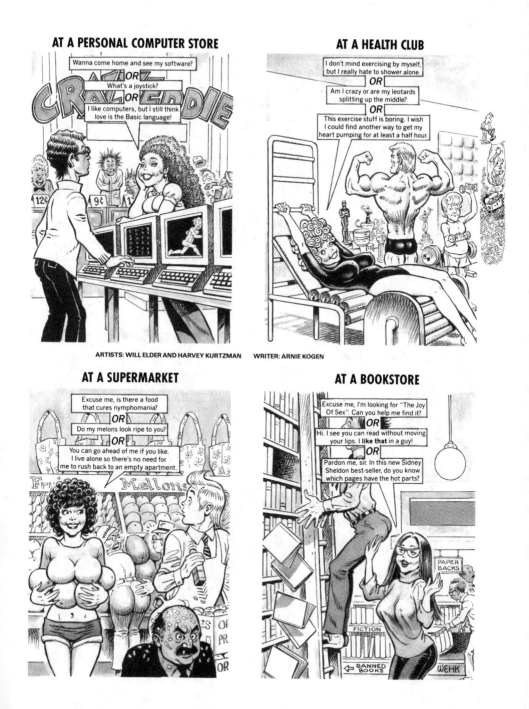

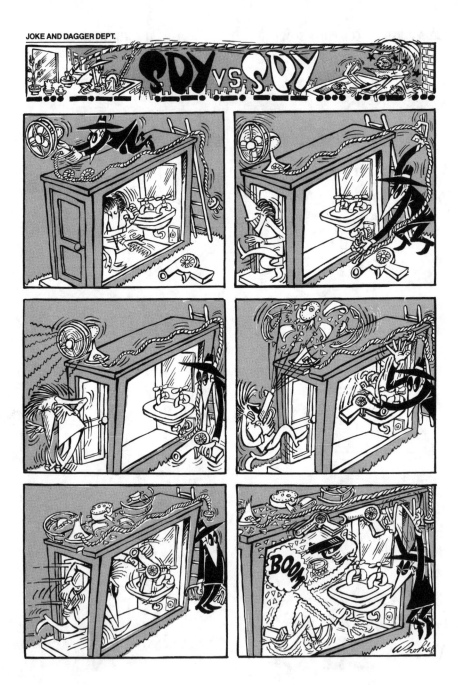

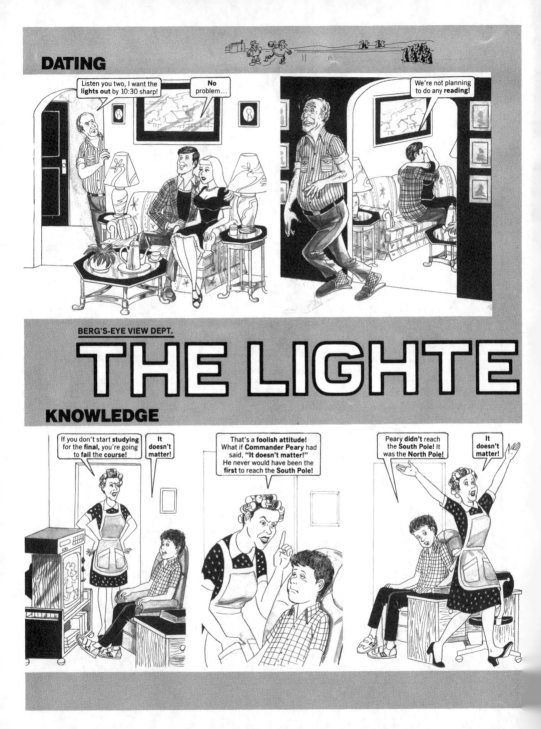

# HORRIFYING CRIME CLICHES...

ARTIST: PAUL COKER    WRITER: FRANK JACOBS

Packing A ROD

Committing A FELONY

Running A RACKET

Putting Out A CONTRACT

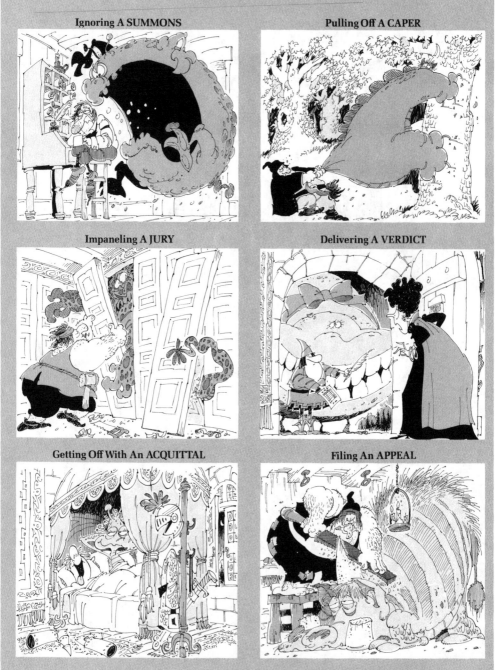

**Ignoring A SUMMONS**

**Pulling Off A CAPER**

**Impaneling A JURY**

**Delivering A VERDICT**

**Getting Off With An ACQUITTAL**

**Filing An APPEAL**

**Ducking A WARRANT**

**Copping A PLEA**

**Beating A RAP**

**Suspending A SENTENCE**

**Overturning A CONVICTION**

**Serving A STIFF TERM**

# THE THREE MILE ISLA

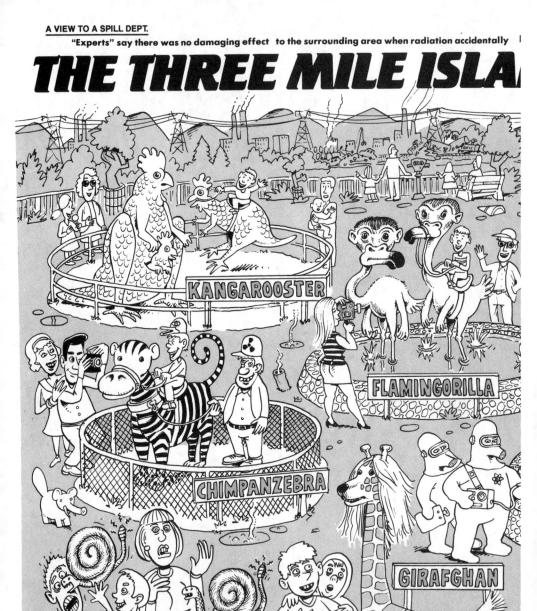

# ND CHILDREN'S ZOO

ARTIST AND WRITER: TOM HACHTMAN

**And now the sharp eyes of MAD take a long hard look at**

# Those Ridiculous *litt*

## TV COMMERCIALS SAY RIDICULOUS THINGS LIKE

*The Do-It-Yourself Emporium is conveniently located in the New Glitzy Mall near East Wuthering Heights.*

### THINKING ABOUT IT THIS MUST MEAN...

The location is "convenient" for everyone who lives in the part of East Wuthering Heights that's near the New Glitzy Mall. From 25 miles away it's a lot less convenient, but they hope you won't realize that until you're already on the road.

## TV COMMERCIALS SAY RIDICULOUS THINGS LIKE

*Dipsy-Cola is now available in handy six-packs at your favorite store.*

### THINKING ABOUT IT THIS MUST MEAN...

They're surely aware that exclusive clothing shops and jewelry salons don't sell soft drinks, so they obviously assume your favorite store is a crowded, smelly supermarket.

## TV COMMERCIALS SAY RIDICULOUS THINGS LIKE

*You must act quickly to get one of these gorgeous stuffed pandas because the supply is limited.*

### THINKING ABOUT IT THIS MUST MEAN...

Even five million lousy pandas can be considered a "limited" supply when compared to the infinite quantities of such things as outer space, rainwater, a Mother's love and the gas you get from eating baked beans.

## TV COMMERCIALS SAY RIDICULOUS THINGS LIKE

*For maximum savings, get Ocean Spritz Cran-Cantaloupe Juice in the big full quart bottle.*

### THINKING ABOUT IT THIS MUST MEAN...

They helpfully call it a "big full" quart bottle so you won't get it confused with some other size of quart bottle, such as the small partly empty quart bottle or the gigantic overflowing quart bottle.

# Things TV Commercials Say!

WRITER: TOM KOCH

## TV COMMERCIALS SAY RIDICULOUS THINGS LIKE

*At Seymour's Citadel of Suits, there's always a full acre of free parking.*

### THINKING ABOUT IT THIS MUST MEAN...

The clothing they sell may shrink, but they give you their unconditional guarantee that the size of their parking lot remains unchanged from day to day.

## TV COMMERCIALS SAY RIDICULOUS THINGS LIKE

*Mudworth House is now available in both regular blend and new decaffeinated. Ask for it by name.*

### THINKING ABOUT IT THIS MUST MEAN...

They prefer you ask for their product by name because it wastes too much time when you play Charades with the grocer to make him guess what it is you want.

## TV COMMERCIALS SAY RIDICULOUS THINGS LIKE

*Pomeroy's Shoe Polish is available at better stores everywhere.*

### THINKING ABOUT IT THIS MUST MEAN...

Don't blame them if you can't find it. The obvious problem is you do all your shopping at worse stores everywhere.

## TV COMMERCIALS SAY RIDICULOUS THINGS LIKE

*Come see us at Smiling Sid's Stable of Sleek Sedans, where we have been serving the community since 1957.*

### THINKING ABOUT IT THIS MUST MEAN...

They're trying to gain your trust and regain their own self-respect with the preposterous claim that a used car lot is somehow "serving the community."

# HEAD TRIP

**ARTIST AND WRITER: SERGIO ARAGONES**

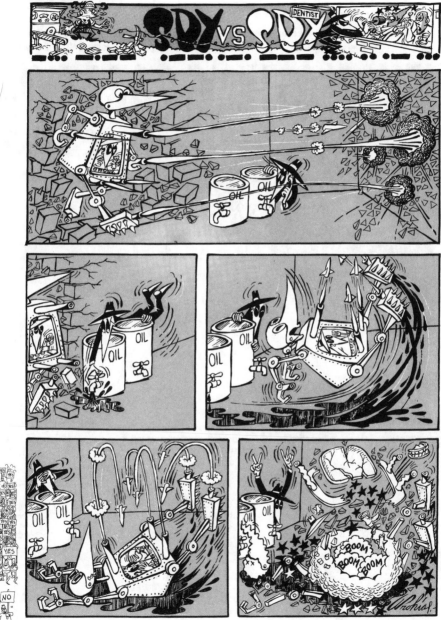

Use any solvent except trichloroethylene.

Those strange doodles shown above are some of the many "Clothing Care Symbols" found on shirts and other garments. We at MAD don't think they are very practical (especially since we never

# NEW CLOTHING CARE SYMB

ARTIST: BOB CLARKE

MADE IN BA

SPARF
SHIRT

Two very, very sharp pins are secretly hidden in this shirt.

If someone filming a detergent commercial suddenly offers you $20 for this shirt, *TAKE IT!!*

European styling will emphasize the American beer belly.

Made from itchy, 100% unnatural fibers. More cotton can be found in the top of an aspirin bottle.

**Use chlorine bleach as directed on the container label.**

 **Hand washable using lukewarm water.**

 **Do not press or iron.**

do laundry)! We think garment makers could do us all a favor by using symbols for information that's *really* important! So, with that in mind, we take unusual pleasure in introducing these...

# OLS THAT TELL IT LIKE IT IS

WRITER: CHARLIE KADAU

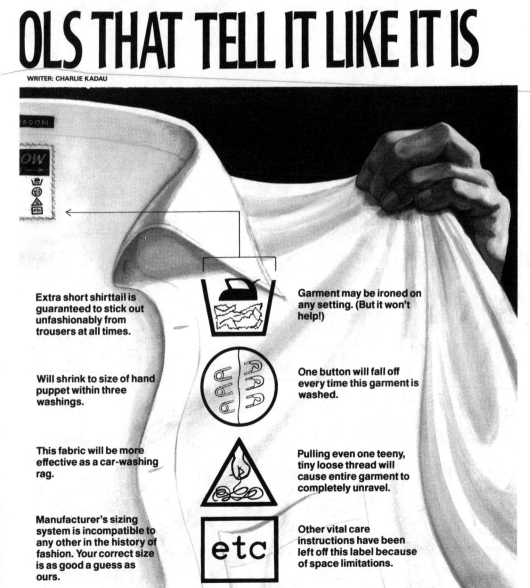

Extra short shirttail is guaranteed to stick out unfashionably from trousers at all times.

Will shrink to size of hand puppet within three washings.

This fabric will be more effective as a car-washing rag.

Manufacturer's sizing system is incompatible to any other in the history of fashion. Your correct size is as good a guess as ours.

Garment may be ironed on any setting. (But it won't help!)

One button will fall off every time this garment is washed.

Pulling even one teeny, tiny loose thread will cause entire garment to completely unravel.

Other vital care instructions have been left off this label because of space limitations.

## EDICT AND WEEP DEPT.

Ever notice how strangely people behave...like saying "Thank you!" to check-out clerks in supermarkets? Ever wonder what they're thanking them for? For giving them change for their own money? For over-charging them for several items in their shopping cart? For keeping them waiting on line for twenty minutes? There are a lot of things people do that make absolutely no sense. But everyone does them because everyone ELSE does them! It's as if we're all behaving according to some "unwritten rules" of our society. Like "Don't belch in public!" or "Cover your nose when you sneeze!" Except that most of the time, these "unwritten laws" are arbitrary and silly! How silly...? Well, we'll show you how silly— as we take this MAD look at what it would be like...

# IF SOCIETY'S *Unwritten*

## IN AN ELEVATOR...

## IN A HOSPITAL...

**ALL VISITORS ARE REQUIRED TO LIE TO PATIENTS ABOUT:**
- How fantastic he or she looks
- How the hospital staff must be taking "special care" of them
- How their Medical Insurance will take care of everything
- How you would love to trade place with them and watch television all day long
- How they'll be out "in no time at all, good as new!"

**RULES OF ELEVATOR BEHAVIOR**
(1) Upon entering, each passenger MUST press the button for his or her floor...even if it's already lit up.
(2) Face forward at all times.
(3) No talking—or smiling—or looking at other passengers.
(4) As soon as doors have started to close, one passenger MUST press the "close door" button hard and impatiently.

## AT A FAMILY REUNION...

**INSTRUCTIONS TO DISTANT RELATIVES**
A. Grab my cheeks and shake them vigorously
B. Express amazement at how much I've grown
C. Ask me several inane questions on any topic other than those I'm interested in

## AT A BALLPARK...

**BATTER'S CHECKLIST**
(1) Tap plate with bat three times
(2) Adjust crotch
(3) Spit
(4) Assume stance
(5) Wiggle your bat dramatically
(6) Sneer at pitcher

## AT AN INTERSECTION...

**INTERSECTION WITH VERY LONG TRAFFIC SIGNAL AHEAD**

Prepare to: start singing along with the radio, or drum on the steering wheel in time with the music, or leisurely pick your nose!

# *Rules of Behavior*
## *WERE ACTUALLY WRITTEN DOWN*

ARTIST: GEORGE WOODBRIDGE          WRITER: MIKE SNIDER

### AT A BUSINESS MEETING...

UPON BEING INTRODUCED, EACH PARTY WILL SHAKE HANDS PERFUNCTORILY, SAY HOW GLAD HE/SHE IS TO MEET THE OTHER, AND THEN PROMPTLY FORGET THE OTHER'S NAME!

### AT A CHECK-OUT COUNTER...

READING OF SENSATIONAL TABLOID NEWSPAPER WHILE WAITING ON LINE WITHOUT SNORTING OR SNICKERING IS STRICTLY PROHIBITED!

### ON A MATERNITY FLOOR...

**INSTRUCTIONS FOR NEW FATHERS**
(1) Press forehead firmly against nursery window.
(2) Wave and grin at baby.
(3) Babble like an idiot.

### AT A SPEAKER'S PLATFORM...

MASTER OF CEREMONIES' **REGULATIONS**
Any claim made by you that the Guest Speaker "needs no introduction" must be followed by a complete introduction!

### IN A GARAGE...

While listening to the Mechanic, all Customers are required to: smile knowingly, nod, and grunt in agreement as if they actually know what he's talking about!

CREST AUTO SERVICE

# A MAD GOING LOOK AT

**SERGIO ARAGONES DEPT.**

TO THE MOVIES

**ARTIST & WRITER: SERGIO ARAGONES**

*Years ago life was easier. The most pressing problem folks seemed to face was deciding which radio program to tune in that evening. But times change. Life's complexities have gone way*

# MAD'S MODERI

**Where can you buy a winter jacket the da**

**remaining pleasures don't cause cancer?**

**divorce?**  **Where can you bu**

**What do you serve your vegetarian, holis**

**friend for dinner?** **Is it pos**

**Do you have to buy earrings you**

**them?** **Is $1.35 still "cheap"?**

**Day card for your gay, transvestite step-fat**

**travel to where the residents don't hate or**

**possible to suffer from an illness that Phil**

beyond just moving a little plastic marker from the morning music show to the shadow traffic report. As baffling dilemmas appear, we find ourselves searching desperately for answers to

# N-DAY PUZZLERS

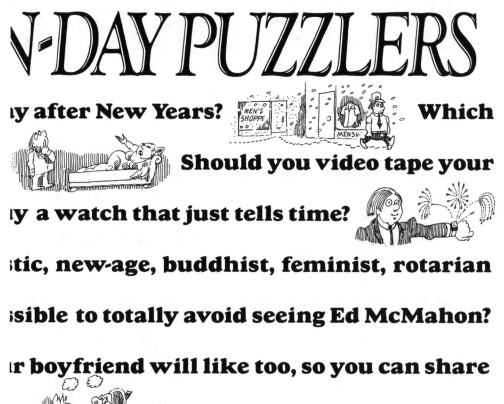

ıy after New Years? Which

Should you video tape your

ıy a watch that just tells time?

ıtic, new-age, buddhist, feminist, rotarian

ısible to totally avoid seeing Ed McMahon?

ır boyfriend will like too, so you can share

Where do you find a Mother's

ıher? What country can you

resent all Americans? Is it

Donahue hasn't covered yet?

WRITER: DAVID AMES

Budding trees signal spring, changing leaves indicate autumn, and heavy snow means winter. But what about that other season—how can we tell when it begins? Beach parties? Picnics?

# SUMMER HAS A...

...LITTLE KIDS SELL LEMONADE FOR 5¢ A GLASS, COMPLETE WITH SAND AND DROWNED

FOR FREE MEALS ENROUTE TO RESORTS YOU CAN'T AFFORD

SURFBOARD

...AND YOU RUN OUT OF DENTAL FLOSS TRYING

FOR NO REASON EXCEPT THAT THE OIL COMPANIES KNOW YOU'LL PAY MORE IN WARM

HAVE BEEN CUT FROM THE NBA PLAYOFFS

..AND T

CONDITIONER ON THE FIRST DAY YOU REALLY NEED IT

UP THE STORM WINDOWS BECAUSE IT'S TIME AGAIN TO PUT UP THE SCREENS

TICKET PRICES REMAIN SKY-HIGH

...AND TV NETWORKS

Think again! (And while you're at it, throw another shrimp on the barbie!) MAD has some other signs in mind... *warning* signs! The signs that mean three months of torture! You know that

# RRIVED WHEN...

ARTIST: PAUL COKER    WRITER: TOM KOCH

**ANTS** ...AND DISTANT RELATIVES UNEXPECTEDLY DROP BY

...AND YOUR LOCAL YUPPIE REPLACES THE SKI RACK ON TOP OF HIS BMW WITH A

TO DISLODGE PIECES OF CORN-ON-THE-COB ...AND GAS PRICES GO UP

**WEATHER.** YES, SUMMER'S HERE... WHEN ALL BUT 8 TEAMS

IE ELECTRIC CO. ASKS YOU TO HELP AVERT A POWER FAILURE BY TURNING OFF YOUR AIR

...AND YOUR FAMILY STOPS BUGGING YOU TO TAKE DOWN THE SCREENS AND PUT

...AND ROCK CONCERTS MOVE OUTSIDE TO BIG STADIUMS, BUT

BEGIN BRAGGING ABOUT THEIR NEW FALL LINEUP–DURING JUNKY RERUNS OF THE SHOWS

**THEY RAVED ABOUT *LAST* YEAR.**   **IT'S DEFINITELY SUMMER...WHEN**

**YOU STOP SETTING YOUR ALARM FOR SCHOOL, BUT THE IDIOT NEXT DOOR WAKES**

**YOU EVEN EARLIER WITH HIS LAWN MOWER**  **...AND YOUR**

**ONLY POSSIBLE CONTACT WITH AN AIR CONDITIONING REPAIRMAN IS HIS ANSWERING**

 **MACHINE** **...AND DAD SAYS HE'LL SPEND HIS VACATION BECOMING**

**YOUR PAL AS THE TWO OF YOU PAINT THE GARAGE TOGETHER**

**...AND PARK RANGERS REPORT THAT THE THREAT OF FLOODS HAS BEEN REPLACED BY**

 **THE THREAT OF BRUSH FIRES** **...AND OVER-EAGER MERCHANTS RUIN**

**YOUR VACATION BY STARTING THE FIRST BACK-TO-SCHOOL SALES.**

# LIVING ON THE EDGE

**ARTISTS: DON EDWING AND HARRY NORTH**  **WRITER: DON EDWING**

# A MAD LOOK AT DATING

ARTIST & WRITER: SERGIO ARAGONES

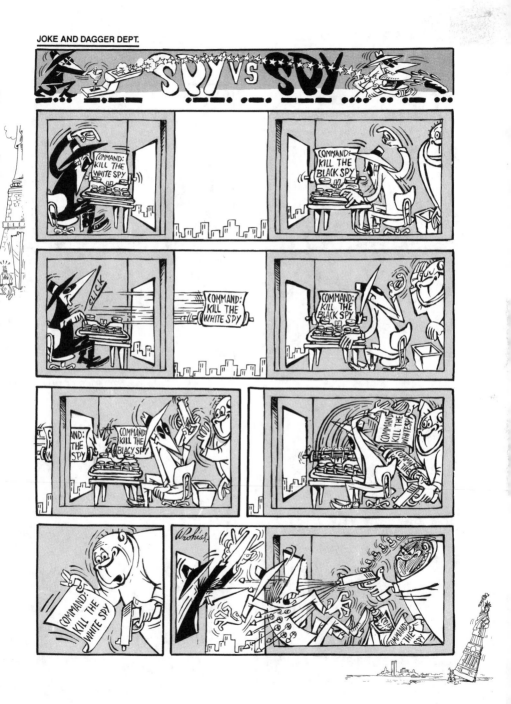

# CLEVER WAYS TO GET OUT OF

### RUNNY NOSE

### GARLIC BREATH

ARTIST AND WRITER: PAUL PETER PORGES

### AN OPEN ZIPPER

### DROOPY PANTYHOSE

# EMBARRASSING SITUATIONS

**DOGGY-DOO SHOES**

**LIMITED ATHLETIC ABILITY**

**DANDRUFF**

**GAMY ARMPITS**

# BACK IN THE OPERATING ROOM WITH DON MARTIN
# DURING A HEART TRANSPLANT

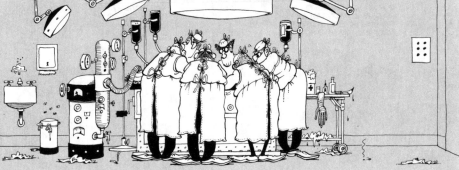

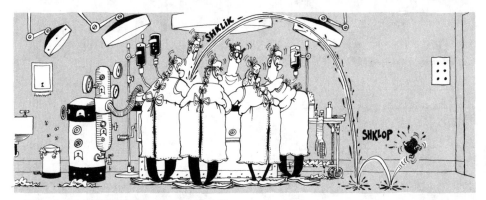

They sit in the dark corners of shopping malls, unwanted and unloved, unable to ask for the attention they so desperately need. Who are these pitiful creatures? Pathetic K-Mart shoppers? Hardly! We're talking about mechanical ponies and rocking boats—the forgotten rides of childhood. Today's kids don't part with their quarters unless they're really stimulated! Which is why we at MAD suggest introducing these...

# NEW AND IMPROVED STORE KIDDIE RIDES

**ARTIST: AL JAFFEE**     **WRITER: DAN BIRTCHER**

## COASTLINE DODGE 'EM!

Hey kids, ever wonder what it's like to be at the helm of a real oil tanker while you're in a drunken stupor? Well, now you can feel the thrill of being completely blitzed at the helm in **Coastline Dodge 'em!**, the ride that recreates the rocky and catastrophic voyage of the Exxon Valdez! You'll feel an exhilarating wave of nausea as you lose control of yourself *and* the ship. True, you won't destroy an entire ecosystem, but the ride *is* rigged to spill some black crud on the floor of the store's menswear department!

**STREEP THROAT** What's dark and deep and filled with the thundering sounds of foreign vowels? Why, it's **Streep Throat**, the amazing new ride which catapults you into the make-believe voice box of one of America's most annoying voices, Meryl Streep! You'll hear her say, "The Nazis made the Gringo take my baby to Flatbush, m'lord" in eleven different accents, including: British, Australian, Polish, Dutch, Estonian and Native Gypsy Ragpicker Dialect. You'll swear you were actually in the mouth of a FOREIGNER! (Must be under 4' 6" to clear gum line.)

**PRESCRIPTION SIGNATURE** In this age of fast video games and slasher movies, kids demand that their rides be fast and slashing too! That's why we've created **Prescription Signature**, the new ride in which you're strapped atop a giant ball-point pen! Feel for yourself the unpredictable jerking of a doctor's moronic scrawl! Believe us, you don't know what excitement is until you've experienced the wild scribbling of a prescription for hemorrhoids in high velocity Latin! It's stimulating, it's bizarre… it's illegible! Be sure to hang on, though, because if you fall— that's all she wrote!

**YUGO-A-GO-GO** When Yugo auto sales took a nose dive, there were still hundreds of thousands of kids who never had the chance to ride in one of these Iron Curtain Wonder cars! That's where the amazing and wacky Yugo-A-Go-Go comes in! After inserting a quarter, simply climb in, turn the ignition key and experience the feeling of absolutely nothing happening…just like actual Yugo owners did! And here's an extra surprise: This ride *isn't* a toy replica! It's a real non-working, cramped and uncomfortable Yugo! Va Va Voom!

## SPACE-AGE CHECK-OUT

We've all seen a grocery clerk scan a package again and again at the check-out, desperately trying to get the bar code to register. Ever fantasized about being treated that way yourself? Then **Space-Age Check-Out** is for you! A giant mechanical hand violently lifts you from the ground and drags you against a hard glass plate. Blinding red lasers flash in your eyes as you are mistaken for an improperly coded canned ham. Ride ends when you are dropped. (Maker of ride assumes no responsibility for kidney damage.)

**SPECIAL DELIVERY** Whoa-ho! It's exciting! Whoo-hoo! It's incredible! Whee-hee! It's **Special Delivery**, the wacky new ride in which you get banged around and mishandled just like a priceless breakable in the hands of an incompetent civil servant! First you're slammed and sealed in an oversized box with an inadequate amount of styrofoam peanuts. Then you're off for Cleveland from Miami Beach via Seattle with lengthy stop-offs at the Post Offices in Peewaukee, Grand Rapids, Intercourse, Wammelsdorf, Cupenluck, Wammelsdorf (again!), and Baktash, South Korea! On the other hand, you may sit around in the back room for weeks, stinking up the joint like a long-forgotten case of rotting gouda cheese!

17

# HIGHER EDUCATION

## BERG'S-EYE VIEW DEPT.

# THE LIGHTE

## EQUALITY

# ABRA-CADAVER

ARTIST: HARRY NORTH    WRITER: DON EDWING

# MAD BASEBALL BOTTOM OF THE SECOND—STILL SCORELESS

## BOTTOM OF THE THIRD—SCORE TIED 1-1...

## TOP OF THE FOURTH—PRESS COVERAGE

ARTIST AND WRITER: SERGIO ARAGONES

# MAD BASEBALL TOP OF THE FIFTH—LOADED BASES...

## RAIN DELAY

ARTIST AND WRITER: SERGIO ARAGONES

# MAD BASEBALL WORLD CHAMPS!

## OPENING DAY—THE FOLLOWING SEASON...

**ARTIST AND WRITER: SERGIO ARAGONES**

**EVERY GUEST ON EVERY TALK SHOW** getting asked to give his Super Bowl "pick."

**A MULTITUDE OF SLO-MO ACTION MONTAGES,** shown over and over, all accompanied by Sinatra's version of "The Winners."

## CERTAIN-T-FORMATIONS DEPT.

Aren't you sick of Super Bowl hype? We are! Every year's the same! Dull and predictable! Who wants to see another "sports profile" about 300-lb. linebackers who knit? We wish they'd cook up some new angles, because otherwise (unless you fall asleep!)...

# EVERY SUPE

ARTIST: PAUL COKER

EMBARRRASSING "RAP" VIDEOS by both teams, shown about 20,000 times.

**YET ANOTHER BONEHEAD PSYCHIATRIST** with another bonehead theory on what our national obsession with football really means.

**DOZENS OF CHEAP ATTEMPTS** to "cash in" on the Super Bowl hype, made by businesses not even remotely connected with football.

**THE UNCEREMONIOUS FIRING** of half of the NFL coaches who just didn't make it to the Super Bowl.

# :R BOWL WEEK YOU'RE SURE OF SEEING...

WRITER: MIKE SNIDER

Mrs. Fleegle, tell us about Danny...you were his substitute teacher for two days in fourth grade...

**MORE BIOGRAPHICAL INFORMATION** on the two opposing quarterbacks than even their own mothers could stand.

**THE SAME STORIES ABOUT TICKET SCALPING** —with the exact same prices—that you remember seeing the year before—and the year before that.

**IDIOT TV REPORTERS** who actually ask the coaches to reveal their surprise game plans.

**HUNDREDS OF "SUPER BOWL MOMENTS"** on TV that make the previous Super Bowls look a lot more exciting than anything you remember.

**PANELS OF WHINY "FOOTBALL WIDOWS"** who get together on the Phil Donahue and Oprah Winfrey shows.

**SENATORS WASTING VALUABLE TIME IN CONGRESS** with goofy penny ante bets.

Many cheered the arrival of the video cassette recorder as another great invention—like the electric toothbrush and the coin machine that dispenses live bait. But now, some are openly questioning the VCR's value to society. Is its ability to bring recent movies into the home such a boon to mankind? Saturday night on the town—at the movies—is an *American tradition..* Do we really want to throw over a cherished custom for some cheap little tape in a plastic box? Of course!! So pause, eject your better judgement, and fast-forward through...

# WHY OWNING A VCR IS BETTER THAN GOING TO THE MOVIES

ARTIST: HARVEY KURTZMAN          WRITER: TOM KOCH

To go to a movie, you must beg for the family car, which your parents often use on Saturday nights.

To watch a VCR you need only the family television, which your parents rarely watch on Saturday evenings—except when they're not out using the car.

Taking a date to the movies costs $10, as long as you don't stop for dinner, which runs you $30 more.

Renting a video tape costs only $2.00, as long as you don't lose it or damage it (assuming it was OK to begin with!), otherwise it runs you $79.95 more.

Driving to the movies on a Saturday night can turn into a frustrating waste of time that leaves you stranded in traffic for almost an hour.

Afternoon drives to the video store are never frustrating, provided you enjoy waiting 45 minutes for service that gets you out just in time for the Saturday night traffic jam.

As a movie-goer, on Saturday nights you have to watch whatever the theatre owner decides to present, even when it is a "Teenage Slasher Film Festival."

Wedging yourself for two hours into a cramped, food-stained theatre seat can lead to spine misalignment and sticky pants.

Chairs will never cause problems in your comfortable home. Uninvited guests will keep you so busy fixing food that you'll never have time to sit down.

At the movies, your enjoyment of the film is always disrupted by lots of people climbing over you to reach their seats.

If you and your date get too personally involved at a movie, you may be interrupted by an usher swinging a flashlight.

No usher will bother the two of you in front of a VCR. However, you may be interrupted by your parents, who frequently swing objects larger than flashlights.

After you've finished a late Saturday night at the movies, you must face the drudgery of driving all the way back home.

As a VCR owner you can watch anything you want—except on weekends, when the only tapes still available are "Friday the 13th Parts III, IV and V."

Before a movie begins you must first sit through boring reminders not to talk, litter or smoke, and previews that can drag on for fifteen minutes.

A VCR lets you get right to the feature, just as soon as you adjust the contrast, brightness, color and tint, which rarely takes more than half an hour.

People seldom crawl over you when you're home with a VCR. They simply ring your doorbell and telephone every ten minutes.

In a public theatre you never know if the stranger next to you is a demented weirdo who's planning to stab you to death.

At home, you are relieved to know that the person next to you is just a demented friend or relative who's merely capable of boring you to death.

When a tape ends on Saturday night, you're already home— at least until Sunday morning, when you must face the drudgery of schlepping it back by 10 AM—or pay for an extra day.

Attending a popular first-run movie on the weekend gives you just one thing to discuss with your friends on Monday morning.

For the same money you can rent **three** VCR films. Unfortunately, all three were seen, discussed, and totally forgotten by your friends about six months ago.

# DRAMA ON PAGE 98

ARTIST AND WRITER: JOHN CALDWELL

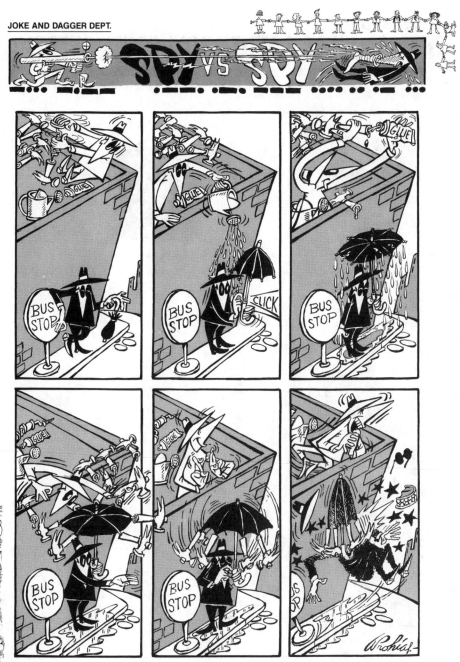

# THE COLOSSAL COURTROOM CONFRONTATION

ARTIST AND WRITER: DUCK EDWING

**THE ENVELOPE, SLEAZE! DEPT.**

You probably know loads of people who receive fat envelopes in the mail that are filled with chances to win fantastic prizes and mucho bucks if they will only send in the entry form (and hopefully order some dumb magazines as well). But, how many people do you know who have actually been a winner in one of these cockamamie contests? Well, we don't know any either! And we thought it was about time we got even with the creeps who keep sending out this stupid trash. So without further ado,

# MAD OPENS A TYPICAL MAGAZINE SWEEPSTAKES PACKAGE

## YOU CAN WIN THESE GRAND PRIZES!

### Super Spectacular Grand Prize #1

Imagine yourself at the wheel of this luxurious 58 foot yacht! Imagine setting sail for such exotic ports as the Caribbean, The French Riviera and the South Sea Islands! If you're our *BIG* winner, you'll be able to imagine all this and more every time you look at your prize—a full-color 8×10 photograph of this luxurious 58 foot yacht!

### Wild Incredible Grand Prize #2

Just think of what your friends will say as you proudly display your new dream house...Complete with 18 rooms, a 4 car garage, patio and in-ground swimming pool! You'll be the talk of your neighborhood, or *wherever* you carry this ¼₄th scale model house...Grand Prize #2 in our amazing magazine sweepstakes!

### Utterly Unbelievable Grand Prize #3

If you're the lucky winner of Grand Prize #3 we'll never send you another piece of obnoxious junk mail like this again...ever! Imagine your satisfaction as everyone you know receives phony magazine contest come-ons except *you*! If that isn't enough of an incentive for entering this contest, we don't know what is!

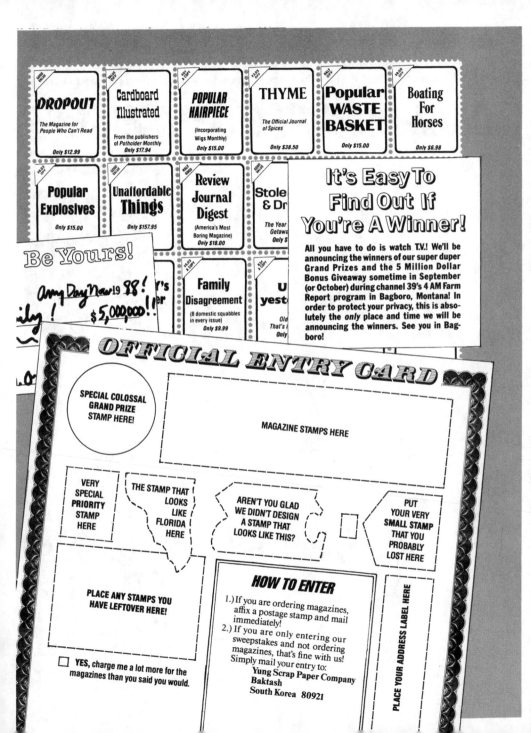

What's a working mother to do? She makes breakfast, sends the kids to school, cleans the house and then rushes to the office where she types, prepares reports and attends business meetings.

# DUAL-PURPOSE OFFICE SUPPl

ARTIST: AL JAFFEE

## SIDE-BY-SIDE FILE CABINETS AND WASHER/DRYER

Color-coordinated to fit any decor, each of these stainless steel file cabinets houses a full-load capacity washer and dryer. Whether washing your kid's grungiest clothes or just a handful of dainties, you'll be able to do a week's worth of laundry and file those important contracts all at the same time. As a bonus, you can file detergent under "D," fabric softener under "F," etc.

## COMPUTER TERMINAL/MAKEUP MIRROR

Finally, a way to apply your morning makeup *and* word process at the same time! Each of these powerful 20 megabyte PCs is connected to a central mainframe and comes with a highly reflective monitor screen with adjustable makeup lights. Peripherals include the disk drive/nail polish dryer and the cosmetic tray/letter quality printer.

## PAPER SHREDDER/PASTA MAKER

In one easy step this handy, handsome appliance allows you to shred confidential documents *and* add bulk to your family's diet! The stainless steel cutting edges never need sharpening and each unit includes settings for making rigatoni, ravioli and fettucine, as well as destroying photos, blueprints and other top secret memoranda.

Wouldn't it be great if she could do her office work at home or her house work at the office? Yes! That's why MAD envisions in the not-too-distant future a catalogue full of new and innovative...

# LIES FOR WORKING MOTHERS

WRITER: JOHN RIOS

## EXECUTIVE DESK/IRONING BOARD

A handsome in-laid mahogany base topped off by a smart, fire-retardant ironing board. Its extra large surface means you'll never have to be more than an arm's length from office reports, balance sheets and wrinkled blouses and skirts. The three drawers (with solid brass handles) can accommodate office supplies, stationery and spray starches.

## PEN AND PENCIL SET/STEAM IRON

The perfect accessory for the Executive Desk/Ironing Board! The base of this attractive gold-plated pen and pencil set is a heavy-duty steam iron. Adjust the pen position for "linen," "cotton" or "synthetics," and push the pencil to the left for "steam." Guaranteed not to scorch, drag or leak ink.

## STAMP PAD/SPICE RACK

Mounted on the bottom of each bottle in this unique and stylish spice rack is a durable rubber stamp. Season your recipes and stamp office correspondence accordingly! Each set includes Thyme/Paid, Cloves/Void, Pepper/Pending, Garlic Powder/First Class, Bay Leaves/Received and Basil/Cancel.

# THE STUPEFYING SUICIDE SITUATION

ARTIST AND WRITER: DUCK EDWING

# ORTS FOR THE VERY DARING AND THE SUPER STUPID

**TURNPIKE TENNIS**

**CONCRETE FLOOR WRESTLING**

**DEMOLITION RELAY RACE**

**SHARK-INFESTED WATER POLO**

Every year, thousands of long-winded Astrology books are sold which describe the personalities and habits of people born under the 12 Signs of the Zodiac. Well, now there's no need to wade

# MAD'S INSTA
# ZODIA

ARTIST: HARRY NORTH

## ARIES

Aries people (Mar. 21–Apr. 20) are bold, fearless, rebellious and pioneering. You know this from the way they:

| | |
|---|---|
| Tattoo their neighbors' children. | Punch out their UPS delivery men. |
| Jog underwater. | Train their parakeets to maim. |
| Put tabasco sauce on their ice cream. | Turn over broiling barbecue steaks with their bare hands. |
| Act nonchalant after walking through plate glass windows. | Entertain guests with color slides of accident victims. |

## TAURUS

Taurus people (Apr. 21–May 21) are patient, practical, serious and solemn. This is evident from the way they:

| | |
|---|---|
| Describe the 100-Years' War battle by battle. | Bore their computers. |
| Show a passionate interest in storage batteries. | Count cows while driving cross-country. |
| Are mistaken for mummies. | Frame Tommy Hearns witticisms above their fireplaces. |
| Take long weekends in their cellars. | Turtle Wax their shoe trees. |

through all those pages just to find out if your Aquarian sweetheart is the girl of your dreams, or if your Capricorn brother is the schmuck you think he is. You can find out fast by using...

# NT GUIDE TO
# C TYPES

WRITER: FRANK JACOBS

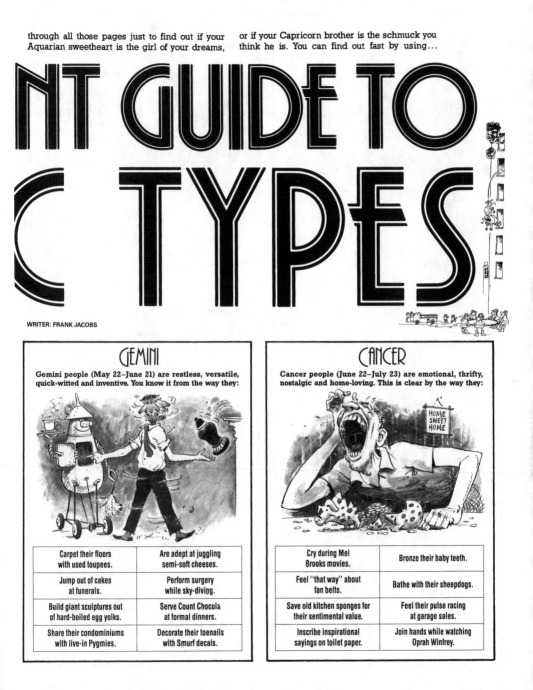

## GEMINI

Gemini people (May 22–June 21) are restless, versatile, quick-witted and inventive. You know it from the way they:

| | |
|---|---|
| Carpet their floors with used toupees. | Are adept at juggling semi-soft cheeses. |
| Jump out of cakes at funerals. | Perform surgery while sky-diving. |
| Build giant sculptures out of hard-boiled egg yolks. | Serve Count Chocula at formal dinners. |
| Share their condominiums with live-in Pygmies. | Decorate their toenails with Smurf decals. |

## CANCER

Cancer people (June 22–July 23) are emotional, thrifty, nostalgic and home-loving. This is clear by the way they:

| | |
|---|---|
| Cry during Mel Brooks movies. | Bronze their baby teeth. |
| Feel "that way" about fan belts. | Bathe with their sheepdogs. |
| Save old kitchen sponges for their sentimental value. | Feel their pulse racing at garage sales. |
| Inscribe inspirational sayings on toilet paper. | Join hands while watching Oprah Winfrey. |

# LEO

Leo people (July 24–Aug. 23) are regal, commanding, egotistical and gregarious. You know this from the way they:

| | |
|---|---|
| Monogram their dentures. | Send mash-notes to themselves. |
| Are proud to park in spaces reserved for the handicapped. | Instruct their wives to address them as "Bwana." |
| Train their pit bulls to curtsey. | Demand tribute from their Street-Cleaners. |
| Show movies of their appendectomies on giant screens. | Wear designer hearing aids. |

# VIRGO

Virgo people (Aug. 24–Sept. 23) are proper, painstaking, fastidious and discriminating. You know from the way they:

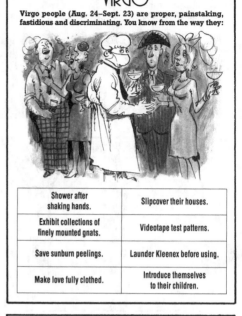

| | |
|---|---|
| Shower after shaking hands. | Slipcover their houses. |
| Exhibit collections of finely mounted gnats. | Videotape test patterns. |
| Save sunburn peelings. | Launder Kleenex before using. |
| Make love fully clothed. | Introduce themselves to their children. |

# SAGITTARIUS

Sagittarius people (Nov. 23–Dec. 21) are adventurous, outspoken and unpredictable. You can see by the way they:

| | |
|---|---|
| Decorate their Christmas trees with shrunken heads. | Make obscene phone calls to their Congressmen. |
| Throw up during soft drink commercials. | Housebreak ostriches. |
| Sleep on all fours. | Do warm-ups for terrorists. |
| Enjoy group sex in hammocks. | Catch Frisbees with their teeth. |

# CAPRICORN

Capricorn people (Dec. 22–Jan. 20) are traditional, set in their ways, loyal and solemn. You know by the way they:

| | |
|---|---|
| Gargle in waltz time. | Still support Judge Bork. |
| Feel at home with bison. | Mourn the current lack of interest in Lincoln Logs. |
| Place fig leaves over pictures of Donald Duck. | Perspire freely while watching "The People's Court." |
| Molt after they reach 50. | Display the earwax of their ancestors in mason jars. |

# LIBRA

Libra people (Sept. 24–Oct. 23) are helpful, indecisive, undemanding and peace-loving. This is evident because they:

| | |
|---|---|
| Get lost in closets. | Take the person who mugged them to lunch. |
| Dial "Weather" and are put on hold. | Turn themselves in for jaywalking. |
| Find momentary beauty in quicksand pools. | Are usually mistaken for large shrubs. |
| Grovel before busboys. | Floss the teeth of stray dogs. |

# SCORPIO

Scorpio people (Oct. 24–Nov. 22) are powerful, secretive, intense and possessive. You know from the way they:

| | |
|---|---|
| Fingerprint their children. | Outstare killer whales. |
| Put out contracts on yodelers. | Mutter to "The Battle Hymn of the Republic." |
| Spoon-feed their cobras. | Run in marathons wearing jack-boots. |
| Crouch in swamps during the full moon. | Plant land mines in their front lawns. |

# AQUARIUS

Aquarius people (Jan. 21–Feb. 19) are unconventional, creative and open minded. You can tell from the way they:

| | |
|---|---|
| Watch "60 Minutes" naked. | Root for the werewolf in horror films. |
| Swallow billiard cues. | Ward off disease by wearing garlic Speedstick. |
| Have grandparents who are into leather. | Meet their lovers in the rear of Chinese laundries. |
| Fit out their giraffes with mesh stockings. | Vacation in wind tunnels. |

# PISCES

Pisces people (Feb. 20–Mar. 20) are dreamy, unambitious, mystical and vulnerable. This is evident by the way they:

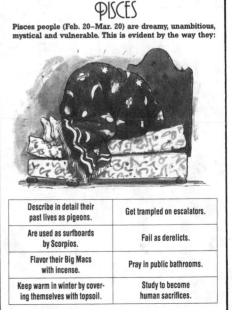

| | |
|---|---|
| Describe in detail their past lives as pigeons. | Get trampled on escalators. |
| Are used as surfboards by Scorpios. | Fail as derelicts. |
| Flavor their Big Macs with incense. | Pray in public bathrooms. |
| Keep warm in winter by covering themselves with topsoil. | Study to become human sacrifices. |

*According to a recent study 76.4% of all MAD readers think 48.9% of all MAD intros are funnier than the articles they introduce. We figure this means one of two things: either 48.9% of our articles are absolute clinkers or 76.4% of our intros are masterful works of comic*

# TELL-TALE COMIC STRIP

ARTIST: BOB CLARKE

*genius. Whatever the case, we worked very hard at keeping this intro especially uninteresting and bland so the article which follows will seem clever and witty in comparison. But the only way you'll know whether we were successful in achieving this is by taking a look at...*

# BALLOONS [The Sequel]

WRITER: DUCK EDWING

We all know how the government works—wait! That's a contradiction in terms! Maybe we should

# A MAD LOOK AT REAL-LII

ARTIST: HARRY NORTH

## GOVERNMENT "LOGIC" is...

...passing a "tax simplification" act...

...that's <u>850 pages long</u>!

## GOVERNMENT "LOGIC" is...

...continuing to promote nuclear power plants as "totally safe"...

...even though no insurance company will insure them—at <u>any</u> price!

## GOVERNMENT "LOGIC" is...

...requiring competitive bids on government contracts...

...then paying whatever outrageous "cost overruns" contractors can claim with a straight face!

say "…how the government *thinks*"—naw, they don't do that either! See what we mean as we take

# FE GOVERNMENT "LOGIC"

WRITER: MIKE SNIDER

## GOVERNMENT "LOGIC" is...

…saving other countries from the oppression of left-wing dictatorships…

…by supporting equally oppressive <u>right</u>-wing dictatorships!

## GOVERNMENT "LOGIC" is...

…entrusting the protection of our national parks and wilderness areas…

…to the same people who give out strip-mining and oil-drilling rights!

## GOVERNMENT "LOGIC" is...

…turning down a plan that would eliminate all nuclear missiles…

…so that we can build a trillion-dollar "star wars" system to defend us from the very missiles we could have eliminated!

# GOVERNMENT "LOGIC" is...

...diligently keeping "unde-
sirables" out of the U.S....

...but welcoming with open arms the
likes of Ferdinand and Imelda Marcos!

# GOVERNMENT "LOGIC" is...

...punishing states with too many speeders...

...by cutting off their Highway Construction
funds—and making roads <u>twice</u> as dangerous!

# GOVERNMENT "LOGIC" is...

...maintaining public health and safety
by regulating everything under the sun...

...<u>except</u> cheap, easily concealed handguns!

# ONE EVENING AT A MASQUERADE PARTY

If you think the Surgeon General's Warning printed on cigarette packages still only says "Smoking May Be Hazardous To Your Health," think again! That line's as outdated as a 50¢ pack of menthols. Smoking hasn't gotten safer—ha!—just the opposite. These days it's so hazardous that just one warning isn't enough! That's why the Surgeon

# NEW CIGARETTE WARNING LA

SURGEON GENERAL'S WARNING:
Stopping Smoking Now Greatly Increases The Need For Tobacco Farm Subsidies. What'll It Be, Clean Lungs Or Lower Taxes?

SURGEON GENERAL'S WARNING:
Since Cigarette Smoke Contains Carbon Monoxide, You Could Probably Save Lots Of Money By Sucking On Your Car's Exhaust Pipe.

SURGEON GENERAL'S WARNING:
Athlete's Foot Is About The Only Thing You Can't Catch From Smoking.

SURGEON GENERAL'S WARNING: Smoking By Fetuses May Result In Injury To Pregnant Women.

General introduced a series of new, harsher warnings (some of which you may have already seen) to be placed on all cigarette packs. Of course, the tobacco companies would prefer you not even think about this, but we at Mad care! Remember, if you *must* get a bad taste in your mouth, you don't have to smoke—you just have to read...

# ABELS YOU MAY HAVE MISSED

PHOTOGRAPHER: IRVING SCHILD    IDEA: ANNE GAINES    WRITERS: JOE RAIOLA & CHARLIE KADAU

SURGEON GENERAL'S WARNING: Contrary To Popular Belief, You Cannot Determine The Age Of A Smoker By Counting The Layers Of Nicotine Stains On His Fingers.

SURGEON GENERAL'S WARNING: Smoking Causes Lung Cancer, Emphysema, Arteriosclerosis, Heart Disease, Tuberculosis, Black Lung, Asthma, Tumors, (list continued on next pack)

SURGEON GENERAL'S WARNING: People Who Walk Around With Cigarettes Behind Their Ears Look Like Schmucks.

SURGEON GENERAL'S WARNING: Smoking In A Crowded Restaurant Greatly Increases Your Chances Of Getting Soup Poured On Your Head.

What would happen if they dropped The Bomb? (No, not the next issue of MAD! Idiot! We mean the *nuclear* bomb!) Our government assures us that life would go on—just as soon as the Feds reinstated mail delivery and taxes! Right! Like we'd really be looking forward to squatting in our shelters, eating Spam and waiting to hear from the IRS!!! It takes *years* for radiation to leave the environment—that's a lot of Spam! So we'd need something to help pass the time...like some magazines! And we can guess what they'd be like! (After all, who knows more about the trashy future of publishing than us?!) So here's a selection of

# MAD'S
# POST-NUCLEAR

**U.S. News** & WORLD REPORT

## RONALD REAGAN ON THE CURRENT CRISIS: *"WHAT HAPPENED??"*

"Did something happen? ...Why wasn't I told about it?...Do you expect me to remember every little detail? ...I have a special committee looking into it...The media has blown (sorry!) this way out of proportion...Well... Nancy, where's my security blanket?..."

Exclusive Photos—
THE *NEW* GRAND CANYON
(formerly downtown Cleveland)

**People** weekly

**ROYAL BREEDER'S REACTION:
Princess Di's Siamese Sextuplets**

## LIZ TAYLOR

**She's introducing the "Telly Savalas Look" for women**

**JOHNNY CARSON'S TRAGIC STORY:
"All of my ex-wives' lawyers survived!"**

# PLAYBOY

**Playboy's Exclusive Pictorial: Those Naughty Mutant Girls of Lawrence, Kansas**

**"Hey, Baby, We're Going to Die Anyway!"
—or How to Use the Nuclear Disaster to Get Your Own Way in Bed**

**A Playboy Preview: Hef's Swinging New Bomb Shelter**

**Can Nuclear Radiation Particles Interfere with Your New Stereo?**

# Consumer Reports

## STAR WARS RE-EVALUATED
Were We a Bit Too Hasty in Giving It a Passing Grade?

**C.R. RATES:**
Laetrile Hamburger Helper • Lead-lined jock straps • Cement denture cream • Exploding welcome mats (for those unexpected shelter visitors)

**WE TEST THAT**

**FUNNY-LOOKING MILK**

**FROM TWO-HEADED COWS**

# COSMOPOLITAN

How to Tell if He's Falling Over You, or Just Overcome with Radiation Sickness

Can a Nuclear Winter Deplete the Nation's Supply of Eligible Men?

Jane Fonda's New Post-Apocalypse Exercise Program

Is He Using the Nuclear Holocaust to Avoid Making a Deeper Commitment?

# PUBLICATIONS

ARTIST: BOB CLARKE     WRITER: BARRY LIEBMAN

# Good Housekeeping

How to Make a COZY SHAG RUG from the Skins of those 39-inch Mutant Rats

46 TERRIFIC MICROWAVE DISHES That You Can Make on the Top of Your Head

Dyeing Your Drapes to Match the Colors of Your Own Personal SKIN RASH

# True Romance

A CALIFORNIAN'S INTIMATE MEMOIR
We made love and the earth moved...
RIGHT INTO THE PACIFIC OCEAN!

I fell in love with his blue eyes and cleft chin...
AND NOW I KEEP THEM IN A PICKLE JAR!

A nostalgic suburbanite remembers a night of romance...
SNUGGLING UP BY THE LIGHT OF HER HAMSTER!

# THE DISASTROUS DESERT DRAMA

ARTIST AND WRITER: DUCK EDWING

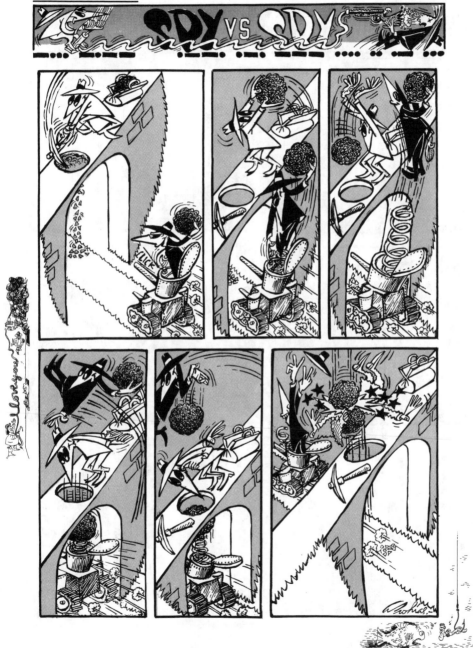

# DRAMA ON PAGE 134

ARTIST & WRITER: JOHN CALDWELL

And now, as a public service to all you would-be artists out there, MAD Magazine, in cooperation with the Famous Artists' School of Wammelsdorf, now proudly presents...

# A BEGINNERS GUIDE TO CARTOON SOUND EFFECTS

ARTIST: PAUL COKER     WRITER: DUCK EDWING

...someone sneezing with a spittoon over his head.
...a push button switchblade accidentally opening in a punk's front pocket.
...someone using a flamethrower to flush an Eskimo from his igloo.

...an elephant experiencing relief.

...a skydiver getting caught in a plane's propeller.

...Batman flushing.
...a fish blowing air bubbles into a fat man's navel.

...a killer clam attacking a sunburnt octopus.

...a Ubangi deep-lipping an entire pizza with anchovies.
...Superman landing directly in doggie-doo.
...a fast zipper-upper catching himself on his denim fly.

...a guy sticking his head inside a lawn
mower to see if he can get it started.

...a tennis player snagging on the net he tried to jump.
...a suicide jumper hitting the 9th floor flagpole.

...an Italian ship being christened with a pizza.

...an elderly crocodile gumming a frantic native.

...a Col. Sanders look-a-like visiting a chicken farm.
...a teenager accidentally knocking his radio into the bathtub.
...an apprentice tie salesman tying a Windsor knot for his first customer.

...a horsefly landing in a bowl of semi-cooled Jello.

...a man with three fingers cracking his knuckles.
...a doctor trying to jump-start a pacemaker.

# A MAD LOOK AT STAY

ARTIST AND WRITER: SERGIO ARAGONES

# THE MANHATTAN MONSTER MONKEYSHINE

ARTIST AND WRITER: DUCK EDWING

Words are funny little creatures. They can bring joy or sadness, hope or despair. And often it doesn't matter what the words are, as much as

# SAME WORDS...*DIFFER*

### EVERYONE MUST PASS THROUGH THE METAL DETECTOR!

### HE'S T

*...is comforting when entering an airport.*

*...frightening when entering your high school!*

*...is terrific when your girlfriend is describing you to her parents*

### I'M A WOMAN AND I DEMAND TO BE TREATED AS ONE!

### TODAY, WE'RE INDICTIN

*...is encouraging when it's your daughter fighting for equality at her work place.*

*...discouraging when it's your son making an announcement at the dinner table!*

*...is reassuring when the D.A. is prosecuting members of a local auto theft ring.*

### JUST SAY "NO!"

### YOURS IS THE BIGGEST

*...is good advice when a friend offers you drugs.*

*...bad advice when an addict puts a gun to your head and demands money!*

*...is thrilling when a friend is checking out your new engagement ring.*

who's saying them and to whom they are referring. Get it? Neither did
we, until one of our hack writers came up with this MAD guide to…

# ENT CIRCUMSTANCES!

ARTIST: PAUL COKER    WRITER: J. PRETE    IDEA: CHRISTOPHER ALLEN

## IE ONE!

*…not so terrific when you're
standing in a police line-up!*

## YOU'RE TOTALLY COVERED!

*…is reassuring when it's an insur-
ance agent discussing your claim.*

*…alarming when it's anyone
discussing your burning rash!*

## G ANOTHER 12 PEOPLE!

*…less reassuring when the
D.A. is prosecuting members
of the White House staff!*

## EASY AS A, B, C!

*…is good when someone's
talking about the computer
program you just bought.*

*…is horrible when
someone's talking
about your sister!*

## ONE I'VE EVER SEEN!

*…not so thrilling
when it's a doctor
examining your goiter!*

## HE LIKES TO BITE MY FEET WHILE I'M ASLEEP!

*…is adorable when hearing
about someone's new puppy.*

*…really gross when hearing
about someone's new boyfriend!*

# A MAD LOOK

ARTIST AND WRITER:

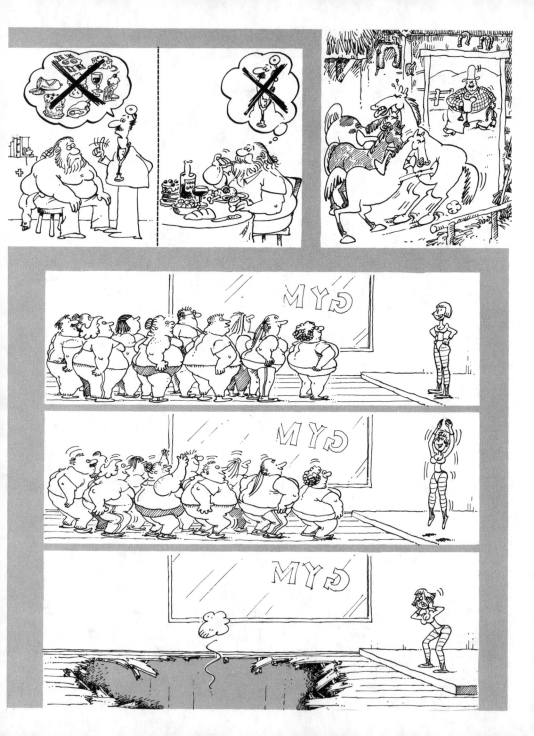

# We're looking for people who are looking for a course on how to write children's books.

**By Chic Glitz**
Dean of Words

Home of the Home Study Institute for the Discovery of Hidden Talents in the Field of Writing Children's Books deep in the Connecticut woods. The Institute is located in a dilapidated shack behind this Victorian mansion.

RECENT GOVERNMENT FIGURES INDICATE there's now a better than 50/50 chance that everyone reading this ad was once a child. That means you've already done all the necessary research needed to create a child's book. Now all you have to do is write one!

Writing children's books is as easy as A, B, 3! Kids don't know from grammar, punctuation and style. To them, a book is just a string of words on pages. You don't have to use big words *or* know how to spell correctly!

### Important details

Of course, there *are* fine points to be learned before writing children's books. Should you submit your story in crayon on white paper or type it on a brown paper bag? Who should you submit it to? General Motors or a book publisher? Should your book be illustrated, or maybe have drawn pictures?

That's where we come in. We're the Home Study Institute for the Discovery of Hidden Talents in the Field of Writing Children's Books. We're listed in the Guinness Book of World Records as the learning institution with the longest name! What better reference is there than that?

### Lingering doubts?

You may still ask yourself: Am I qualified to be a writer? If you can write a check in the amount of $350—and the bank is so moved by your writing that they pay the amount of the check to us, then you're qualified!

After receiving Lesson One, "How to Sharpen a Pencil," you will be able to say to your friends, "Hey, I'm a writer"! Then, we will send you (at additional cost, of course) your own business card that says: WRITER. If you so desire, you can add other information like your name, address and phone number, also at an additional cost.

### Learn writing "tricks"

Above all, we'll teach you to be original and avoid common clichés, which is easy as pie! We pledge the grass won't be greener on the other side of the fence any more for you! But, since even the longest journey starts with one step and today is the first day of the rest of your life, remember: He who hesitates is lost! Fill out and mail in the attached coupon now!

If you want to start on the fabulous road to becoming a famous author EVEN FASTER and earn big bucks to help pay off the charges we'll put on your credit card, then call 1-800-WRITER *this second* and give us your VISA, MASTERCARD or AMERICAN EXPRESS number. SPECIAL OFFER: Give us all three credit card numbers and learn three times faster!

### Satisfied students

Here are some comments from our graduates:

"I could hardly believe it when I opened the publisher's envelope and a check fell out! My first sale after mailing out 6,735 submissions! I'll be taking a break from my writing now to decide how to spend my $5 check!!"
—N.M., Poor, NM

"I used to waste valuable time doing nothing. But now, thanks to the Institute, I now waste valuable time writing unpublished kid's books!"—J.W., Skank, OR

"The Home Study Institute for the discovery of Hidden Talents in the Field of Writing Children's Books is the best course in the entire world! I never, ever thought I'd be paid for my writing, but I just got my first check for writing this favorable quote for them to use in their ad!!!"—D.D., Boatbasin, NY

### Don't think, do it!

Our course will get you started on the road to becoming an author of children's books, or children's stories, or maybe just a single children's word. We GUARANTEE you that after taking the course no more than five times, you will definitely be published, or at the very least, xeroxed!

---

**The Home Study Institute for the Discovery of Hidden Talents in the Field of Writing Children's Books**
**11 Verb Place  Noun, Alaska**

Dear Mr. Glitz: Enclosed is my check for $350, which covers EVERYTHING you can think of for the moment. But being extremely creative, I know I can expect many future charges. I understand that once my check clears, I am under no obligation whatsoever to even open my study-at-home course.

Mr.　Mrs.　Ms.　Miss

_____
Please circle one and print name clearly

_____
Street

_____
City

_____
State                              Zip

Elvis Presley died in 1977. At least, that's what most people believe. But there's still a bunch of kooks who think he faked his death and is really alive. Not to mention the fast-buck hucksters living off the Presley legend. Which makes us ask: "What would Elvis say about all this?" Most likely, he'd pick up his guitar and sing…

"DON

# 'T BE FOOLED"

(sung to the tune of "Don't Be Cruel")

There's a *number* folks..are..cal-lin'
(and you know it's *not..toll-free*)
With a *tape* of *some guy..drawl-in'*,
Who is *claim-in'* to..be..me.
*DON'T BE FOOLED!*
*'Cause it just ain't true!*

There's a *girl* in San..Di-e-go,
Who's convinced that *I..ain't..dead;*
Says I *drive* a *Win-ne-ba-go*
With a *para-keet*..named..*Fred.*
*DON'T BE FOOLED!*
*That's a rip-off too!*

They're just *play-in'* with..*your..head;*
*Ev'rybody..knows*
The *King* is dead!

There's a *load* of *im-i-tat-ors*
Comin' off as *El-vis..clones—*
Mainly *crum-my second..rat-ers.*
Makin' *mon-ey* off..*my..bones.*
*DON'T BE FOOLED!*
*That ain't noth-in' new!*

Makes no *diff-rence* how..*they..sound;*
*I'm still bur-ied*
Six feet underground!

There's a *book* by an..ad-mir-er,
Says I live in *Mam-moth..Cave,*
And she *swears* in..the.."*En-quir-er*"
Jimmy Hoffa's *in..my..grave.*
*DON'T BE FOOLED!*
*Not a word is true!*

You can tell the *tab-loid..press,*
*The King's got no*
*Fowarding address!*

If you *want* an *ex-plan-a-tion*
For the *stor-ies* they..*contrive,*
Check the *rise* in..*cir-cu-la-tion*
Ev'ry time I'm "*proved*"..a-live.
*DON'T BE FOOLED!*
*They're all conning you!*

Don't let it *break..your..heart;*
*Where..I've..gone*
There's no Top Forty Chart!

Yes, I'm *push-in'* up..the..*dai-sies,*
But the *uproar* just..*won't..cease,*
'Cause the *world* is *full of..cra-zies*
Who won't *let me rest..in..peace!*
*DON'T BE FOOLED!*
*This I'm tellin' you!*
*DON'T BE FOOLED!*
*What they say ain't true!*

ARTIST: GERRY GERSTEN    WRITER: FRANK JACOBS

McDonald's "McD.L.T." (which keeps the lettuce and tomato cool and the hamburger hot) was promoted as a great new idea in hamburger technology. But isn't this how all burgers are *supposed* to be? Are we so used to lousy goods and services that a company raising its standards to "merely adequate" can claim to be doing us a favor? If so, we hope they introduce...

# OTHER McD. L.T. TYPE IDEAS

## WE'D LIKE TO SEE FROM McDONALD'S

ARTIST: AL JAFFEE    WRITER: MIKE SNIDER

# NEW at McDonald's

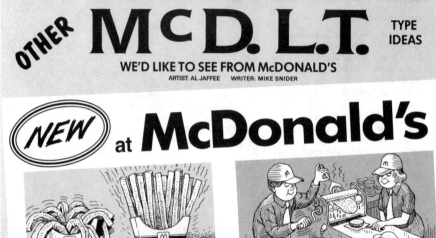

### McRecently-Made Fries
Now, have it two ways... *Regular or Fresh and Hot!*

### The McH.T.G.
One McDonald's burger: "Hold The Grease!"

### Correct McChange
Any employee caught skimming is now immediately transferred to the kitchen crew! No exceptions!

### The McLid
The latest in liquid-containment technology...it actually keeps your soft drink contained in the cup!

### Semi-McLiterate Counterpersons
We've increased our minimum IQ to 90...And— no more droolers!

### The McSpecialized Rag
Now, a separate rag for each of our cleanup chores!

# THE PESKY PECKER PUZZLER

ARTIST AND WRITER: DUCK EDWING

**Attention all you Couch Potatoes with weak Bladders! Do you need more breaks than just the usual commercial interruptions for your bodily functions? Thanks to the following**

# IT'S SAFE TO GO TO TH

article, now you can be sure you won't miss anything important on TV while you're "takin' care of business!" Just what in God's name are we claiming in this introduction? Simply...

# HE BATHROOM WHEN...

ARTIST AND WRITER: PAUL PETER PORGES

# HAND-ME-DOWN

ARTIST AND WRITER: SERGIO ARAGONES

# *MORE*
# *YOU'D BE RICH*
# *IF YOU HAD A*

ARTIST: PAUL COKER    WRITER: CHARLIE KADAU

...For every vacation postcard you send to friends that arrives long after you've already come home.

...For every telephone receptionist who asks if you can "hold" and then puts you on "hold" before you can answer.

...For every time you set off your smoke detector just by cooking.

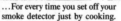

...For every health club ad that says this is your last chance to join before the rates go up.

...For every message on your answering machine that turns out to be a recording of someone hanging up.

...For every take-out pizza you get where there's more cheese stuck to the box than on the pizza.

# NICKEL...

...For every minute you waste in a doctor's waiting room beyond your scheduled appointment time.

...For every politician who claims victory in a primary, even when he finishes second, third, or worse.

...For every blaring car burglar alarm that people completely ignore.

...For every great dream you never get to finish because somebody wakes you right at the best part.

...For every old packet of salt, ketchup, soy sauce and Sweet 'N Low stashed away in your desk drawer.

...For every time MAD runs a sequel to an article that they shouldn't have run in the first place!

ARTIST AND WRITER: DUCK EDWING

# ONE EVENING IN SPAIN

# A MAD LOOK AT FEMALE

# BODYBUILDERS

ARTIST AND WRITER: SERGIO ARAGONES

For the keenly aware in the world, there are little warning signs everywhere — nuances that some kind of trouble, be it big or small, lies ahead. Unfortunately, it's rare that the average MAD reader is keenly aware of anything! Which is why we thought it necessary to compile the following list of...oh, let's call them "tipoffs"...that all is not well in your little corner of the world. Read it carefully and see if (for once) you don't agree with us that...

## IT'S NEVER A GOOD SIGN WHEN...

...People in the car next to you are honking and pointing.

## IT'S NEVER A GOOD SIGN WHEN...

...You're the only one in line to see a movie — on a Saturday night.

## IT'S NEVER A GOOD SIGN WHEN...

...There're three times the normal number of people waiting at your bus stop.

## IT'S NEVER A GOOD SIGN WHEN...

...After a few hours of trying, a repairman asks to use your phone so he can call his boss.

## IT'S NEVER A GOOD SIGN WHEN...

...Your dry cleaner asks you to "describe it."

## IT'S NEVER A GOOD SIGN WHEN...

...Your older brother starts treating you "nice."

# A GOOD

## IT'S NEVER A GOOD SIGN WHEN...

...A friend insists that you first "sit down" before he'll tell you something.

## IT'S NEVER A GOOD SIGN WHEN...

...Your doctor asks to speak to your immediate family out in the hallway.

# SIGN WHEN...

WRITER: J. PRETE

ARTIST: AL JAFFEE

They say you can't stop progress. But we say, **TOO BAD!** The alleged "progress" we've seen has resulted in more suffering and misery than it has in benefits to mankind! To prove it, here's just a smattering of...

# SCIENTIF

The Postal Service saved us tons of time by shortening the abbreviation for Michigan from "Mich." to "MI." Now we waste even more time trying to figure out whether "MI" stands for Michigan, Minnesota, Mississippi or Missouri.

Thanks to science, we no longer get a grating busy signal when we call an overloaded office phone number. Instead, we're put on "hold," and are forced to listen to some bad recorded music, often at a toll charge of fifty cents per minute.

The trash compactor is a modern wonder that makes it unnecessary for us to hunt for valuables we threw away by mistake, because we know, even if we find them, they'll be crushed.

Glass milk bottles that occasionally broke have now been universally replaced by cardboard milk cartons that virtually always leak.

Automated manufacturing has enabled the retail price of the cheapest VCRs to drop well below $200. Interestingly, the cheapest VCRs soon require the services of a repairman who is *unauto-mated* and whose price has risen well above $200.

Jiffy self-service gas stations let you speed up to the pump, walk over and give the cashier your money, walk back to pump your gas, walk back to collect your change and then walk back to your car again—all in less than an hour.

# IC ADVANCES THAT UNIMPROVE OUR LIVES!

**ARTIST: GEORGE WOODBRIDGE**

**WRITER: TOM KOCH**

Amazing medical research will soon increase the human life span to 100, which is 17 years longer than Medicare can be expected to pay your amazing doctor bills without bankrupting the government.

By transferring bulky card files to microfilm, libraries freed up lots of space to accommodate all the additional people who now must wander aimlessly hunting for books because they don't know how to operate a microfilm machine.

The thirst for knowledge has prompted most universities to offer Master of Business Administration degrees. As a result, we now have enough Ivan Boesky clones to defraud every man, woman and child in the country.

# THE EXQUISITE EXECUTION EXPERIMENT

ARTIST AND WRITER: DUCK EDWING

These days, our postal system is clogged with millions of slick, four color catalogs from The Sharper Image, Brookstone, Hammacher Schlemmer and other upscale mailorder companies. They're filled with unusual gadgets, exotic tools and strange contraptions that all have two things in common: They're incredibly overpriced and totally useless! Who needs a $200 computerized cheese scale anyway?? It would be a joy if we could go to our mailbox just once and find a catalog filled with *useful* tools and truly novel inventions. Perhaps a catalog just like...

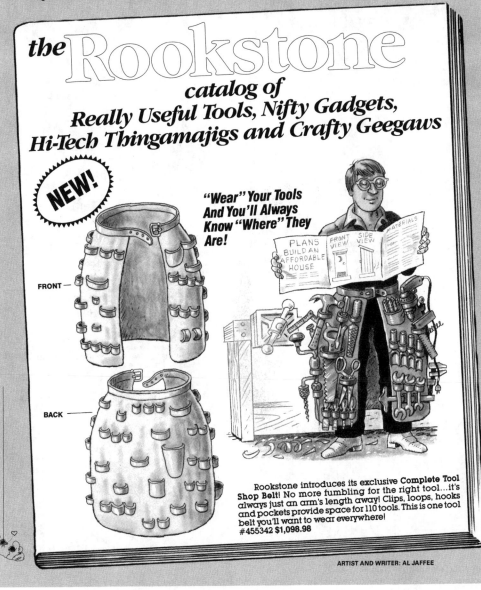

*the* Rookstone

catalog of
*Really Useful Tools, Nifty Gadgets, Hi-Tech Thingamajigs and Crafty Geegaws*

NEW!

"Wear" Your Tools And You'll Always Know "Where" They Are!

FRONT

BACK

Rookstone introduces its exclusive **Complete Tool Shop Belt!** No more fumbling for the right tool...it's always just an arm's length away! Clips, loops, hooks and pockets provide space for 110 tools. This is one tool belt you'll want to wear everywhere!
#455342 $1,098.98

ARTIST AND WRITER: AL JAFFEE

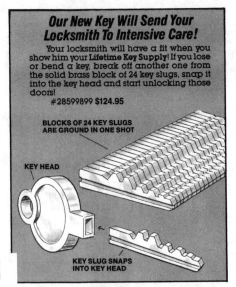

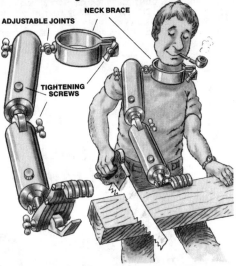

## "Telescopic" Legs Turn Your Hovel Into A Mansion

Cramped city apartment living can no longer prevent you from owning large, regal furniture. By adding these **super adjustable table legs**, you'll be able to fit even the largest sculpted mahogany banquet table into the smallest one-room apartment!
#786512 $735.00

## Stick It On Your Wall In Style!

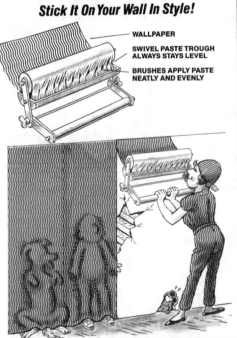

**WALLPAPER**

**SWIVEL PASTE TROUGH ALWAYS STAYS LEVEL**

**BRUSHES APPLY PASTE NEATLY AND EVENLY**

If fuss, mess, glue and goo have prevented you from wallpapering your home, wait no longer! The E-Z-DO Wallpaper Applicator is the fastest method we've found! Imported from Chad.
#675 $299.95

## You've Heard Of Snap-On Tools, Now Take A Look At Snap-off Tools!

Snap-Off Screws and Nuts eliminate the need for greasy, dangerous tools! After using them, "snap off" the installation appendage and toss it. Never buy another expensive gimmicky tool again!
#1 $94.95

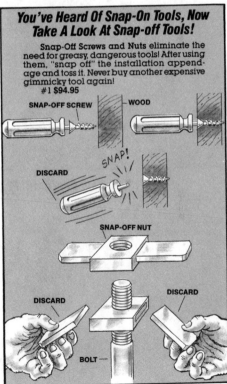

**SNAP-OFF SCREW** — **WOOD**

DISCARD — SNAP!

**SNAP-OFF NUT**

DISCARD — DISCARD

BOLT

# 10-in-1 Bit Gives You The Drill Of Your Life

Borrowing an idea from Medieval England, what looks like a jouster's lance is actually the All-In-One-Drill Bit. Just keep drilling until you reach the hole diameter you want! What you put into the hole is entirely up to you!
#555 $198.98

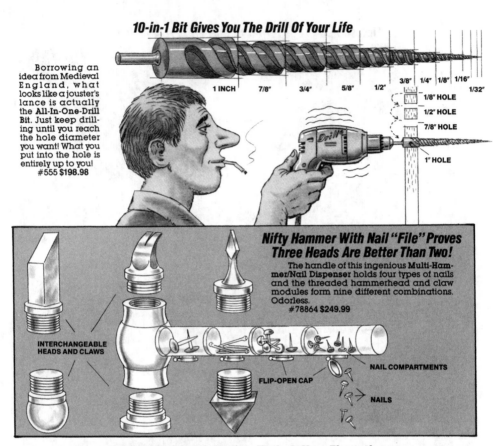

1 INCH  7/8"  3/4"  5/8"  1/2"  3/8"  1/4"  1/8"  1/16"  1/32"

1/8" HOLE
1/2" HOLE
7/8" HOLE
1" HOLE

## Nifty Hammer With Nail "File" Proves Three Heads Are Better Than Two!

The handle of this ingenious Multi-Hammer/Nail Dispenser holds four types of nails and the threaded hammerhead and claw modules form nine different combinations. Odorless.
#78864 $249.99

INTERCHANGEABLE HEADS AND CLAWS

FLIP-OPEN CAP

NAIL COMPARTMENTS

NAILS

## "Just Plain Big" Knife Puts Tools At Your Fingertips

Finally, a **Swiss Army Knife** with full-size tools! Custom-crafted in the alps, each 65 pound knife comes with 10 complete tools. Attach to your belt or push in a wheelbarrow.
#3491067 $325.99

18

# A MAD LOOK AT DRIVER'S ED

**ARTIST AND WRITER: SERGIO ARAGONES**

*Legend has it that college athletes once were clean-living, law-abiding types idolized as role models. But with all the recent scandals, it seems a new breed of jock is emerging — one who's more a role model for aspiring criminals! Which leads us to this rhyming saga of*

# TEN COLLEGE ATHLETES

ARTIST: JACK DAVIS     WRITER: FRANK JACOBS

*Ten college athletes,*
*The best the school could sign;*
*One punched out a campus cop —*
*Slam! Bam! We're down to nine.*

*Nine freshmen athletes,*
*Beefed up and looking great;*
*One OD'd on steroid shots —*
*He's stiff, which leaves us eight.*

*Eight freshmen athletes,*
*With juiced-up Porsches revvin';*
*One was driving stolen wheels —*
*Beep-beep — we're down to seven.*

*Four junior athletes,*
*Unleashed and running free;*
*One shot up a bar and grill —*
*Boom! Boom! We're down to three.*

*Three senior athletes,*
*In class, without a clue;*
*One flunked out and stabbed his prof —*
*Point made — which leaves us two.*

*Two senior athletes,*
*Their school-days nearly done;*
*One got nailed for coed rape —*
*School's out — we're down to one.*

Seven soph'more athletes,
Big spenders with the chicks;
One took payoffs from alums—
Bye, guy—that leaves us six.

Six soph'more athletes,
Each betting he'll survive;
One helped gamblers fix a game—
Bet's off—we're down to five.

Five junior athletes,
Hot stuff and out to score;
One got busted dealing coke—
Toot-toot—that leaves us four.

One college athlete,
Respected, clean, sincere;
My gosh, he's gonna graduate!
Hey! What's he doing here?

35

Look carefully at the Publishers' Sweepstakes envelope below. You probably get one every year, and you probably trash it! You think it's junk mail, and besides, the odds must be crazy that you, out of millions, could be the big winner, right? Wrong! The truth is many people fail to receive their notices. And those who do either trash them or screw up the forms so badly that they're eliminated! So what are you waiting for? Go through your garbage! Get back that entry form and check every box, affix every stupid sticker and rush it in, because MAD has assembled the figures to prove convincingly...

# WHY TO MAGAZ SU

## Among 50,000,000 entries sent out...

...14,168,000 will ruin their Sweepstakes entry forms by throwing up all over them the moment they see the picture of Ed McMahon.

## Of the remaining 35,832,000...

...184,000 will immediately throw the packet away after discovering that no hard core pornographic magazines are among those being offered.

## Of the remaining 30,886,951...

...3,800,957 will be farmers and yahoos living so far out in the sticks that the mailman can't get through until two weeks after the deadline.

## Of the remaining 27,085,994...

...622,460 will be former Mafia informants who got new identities from the F.B.I. and who are afraid to claim mail addressed to their real names.

# YOU ARE SURE [TO] WIN THE NEXT [MAGAZ]INE PUBLISHERS' [S]WEEPSTAKES

**ARTIST: JOHN CALDWELL**  **WRITER: TOM KOCH**

### Of the remaining 35,648,000...

...2,300,049 will be wealthy Wall Street wheeler-dealers and real estate brokers who don't think prizes of yachts or houses are valuable enough to waste time trying to win.

### Of the remaining 33,347,951...

...2,461,000 will be so confused by all the stickers, form letters, bonus seals, and other garbage that they'll give up without ever finding the Sweepstakes entry form.

### Of the remaining 26,463,534...

...16,917,540 will be so busy reading the magazines that they subscribed to last year in hopes of winning that they won't have time to open this year's contest packet.

### Of the remaining 9,545,994...

...924,875 will be so intent on winning the Promptness Bonus by mailing before "midnight tonight" that they'll be arrested for breaking into the Post Office before "midnight tonight."

## Of the remaining 8,621,119...

...892,500 will only read the part that says, "You may have already won $1,000,000!" and assume they don't have to do anything but wait for the money.

## Of the remaining 7,728,619...

...71,000 will be more than 95 years old, and will reason that it's just plain goofy to go after prize money that's paid out in 30 annual installments.

## Of the remaining 7,657,619...

...2,194,350 will skip it for fear that the publicity of a big contest win might cause the I.R.S. to notice that they've never filed a tax return.

## Of the remaining 5,463,269...

...2,432,005 will fail to participate because they can't find the only obscure option among 85 possibilities that lets you enter without buying anything.

## Of the remaining 3,031,264...

...2,350,000 will be loyal members of the National Society To Wipe Out Junk Mail, and are bound by oath to destroy Sweepstakes envelopes on sight.

## Of the remaining 681,264...

...1,868 will consult numerologists who tell them that their assigned numbers are so unlucky that using them could touch off an epidemic of cholera.

## Of the remaining 679,396...

...679,394 will look closely at the photo of last year's winners and decide that they'd rather lose $1,000,000 than risk being seen with this year's roundup of goons and fools.

## Of the remaining 2...

...1 will be none other than prizemeister Ed McMahon, who is ineligible to win his own contest, thus leaving *you* as the only possible choice for first prize!!

# THE UNNERVING UNDERTAKER'S UNDERTAKING

ARTIST AND WRITER: DUCK EDWING

When we're young, we all play fun party games like "Pin the Tail on the Donkey" and "Beat the Crap Out of Phil." But when we get older, some people start playing other games, like "Impress a

ARTIST: AL JAFFEE

*As we travel through life, we begin to see emerging patterns that occur with eerie regularity. If you don't believe us, check your calendar as we review...*

# THE MAD WEEK

ARTIST: PAUL COKER       WRITER: CHARLIE KADAU

## ON SUNDAYS...

...You stay out late to miss the end-of-weekend traffic jam, only to wind up in a traffic jam of other people who stayed out late for the same reason.

...At about 10:30 p.m. you decide it's time to start working on your weekend homework assignment.

...You add the six sections you "still haven't gotten to" to the pile of Sunday newspaper sections you still haven't gotten to from the past 18 weeks.

## ON WEDNESDAYS...

...You step out your door and finally find where the paperboy threw Monday's newspaper.

...You make the unbelievable discovery that every bookstore in town is sold out of the *Cliff's Notes* of the novel you haven't read a page of yet, but have to hand in a book report on by Friday.

...You make a silent pledge to yourself that by the end of this week you'll finish all the work you had pledged to finish by the end of *last* week.

## ON THURSDAYS...

...At about 4:30 a.m., the sound of garbage trucks reminds you that you didn't put the trash out the night before.

...You finally get up enough nerve to ask someone for a date on Saturday night, only to discover they made other plans yesterday.

...You remember that you still haven't returned the video you rented that was due back last Monday.

# ON MONDAYS...

...Five minutes before you have to be at work, it comes to your attention that you forgot to click back on your alarm clock from the weekend.

...Because you never got around to doing the laundry you have to fish underwear out of the hamper.

...You step out your door to discover that the weather is a lot better than it was all weekend.

# ON TUESDAYS...

...You start your day by realizing you only have enough cash left for carfare or lunch—but not both—until payday on Friday.

...At work, you enter that in-between period when people stop asking "How was your weekend?" but have yet to start asking "So what are you doing this weekend?"

...The mailman finally delivers your copy of last week's *TV Guide*.

# ON FRIDAYS...

...You get an agonizing, throbbing toothache in the early evening—just as your dentist is leaving his office for a 3-day weekend.

...For the umpteenth Friday in a row, you don't know or care *who* ABC News is planning to choose as its "Person of the Week."

...For the first time all week, you can stay up as late as you want—but you get drowsy and fall asleep at your regular time anyway.

# ON SATURDAYS...

...While standing in line at the checkout counter you discover that all the coupon specials you clipped out of last Sunday's supermarket circular are now out-dated.

...Dozens of nuisance chores once again prevent you from watching the hours and hours of video tapes you've recorded over the last two months.

...You make it a point to get home in time to catch "Saturday Night Live" only to be disappointed by the show yet again.

*"Gruesome! Disgusting!! Loathesome!!!"* you bark. But wait! Before you respond too negatively to something, you should consider its alternative. It may be even more vile! So don't just sit there—get up and exercise your decision skills! You have some ugly choices to make as…

# MAD A THE LESSER

**ARTIST: PAUL COKER**

Sleazy "unauthorized biographies" that trash the reputations of defenseless dead celebrities…

**OR**

…the sickeningly pompous "vanity books" celebrities write about themselves while they're still alive?!!

Young pop singers closer to infancy than puberty who are crooning about love and sex…

**O**

Issuing a "Christmas Wish List" ot what you really want—and looking like a greedy, materialistic pig…

**OR**

…taking your chances—and bracing for an onslaught of socks, underwear and fountain pens?!!

Coin-operated video games so addictive, you wind up wasting all your spare cash on them…

**O**

Slick TV commercials produced by ad agency weasels who know all of the "subliminal tricks" in the book…

**OR**

…sub-moronic "home-made" spots put together in a half hour by the company president's brain-dead son-in-law?!!

The repulsive dictators the U.S. associates with in the name of "national security interests"…

**O**

# SKS: WHICH IS OF TWO EVILS???

WRITER: MIKE SNIDER

 ...way-past-their-prime "legends of rock-n-roll" who expect us to believe they're still sixteen?!!

Academy-Award Show production numbers that prove Hollywood has more than its share of tone-deaf clods... **OR** ...the too-horrible-to-contemplate alternative—an evening of uninterrupted acceptance speeches?!!

 Nintendo home versions of the same arcade favorites that merely consume all of your spare time?!!

Missing important calls because bird-brain friends and relatives are always tying up your line... **OR** ...getting Call Waiting—and constantly having your important calls interrupted by the same boobs?!!

 ...the even more loathsome vermin who usually wind up replacing the dictator when he's overthrown?!!

Secretive capitalists who wheel and deal in back rooms, away from the scrutiny of the public eye... **OR** ...self-promoting ego-maniacs of high finance who won't stay out of the public eye for a minute?!!

# THE DIABOLICAL DUNGEON DECEPTION

# THE HAUNTING HUNTING HULLABALOO

ARTIST AND WRITER: DUCK EDWING

These days we're bombarded with information from TV, books, movies, parents, teachers and even worthless humor magazines! Most times, the information is either stupid, useless, embarrassing or too late to do you any good! To see what we mean, think back and consider all of the information you were given lately. Then sit back and ask yourself...

# Do You RE

ARTIST: AL JAFFEE

...Exxon's side of the oil spill story?

...most of the statistics that baseball announcers spew at you?

...the plot line in a porno movie?

...that some guy died in the bedroom of the apartment you just rented?

...the weatherman's five-day forecast, when he usually can't get it right for just one day?

...anything about your Uncle Beppe's goiter operation?

# ALLY Need To Know...

IDEA: MARY PAT LINDL    WRITER: J. PRETE

... how many times a co-worker calling in sick threw up?

...that your dinner companion found a hair in his linguini?

...the number of guys your girl was with before you?

...that your subscription to Time magazine runs out in just 113 more issues?

...how much better a student your older sister was than you?

...at the end of a film, who the "Best Boy" was?

BLUNDER ENLIGHTENING DEPT.

Way back in MAD #254, we presented chapter one of "The MAD 'DON'T' Book," a feature created to explain the value in knowing what <u>not</u> to do in a given situation. We also promised to

# THE MAD "D(

## (Chapte

## CHAPTER 2:
### WHAT <u>NOT</u> TO DO ON A FIRST DATE

DON'T bring your date second-hand flowers.

DON'T try to earn the admiration of your date by exhibiting your pickpocketing skills.

DON'T try to get on the good side of your date's father by showing off your extensive knowledge of pornographic films.

## CHAPTER 3:
### WHAT <u>NOT</u> TO DO AT A HOSPITAL

DON'T take used hypodermic needles from the trash and fashion makeshift "squirt toys" out of them.

DON'T use a patient's oxygen tank to inflate a bunch of "Get Well Soon" balloons.

DON'T try to cheer up a convalescing friend by giving them a cake baked in the shape of the diseased organ they just had removed.

present additional chapters in future issues, although we desperately tried <u>not</u> to do so!
But sadly, recently passed "Truth in Magazine" legislation forces us to finally publish…

# ON'T" BOOK

## 's 2–5)

ARTIST: PAUL COKER    WRITERS: CHARLIE KADAU AND JOE RAIOLA

## CHAPTER 4:
### WHAT <u>NOT</u> TO DO
### IN A CROWDED ELEVATOR

## CHAPTER 5:
### WHAT <u>NOT</u> TO DO
### IN A COURTROOM

**DON'T use the elevator as an intimate catering hall for your wedding reception.**

**Just before declaring a guilty verdict, DON'T convince fellow jurors to join you in doing the "wave."**

**DON'T use the elevator to do research for your term paper, "The Study of Hornets in a Closed Environment."**

**DON'T insist that your attorney attempt to trick a stubborn witness by cross-examining him with a ventriloquist's dummy.**

**DON'T tell a stranger that the last elevator you rode in was so shaky it released all of the toxic gases you carry in your briefcase.**

**DON'T try to sway the jury by filling the courtroom with a flock of parrots, all of whom have been trained to say "not guilty."**

# THE DREADED DENTAL DEBACLE

ARTIST AND WRITER: DUCK EDWING

Today, government agencies, private business and frazzled individuals all have a lot of bad news to dish out that they don't want us to hear. How, then, do they do it? Simple! They bury the negative facts under a heavy layer of positive hot air! This technique of putting us in a good mood before they hit us with the awful truth is a sneaky skill that all MAD readers should learn to recognize—mainly so they can employ the same techniques themselves when the occasion arises. So join us now as we carefully examine some blatant examples we've collected of:

# THE ART OF BREAKING BAD NEWS GENTLY

WRITER: TOM KOCH

## IBEX Industries
### Public Relations Dept.

To All News Editors
FOR IMMEDIATE RELEASE

Ibex Industries is delighted to announce the appointment of Harley J. Pitlik, Jr., to the office of Chairman of the Board. Mr. Pitlik, a loving father as well as a college graduate, replaces C.J. Winterhorn, who retired recently after 36 years of devoted service to the company.

Ibex spokesmen said that Former Chairman Winterhorn is now enjoying a well deserved vacation in Brazil. He has purchased a comfortable villa near Rio de Janeiro with part of the $6,000,000 in company funds that he apparently saw fit to take with him.

## HAVE YOUR OLD FROSTY FRIDGE

### SERVICED FREE

Most refrigerator companies would charge $50 or more to inspect and service their old 1988 models. Not Frosty Fridge! We don't forget our friends just because their warranties have expired. So hire a truck to bring in your old Frosty Fridge—and just look at what you'll receive with our compliments:

1. **FREE** inspection of all moving parts.
2. **FREE** oiling of door hinges.
3. **FREE** water to refill ice cube trays.
4. **FREE** replacement of N-16 valve, which the government claims is defective and could cause your refrigerator to explode.

### HURRY! THIS GENEROUS OFFER MADE FOR A LIMITED TIME ONLY!

## Mandamus & Fleece
### Attorneys at Law

Mr. Jimmy Joe Boxford
c/o Shorty's Pinball Arcade
Beachfront Park

Dear Mr. Boxford:
   Did you know that your blood type (J-Negative) is so rare that it can prove kinship to lost
relatives you didn't even know you had? A
Michigan judge recently decided a $500,000
inheritance case in favor of a lad like you, just
because he and his uncle both had J-Negative
blood.
   Based on that Michigan decision, we soon
hope to unite you legally with your "missing"
infant son. His mother's paternity suit against
you, which will bring about that happy event,
begins at 10 A.M. on Sept. 23 in Circuit Court.
Please be there so I can congratulate you personally on becoming a father.
                              Yours truly,

                              *Fillmore Fleece*
                              Fillmore Fleece

---

Deer Mom and Dad,
I am fine. The reeson I
boam to go Camping out ~~at~~
~~the~~ desert with sum guys
met. They are neet guys.
Cook meels for ~~xx~~ me out
Also, they say you shood
Put $50,000 in the fone
booth by the Bus Stashion
~~at~~ wonce. If you doant,
They say they will stop cookin
Meals for me outdoors and will
leave me hear to rot.
        Luv, Ste...

---

## AMERICAN OINTMENT WORKS, INC.
## REPORT TO STOCKHOLDERS -
## A MESSAGE
## FROM YOUR PRESIDENT

   Successful efforts by Management to slash plant maintenance
and operating costs highlighted the brilliant fiscal year just
completed by American Ointment. Target goals were far surpassed
as the annual outlay for utility service was cut by 87 per-cent.
Similar encouraging reductions were made in purchases of
washroom towels and new pencils.
   The deep cuts were primarily attributable to the permanent
closing of our main factory in April. Department heads optimisti-
cally look forward to even bigger cost reductions this year, once
your company has gone out of business altogether.

---

### WHILE YOU
### WERE OUT

**TIME**
12:30 pm
**MESSAGE**

Your wife wants
you to bring home
romantic incense,
wine and a Phil
Collins CD. She
says they'll help
you make out with
some new babe,
now that she's
leaving you.

left
in
I
They
doors.

'G

# PUBLIC NOTICE

Commuting time between this locality and downtown will soon be cut in half, thanks to construction of the projected Suburbia Freeway. Surveys indicate that the easier access will cause most home values in this area to double. The few homes which will not enjoy this phenomenal increase are those which must be torn down to make room for the Freeway. Fortunately, that only includes the homes in this block. Please be a good neighbor and move your junk out by Thursday so the bulldozer crews can begin their community improvement work.

## FORDYCE PLANCHET CORP.
### ELKPATH, IDAHO

OFFICE OF THE PRESIDENT

Dear Employee:
Sometimes, it pays to count our blessings. That's why I am taking a moment to remind you that the community where we all work is in the heart of a natural wonderland that abounds in fish and game.
If you're like me, you probably wish you had more time to enjoy outdoor pursuits. Now, thanks to the loss of the Snively Lumber account, you'll have unlimited free time following your early retirement. I'll be filled with envy as I picture you cleaning out your locker and leaving this stuffy building forever by 5 P.M. next Friday.

*J. L. Fordyce III*

Signed by Emma Lu Vitsman for Mr. Fordyce, who is out of town on vacation

# A WARM INVITATION TO ALL!!!

Local residents are cordially invited to a free lecture by Police Chief Hugh Newby at the High School next Tuesday evening. The Chief's subject will be, "Making Your Home More Secure." Cookies and Dr. Pepper will be served afterward.

This helpful talk consists of easy-to-follow advice for installing dead bolts, window latches and similar home improvements that may protect citizens from the four maniacs who escaped from the State Work Farm last night and reportedly are heading this way.

If you get goosebumps when a *Home Shopping Network* seller gives you a "toot"...*GET A LIFE!!!!!!!!!!!!!*

If you always make it a point to sit up front on a bus so you can "chat" with the driver...*GET A LIFE!!!!!!!!*

If you are on a first-name basis with all of the security guards at your local shopping mall...*GET A LIFE!!!!!*

## TAKING A SCHLEP IN THE RIGHT DIRECTION DEPT.

There are basically two kinds of people in the world: those who lead rich, exciting lives and those who do not. What group are you in? We're betting, based on the fact you're reading this intro, that you're part of the group that does not—the losers, the sticks-in-the-mud...the dull dweebs! Well, MAD wants to help you change! We're offering the following examples in the hope that they will motivate you to finally get off your butt, hold your head high and go out there and...

**GET**

ARTIST: JACK DAVIS

If you only need to catch the episode where Mr. Drysdale falls into Granny's vat of homemade possum-fat soap to complete your "Beverly Hillbillies" checklist...*GET A LIFE!!!!!!!!!!!!*

If you still own and operate a C.B. radio and you are not a licensed, interstate truck driver...*GET A LIFE!!!!!!!!!*

If your monthly phone bill includes over $75 worth of calls to "Entertainment Tonight" 900# Opinion Polls...*GET A LIFE!!!!!!!!!!!!!!*

If you eagerly anticipate the day your jury duty notice arrives in the mail ... *GET A LIFE!!!!!!!!!!!!*

If you program your VCR to record *The Weather Channel* while you're not at home ... *GET A LIFE!!!!!!!!!*

If you've ever yelled "One more time!" to a wedding band that just finished playing "The Alley Cat" ... *GET A LIFE!!*

# A LIFE !!!!! !!!!

WRITER: CHARLIE KADAU

If you mail back your Publisher's Clearing House Sweepstakes entry form registered, return receipt requested ... *GET A LIFE!!!!!!!!!!*

If you've ever bragged to anyone that your next door neighbor's best friend is Wink Martindale's barber ... *GET A LIFE!!!!!!!!!!!*

If you think you're really putting one over on your bank by cleverly placing two Canadian cents in the centers of your rolls of saved-up pennies ... *GET A LIFE!!!!!!!!!!!!!!*

Spend two minutes with your grandparents and you realize their favorite phrase is "When I Was Your Age..." They can drive you nuts with their recollections! But here's the problem: EVERY generation likes to talk about when they were young! And in just a scant 40-50 years, today's youngsters will be the babblers—boring kids with *their* reminiscing! What will their stories be like? Here's...

# "WHEN I W
## TODAY'S KIDS WIL

**ARTIST: GEORGE WOODBRIDGE**     **WRITER: MIKE SNIDER**

When I Was Your Age...**oxygen masks** were things only **sick** people wore!!

When I Was Your Age...we thought nothing of **walking** from one end of the mall to the other!

When I Was Your Age...I spent only **$1,000** on **Prom Night**—and had **just** as good a time as the kids who spent the **big** bucks!

# AS YOUR AGE... "STORIES
## L BE TELLING THEIR GRANDCHILDREN

When I Was Your Age...folks only needed **three** deadbolts to lock their doors!

When I Was Your Age...they only had **ten** movie screens in one theatre!

When I Was Your Age...only ½ the teams in the NBA made it to the playoffs!

When I Was Your Age...it was the **Mexicans** who snuck into **America** to get the decent-paying jobs!

When I Was Your Age...we had a thing called **"the ozone layer"** to protect us from the sun!

When I Was Your Age...Debbie Gibson and Fred Savage hadn't even **gotten** into **politics** yet!

When I Was Your Age...we had Tone Loc, DJ Jazzy Jeff and the Beastie Boys—now **there** were some **great songwriters!**

When I Was Your Age...our family was so poor, we could only afford to put a phone in **one** of our cars!

When I Was Your Age...Mom **always** made us home-cooked meals—no matter **how** many minutes she had to sweat over the microwave!!!

"You gotta be in it to win it," "All you need is a dollar and a dream," and on and on. Lotteries are big business these days and they run catchy slogans to get you to play. "For a buck, what the—heck!" Well, you've got nothing (much)

# Some Truly Joy
# Could Do If You

End the embarrassment of trying to pass "10¢ OFF" coupons that you know have already expired.

Spend 40¢ a gallon more for what is laughingly called "Full Service" so that you won't have to walk around all day reeking of gasoline.

Wear your clothes once. Then throw them out and buy new ones, so you can avoid those weirdos you meet late at night at the laundromat.

Give every beggar you encounter a quarter to lessen the chances that he will suddenly snap and strangle you for rejecting him.

Put a whole hour's worth of money in the parking meter to escape the pressure of trying to finish all your Saturday errands in 12 minutes.

Replace those cheap ball-point pens in your kitchen drawer that refuse to work until you make a whole page of ovals just to get them started.

to lose. And you might even win! Then you could sail around the world and buy everyone you know a house. And when you tired of that mindless extravagance and wanted to buy *real* happiness, then you could consider our MAD suggestions for..

# ous Things You
# Won The Lottery

**ARTIST: PAUL COKER**   **WRITER: TOM KOCH**

This year, stop waking up your poor mother at 2 a.m. to wish her Happy Birthday just because the long distance rates are lower then.

Hire a fix-it man to figure out where to put that drawerful of parts you have been saving because you assume they fell off something important.

Rejoice that you can now afford to buy 2 hot dogs, a large soda, and a pretzel at an N.F.L. game and still have enough money to buy a ticket.

Hire a cleaning lady. Then hire a translator to help you communicate with your cleaning lady in whatever language it is that she understands.

Avoid those long supermarket check-out lines by shopping exclusively at 7-Eleven, since now you can afford to pay their usual double-mark-up prices.

Stop wasting energy kicking vending machines that take your money and don't give anything back. (Hire a hefty teenager to kick them for you.)

You've done it again—you've said the wrong thing. You've offended someone. And now he's going to punch your lights out. Should you clam up? No! Keep talking! If You keep talking you might

# MORE QUICK R
## EMBARRASSIN

**IN A PUB**

Is that Mrs. Kelly? I hear she **puts out** . . .

Hey, **Kelly!** Telephone!

. . . some **nice snacks** during Happy Hour!

**AT A FUNERAL**

This is one guy **no one** will ever miss . . .

He was my **brother.**

. . . **half** as much as **I will!**

**AT A RESTAURANT**

**Read** my lips, **Mac!** No one gets in here without a **reservation** . . .

**Please, Mad dog!** Don't make **trouble!**

. . . **unless** accompanied by a **beautiful** and **intelligent** date!

**IN A PRIVATE HOME**

Can you **imagine anyone** plunking down **hard earned cash** for a thing like **that** . . .

Yes. **I did.**

. . . when it **clearly** belongs in a **museum** for the **whole country** to enjoy!

# DRAMA ON PAGE 218

**ARTIST AND WRITER: JOHN CALDWELL**

# An Important Message for Unsuccessful People Everywhere From Sheldon Vinegar, D.D.S., President of the

# 2 HOUR SCHOOL OF DENTISTRY

ARTIST: TOM BUNK    WRITERS: JOE RAIOLA AND CHARLIE KADAU

**BIG PROFITS!**

You betcha! In just **TWO SHORT HOURS**, we'll show you all you need to know to become a qualified and **WELL-PAID** dentist! Take our class this morning and be drilling this afternoon—sooner if you skip lunch!

**HOW** do we do it? We don't waste time on unimportant things like X-rays and Novocain. You learn by doing! In just 120 minutes we'll teach you EVERYTHING you need to be familiar with as a graduate of the 2 HOUR SCHOOL OF DENTISTRY, including:

DRILLING AND FILLING
ROOT CANAL
MALPRACTICE SUITS
GUM REBUILDING

OUT OF COURT SETTLEMENTS
TOOTH CAPPING
PLEA BARGAINING
CHANGING YOUR IDENTITY

**Take this short quiz to see if you qualify:**

This man's problem is
A) Pyorrhea
B) Plaque buildup
C) Agreeing to pose for this photo

**ANSWER:** It doesn't matter! If you took the time to take this quiz, you're qualified!

Who needs college? Who needs high school? Just have your patients say "ahh" and get right in there! Send for our full-color brochure and a free canister of nitrous oxide!

10:00    12:00

Remember, you don't need **five years** of **medical training** to tell someone to **"spit"**!

## THE 2 HOUR SCHOOL OF DENTISTRY
P.O. Box 181, New York, NY 10108
Approved and recommended by the same people who run
The Six Minute School of Eye Surgery

T. BUNK

The guy from your class who used to be a flaming liberal calls and says he's now selling tax-free municipal bonds.

You offer your old Rubik's Cube at a garage sale, and the neighbor kids don't know what it is.

Your childhood baseball idol gets elected to the Hall of Fame.

# 12 SURE SIGNS THAT YOU'VE

You read in the paper that Jane Fonda has a daughter who is only about five years younger than you assumed Jane Fonda to be.

You can recall when this season's new fashions were popular the first time.

Your friends stop regarding you as macho when you drink a lot, and start regarding you as a slobbering idiot.

The cop who pulls you over is a guy you went to grade school with.

You realize that 50,000,000 Americans are too young to recall a time when we had a President who wasn't a Republican.

Telephone solicitors give you their sales pitch instead of asking to talk to your mother.

# REACHED ADULTHOOD

ARTIST: RICK TULKA    WRITER: TOM KOCH

The rock group you worshipped as a kid is now heard only as Muzak in medical building elevators.

You begin looking for tell-tale signs that you've inherited your father's baldness.

Your mother stops complaining that you're too young to go steady, and starts complaining that you still haven't made a commitment to anyone.

IT'S A NO DARWIN SITUATION DEPT.

*Darwin's theory of evolution holds that human beings, with the exception of a few Republicans, progressed from monkeys and are forever moving forward in a constant state of change. But we*

# A MAD GUIDE TO

## COMEDY GROUP

**The Three Marx Brothers**

**The Three Stooges**

**The Three Amigos**

## TOP NATIONAL ISSUE

**Civil Rights**

**Watergate**

**Flag Burning**

## TV DOCTOR

**James Kildare**

**Hawkeye Pierce**

**Doogie Howser**

## ARCHITECTURE

**The Pyramids**

**The Great Wall of China**

**Trump Tower**

# ⊃ DEVOLUTION

WRITER: HY BENDER

## DOG ROLE MODEL

Lassie

Benji

Spuds MacKenzie

## FAMOUS SHIPS

The Nina, the Pinta,
and the Santa Maria

The Monitor
and the Merrimack

The Exxon Valdez

## CRUSADING JOURNALIST

Edward R. Murrow

Dan Rather

Geraldo Rivera

## NURTURING TV MOM

June Cleaver

Maude Findlay

Roseanne Conner

# THE LUSTY LEDGE LEGEND

ARTIST AND WRITER: DUCK EDWING

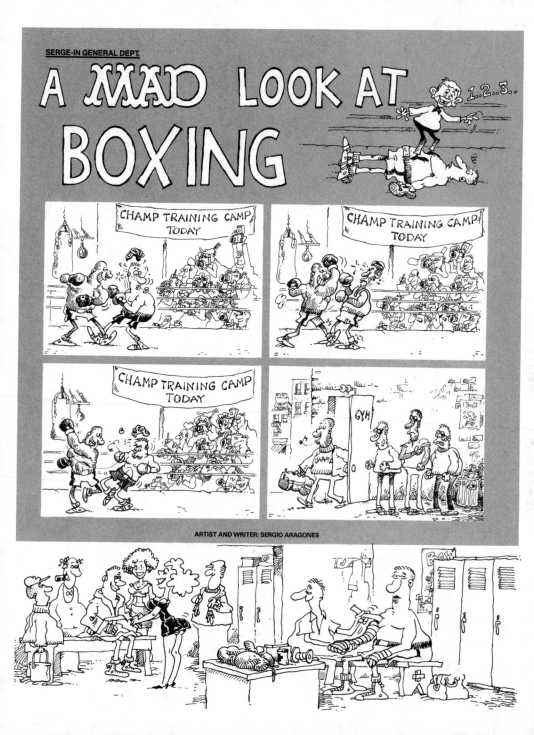

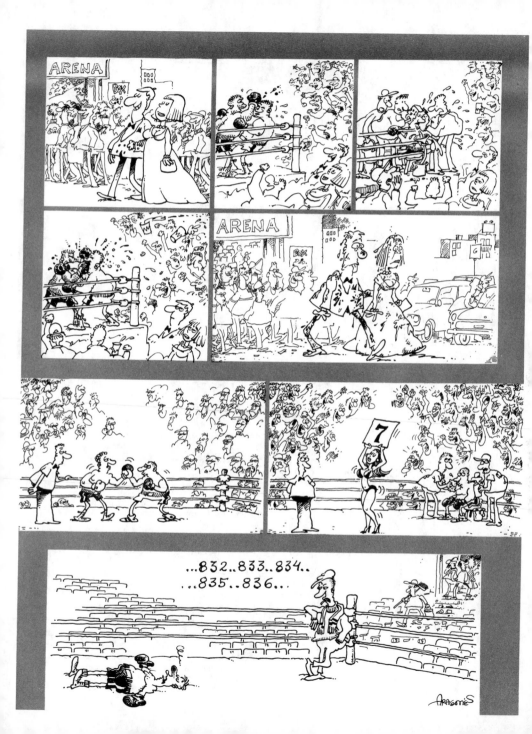

*Reall Di*

Believing anything Exxon says.

Centering a Band-Aid on certain body parts on the first try.

Scalping tickets for a New Jersey Nets/Miami Heat basketball game.

Removing the soap from your body after the water turns cold in the middle of a shower.

Maintaining a friendly expression after a friend tells you that his rottweiler can "smell fear."

Looking calm during a physical exam when your doctor suddenly brings out some weird instrument and tells you to take off your clothes.

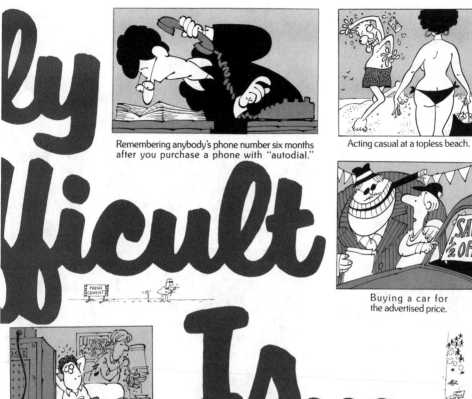

Remembering anybody's phone number six months after you purchase a phone with "autodial."

Acting casual at a topless beach.

Buying a car for the advertised price.

Watching a steamy R-rated film with your mother in the room.

ARTIST: PAUL COKER    WRITER: FRANK JACOBS

Retrieving a contact lens that's traveled up to the back of your eye —or watching someone else do it.

Mending something with Super Glue and not winding up with your fingers stuck together.

# Really Difficult Is...

Getting through to the Department of Motor Vehicles by telephone.

Finding the little screw that just popped out of your glasses.

Getting a giant plastic bag of trash into the can once it splits.

Getting excited about the annual Bud Bowl.

Programming a VCR for a show airing two weeks from Sunday.

Telling the saleslady that she gave you change for ten dollars, when you only gave her five.

Resisting the temptation to pick up that last piece of incredibly delicious chocolate cake that just fell on the floor, and eat it.

ENDORSE OF A DIFFERENT COLOR DEPT.

This nauseating travesty is no doubt familiar to anyone who watches sports on TV: Convinced that 90 minutes of commercials in a 3-hour sportscast isn't enough, networks and advertisers are now "encroaching" on the games themselves! So far, these annoying mini-ads have been limited to kickoffs, home runs and the like, but you can bet your Miller-Lite Beer mug that there will come a day pretty soon...

# WHEN TV SPORTS ADVERTISERS
## decide to "SPONSOR"
# MORE than just
# KICKOFFS & HOME RUNS

ARTIST: JACK DAVIS      WRITER: MIKE SNIDER

THE NATIONAL COUNCIL OF CHURCHES—
*When you haven't got a prayer, come see us!*

**CARNIVAL CRUISES—**
*The next most popular crowd activity in the world!*

**THE SEARS DIE-HARD BATTERY—**
*Your protection against False Starts!*

**BLUE CROSS/BLUE SHIELD—**
*Offering more superior protection than even the best offensive linemen!*

**WARNER COMMUNICATIONS—**
*Producer of the blockbuster motion picture "Batman," now available everywhere on videocassette!*

**MAD MAGAZINE—**
*Delivering cheap shots since 1952!*

**DECIBILL OF GOODS DEPT.**

Here's a word you've probably missed: *onomatopoeia*. Since we're a humor magazine, you may think we made it up, like we did those other silly words, *nerfecsterpoc* and *vog*. YOU FOOL!! An onomatopoeia is a word that sounds like the thing it denotes. For example, "buzz" is an onomatopoeia. Get it?? Probably not, which is why we're scrapping our plans to call this article "A MAD Look at Brand Name Onomatopoeias," and simply calling it

# REALLY

# APPROPRIATE

# BRAND NAME

ARTIST: JOHN POUND    WRITER: RUSS COOPER

# THE EXTRAORDINARY EULOGY ENTRAPMENT

ARTIST & WRITER: DUCK EDWING

Tens of thousands of kiddies have grown up reading about Babar, the king of the land of the elephants. Babar lives in a kinder, gentler world where everything turns out for the best for the elephants and their friends. Yet who knows? Maybe one day they'll have to deal with the not-so-kind, not-so-gentle real world, and we'll have to read

# BABAR'S
# FINAL ADVENTURE

ARTIST: BOB CLARKE          WRITER: FRANK JACOBS

King Babar and Queen Celeste were enjoying a wonderful picnic in a happy meadow in the glorious land of the elephants.

Celeste, who was eating an apple, turned her back to Babar while she threw up. "The apple did not please me," she said.

"Of course it pleased you," said Babar. "It had itself sprayed with chemicals so that it was red and shiny and lovely to look at."

"But it made me sick," Celeste said.

Babar chuckled. "How better could the apple tell you that you shouldn't eat it?"

Celeste threw up again, then smiled. "You're right. It was a most considerate apple."

"Oh, look," Celeste exclaimed. "A truck is taking away Zephir the monkey. I am sad to see him go."

"You shouldn't be," Babar said. "He is being given a chance to help humanity."

"I thought he liked it here," said Celeste.

"He did, but now he will serve medical research by being injected with viruses and implanted with electrodes."

"How nice for him," said Celeste, waving her trunk. "Bye-bye, Zephir. Be sure and write."

Suddenly they saw dozens of animals fleeing from a great fire. Babar recognized his old friend, Duane the giraffe.

"The rain forest is burning!" Duane gasped. "It's a disaster!"

"No, silly," Babar said reassuringly. "It's progress. The timber companies cut down the trees, providing space for the gold miners and cocoa plant growers. What they haven't cut, they burn. Everyone profits!"

"But what about the animals who lose their homes?" asked Celeste.

"They are given the opportunity to relocate and discover if they have the ability to survive," Babar explained.

"In other words, they're being given a *fresh start!*" Celeste exclaimed.

"Exactly," said Babar.

"Let's visit Maurice the alligator," said Celeste.

Babar thought this a splendid idea, and they soon reached the bank of a great river.

"The water once was blue and clear, but now it is brown and polluted," Celeste said in wonderment.

"It's another sign of progress, Babar explained. "Pollution tells us that industries are busy and that the economy is good."

"Look—floating on the surface! That *is* Maurice, isn't it?" asked Celeste.

"That *was* Maurice," said Babar.

As they left the river, Babar and Celeste were dazzled by a very bright glow. The glow was coming from Leonard and Louise Mole.

"Well, just look at *you*," Babar exclaimed as he and Celeste put on their sunglasses. "Are you into Day-Glo these days?"

"Hardly," said Leonard. "We got too close to a nuclear plant, and now we're radioactive. We were among the few lucky ones who survived."

"Look on the *bright side*," Babar said, making a clever play on words. "when you burrow in your hole, you'll always be able to see where you're going."

Nearing a thicket, Babar and Celeste heard someone moaning. Looking down, they saw Darius the fox, his body held fast in a steel trap.

"Looks like you really stepped in it," Babar said.

"Tell me about it," Darius moaned. "Somebody should have warned me about fur trappers."

"It's really not the end of the world," Babar said. "Your pelt will be part of a beautiful coat that will keep some lovely woman warm. Don't you agree, Darius? Darius? Darius?"

"I don't think he can hear you," Celeste said.

"He never was much for conversation," said Babar.

Returning home to their city, Babar and Celeste had a great surprise.

"Look," Celeste said. "Our people are all lying on the ground and have lost their tusks. Are they taking a nap?"

"No," said Babar, "they have given their lives to the ivory poachers. Of course, they would have died eventually anyway, but now their ivory can live forever. Why else would we have been given tusks?"

"Good point!" said Celeste.

All the elephants had been killed except Babar and Celeste. The years passed, but Babar still remembered his elephant family, especially when he played the piano.

"Here's cousin Arthur," Babar said, striking a white key.

"And next to him is old Cornelius," said Celeste, pointing to another white key. "So many of our loved ones are with us. Still, I sometimes wonder if it was right, the wiping out of elephants by humans."

"Of course it was right," Babar said wisely. "After all, humans are the most intelligent species in the world."

**THE END**

**MAD's Handy Clues, Hints And Tipoffs That You're Really, Unquestionably, Without A Doubt...**

When you're playing the piano you frequently lose your grip on the bow.

You go to bed and accidentally fluff up your head.

You're absolutely convinced that nostalgia is a thing of the past.

**ARTIST: SERGIO ARAGONES**

You've caught yourself waving "Goodbye" instead of "Hello" when answering the telephone.

You put a higher antenna on your mailbox in an attempt to receive mail from people farther away.

You go to bed and family members attempt to fluff up your head.

Your neighbor's radio blares at three A.M. and you angrily call him up to demand that he change the station at once.

People repeat everything they say to you because you look way too stupid to grasp things the first time around.

People repeat everything they say to you because you look way too stupid to grasp things the first time around.

You go to bed and purposely fluff up your head.

**WRITER: DAN BIRTCHER**

You purchase season tickets to the Super Bowl.

You have trouble picking your shadow out of a crowd.

You fret over the fact that they never mention what a hurricane's last name is.

You find yourself complaining to a waitress that the straw in your glass is upside down.

You find yourself wondering what branch of the military Captain Kangaroo was in.

Your biggest worry about marriage is getting that little ring over your loved one's head, down their arm and onto their second finger.

You find yourself trying to convince a policeman who's pulled you over for a burned-out headlight that he merely has one eye closed.

You worried about a sore that wouldn't heal, only to find out later that it was a natural body opening.

# THE HYMN OF THE

ARTIST: GEORGE WOODBRIDGE    WRITER: FRANK JACOBS

Our eyes have seen the sorrow of a nation gone to pot,
Where the loonies carry handguns and the passersby get shot,
Where the farms are going under and the cities burn and rot—
    The Glory Days are gone!

    Lordy, Lordy, how'd we do..it?
    Now..we have to suffer through..it!
    Had..our chance but really blew..it!
        The Glory Days are gone!

We've a budget we can't balance, though we once were in the chips;
We've been overspending billions for outmoded planes and ships;
If you haven't figured out who'll foot the bill, just read our lips—
    The debt keeps piling on!

    Kindly, gently, how they stroke..us
    With..their fiscal hocus-pocus!
    All..the time they're out to soak..us!
        The debt keeps piling on!

We have seen the big polluters fill our waterways with swill;
We have smelled the fishes dying from the latest tanker spill;
If the oil doesn't kill them, then the garbage surely will—
    The crud keeps flowing on!

    Pity, pity, our poor na-tion!
    Who..can stop the devasta-tion?
    May-be Bo knows conserva-tion!
        The crud keeps flowing on!

We get smacked by soaring prices when we gas up at the pumps;
We have seen the reckless loggers turn our forests into stumps;
Now we're bailing out the S&Ls who've played us all for chumps—
    The greed goes marching on!

    Surely, surely, trouble's brew-ing
    From..the damage that they're do-ing!
    We're..the ones who get the screw-ing!
        The greed goes marching on!

We have heard those scuzzy rappers spouting sleaze for easy cash;
We're turned off by TV sitcoms spewing out their mindless trash;
All which makes us very thankful for old episodes of "M*A*S*H"—
    The drek keeps coming on!

    Cowabunga! how we're hat-ing
    What..they'll do to get a rat-ing!
    Like..a whale regurgitat-ing!
        The dreck keeps coming on!

In the alleys of our cities where the poor and homeless dwell,
You can see the victims dying from the crack that pushers sell,
While the bankers launder money for the Medellín cartel—
    The crime keeps marching on!

    Spurting, gushing, blood is flow-ing,
    While..the murder rate is grow-ing!
    Down..the tubes we're surely go-ing!
        The Glory Days are gone!

# Battered Republic

*Why do we study history? Because they make us! And because they're right—those who don't remember the past are doomed to relive it! But things never happen quite the same way*

# SMALL SCALE EX
# HISTORY REP

**50,000 B.C.** Through sheer will power, man makes it through the Ice Age.

**1860** The Pony Express begins, with riders taking care of the horses at every opportunity.

**2200 B.C.** Lust for immortality spurs the Egyptians to wrap themselves in precious linens.

**1778** Love of country prompts George Washington to spend cruel winter at Valley Forge.

**Today** Through sheer will power, man makes it through the Ice Capades.

**Today** the U.S. Postal Service continues, with employees taking every opportunity to horse around.

**Today** Lust for high office spurs politicians to wrap themselves in precious linens.

**Today** Love of Bon Jovi prompts Sally Greps to spend cruel night in line at arena ticket office.

**1787** The Founding Fathers create a new nation at the Constitutional Convention in Philadelphia.

**2 Billion B.C.** Life forms in a swamp's ancient, soupy goo.

**1839** Samuel Morse sees his telegraph is built and taps out "What hath God wrought?"

**1804** Curiosity spurs Lewis and Clark to go explore the Louisiana Territory.

twice! Sometimes you have to look pretty closely to spot the repetition…or let us look for you! So, without further ado (and just in time for that big test!), we proudly present some

# AMPLES OF HOW
# EATS ITSELF!

ARTIST: TOM BUNK    WRITER: DAN BIRTCHER

**Today** Fred's father creates a sensation at the Confectioners' Convention in Atlantic City.

**Today** Life forms in a diner's old, gooey soup.

**Today** Mr. Fiksman sees his telephone bill and shrieks out, "Who in God's name can afford this?!"

**Today** Curiosity spurs Louis and Claire to consider going to a different bowling alley.

**30 million B.C.** Apes leave the trees and regroup on the ground in order to achieve a better life.

**1810** Napoleon is painted with his hand in his coat because that is the style in France.

**1620** Desire to be free of England drives pilgrims to the New World.

**1066** The Normans invade England and make it their home.

**Today** The Monkees leave retirement and regroup on the stage in order to recapture the good life.

**Today** Congressmen are videotaped with their hands in the cookie jar because that is the style in D.C.

**Today** Desire to be free of wife drives Mr. Hanrahan to his basement workshop.

**Today** Norman's uncle invades his apartment and makes it his home.

The Jolly Green Giant. The Pillsbury Doughboy. Spuds MacKenzie. The California Raisins. The list is endless! All of them the products of an ad executive's limited imagination, and all of them rammed down our throats until they become the beloved symbols of the goods they were

# ADVERTISING CHARACTER
## THAT BETTER REFLECT THE MISERA

**EXXON'S**
Oscar, the
Oily Otter

**KENMORE'S**
Bait & Switch, the Shady
Sears Appliance Salesmen

**HUMANA HOSPITAL'S**
Hank, the Talking Bag of
Infectious Medical Waste

**COCA COLA'S**
Dancing Decayed
Teeth

**THE NATIONAL FOOTBALL LEAGUE'S**
Anabolic
Steroid Family

ARTIST: GEORGE WOODBRIDGE     WRITER: CHARLIE KADAU

created to huckster for! We've always found something phony about these characters, though. We just don't think they truly represent what their respective companies are like! Besides truth in advertising, we'd like to see some truth in advertising *characters!* We'd like some...

# S & CORPORATE MASCOTS
## BLE COMPANIES THEY WORK FOR

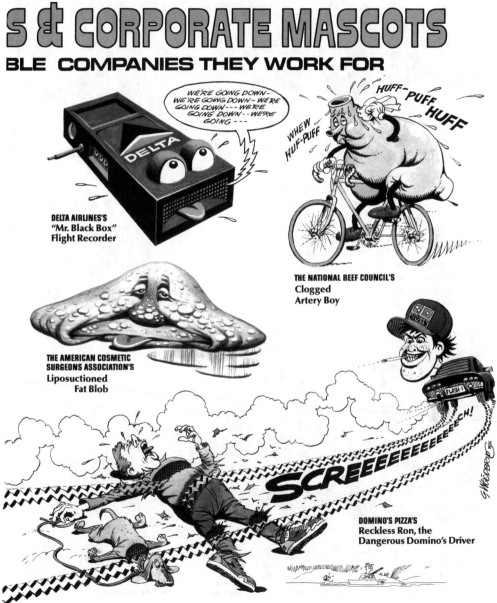

DELTA AIRLINES'S
"Mr. Black Box"
Flight Recorder

THE NATIONAL BEEF COUNCIL'S
Clogged
Artery Boy

THE AMERICAN COSMETIC
SURGEONS ASSOCIATION'S
Liposuctioned
Fat Blob

DOMINO'S PIZZA'S
Reckless Ron, the
Dangerous Domino's Driver

The latest VCRs can be set to record a program two weeks from now, by which time any show worth watching will probably have been cancelled.

Many new cigarette brands have been developed to attract very specific economic and ethnic groups, which means that all Americans now have an equal opportunity to get lung cancer.

### THERE'S ALWAYS GLOOM FOR IMPROVEMENT DEPT.

Most Americans know Murphy's Law—"Whatever can go wrong will go wrong!" And you probably know the Peter Principle ("Individuals rise to their levels of incompetence.") and Parkinson's Law ("Work expands to fill the time left for its completion."). But do you know the theory that really explains what's wrong with modern life? Find out! Follow us into the informational void as we take...

**THE MAD MAXIM:
"EXPERTS NEVER STOP MAKING
'IMPROVEMENTS' UNTIL
EVERYTHING BECOMES IMPRACTICAL!"**

# A MAD LO
# HOW
# WE'VE

ARTIST PAUL COKER

By spending hundreds of billions of dollars, the Pentagon has developed a new and sophisticated military establishment that can allegedly win a full scale nuclear war in outer space—but not in Central America.

So many glitzy accessories have been added to new cars that buyers who only want an AM radio and a heater are warned that they're now going to have to pay substantially more for such a unique "customized" model.

# OK AT

# FAR COME

WRITER: TOM KOCH

Educators keep writing simpler textbooks hoping that they will encourage underachievers, with the result that bright kids now don't learn anything except how to underachieve.

To enable more fans to enjoy major league sports, many new expansion teams have recently been formed, all manned by players who definitely belong in the minor leagues.

Colleges across the U.S. have become so expert in obtaining TV revenue for their football teams that they can now be profitable without having any real students at all.

**THE MAD MAXIM:
"EXPERTS NEVER STOP MAKING
'IMPROVEMENTS' UNTIL
EVERYTHING BECOMES IMPRACTICAL!"**

Organizational skill within professional boxing can be thanked for giving us so many different weight divisions and so many different Federations that every fighter in the world is now the champion of something.

The miracle of direct long distance dialing has become so widespread that it is now possible for almost any drunk anywhere in the world to wake you at three in the morning.

Pharmaceutical companies have introduced so many new life-saving drugs that hospital emergency rooms have become filled with scores of people suffering from the harmful side effects of taking them.

Increasingly creative corporate financing has made it possible for virtually any kid with a lemonade stand to take over General Motors just by issuing enough junk bonds.

Bicycles, which became popular as inexpensive alternatives to the automobile, have been so upgraded that the same people who could not afford to buy a car now also cannot afford to buy a bicycle.

In our complicated, modern world, there are tons of books around which explain how complex and sophisticated contraptions such as the Stronifium Zertometer and the Digital Shovel operate. But here at MAD, we are bold enough to ask: "Of what use is it to know the innermost workings of an Autoflab HamChip, if you have no appreciation for life's simple pleasures??" Wise words indeed. Well, Here at MAD, no one is as simple-minded as Al Jaffee, who concocted this handy guide explaining how simple things work! Coincidentally, the name of this article is...

# A MAD GUIDE TO
# HOW SIMPLE THINGS WORK PART II

## THE COTTON SWAB

The cotton swab (or "Q" tip, as it's commonly referred to) is a soft plastic stick with little pieces of cotton wrapped on each end.

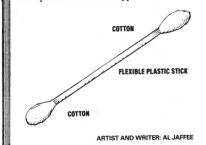

COTTON

FLEXIBLE PLASTIC STICK

COTTON

**ARTIST AND WRITER: AL JAFFEE**

The cotton swab has no equal when it comes to cleaning out any orifice in the human body. However, since this is a family magazine, we will only discuss cleaning wax out of the ears.

As with any product that is inserted into part of the anatomy, special care must be taken to avoid injuring delicate tissue.

If for some unexpected reason the cotton swab has been inserted too far, you may want to consult an ear doctor. If it has been inserted way too far, you may want to consult a brain surgeon!

## THE DOG LEASH

The dog leash is a leather or cloth strap with a clasp at one end and a loop at the other end.

**COLLAR CLASP**

**STRAP**

**HAND LOOP**

To use, you simply open the clasp to the desired width and gently clip it to the dog's collar ring.

## THE KEY CHAIN

The key chain is simply a length of chain with a metal or plastic clasp on one end and a key ring on the other end.

**BELT CLASP**

**KEY**

**KEY RING**

**CHAIN**

The clasp easily attaches to a belt or belt loop while the keys at the other end are safely tucked into a pocket.

## THE NUTCRACKER

The basic nutcracker consists of two steel handles joined by a hinge. Each handle has teeth with which to hold the nut in place.

**HANDLE**

**HINGE**

**TEETH**

**HANDLE**

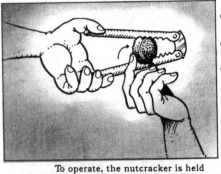

To operate, the nutcracker is held in one hand while the nut is placed between its teeth with the other hand.

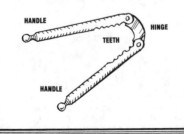

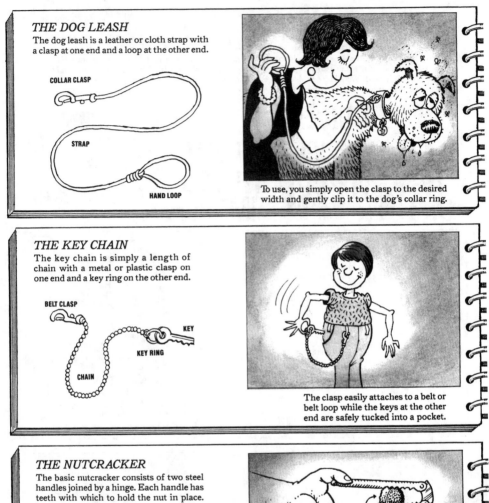

It is now easy to walk the dog while controlling its movement. If the dog is large, you may want to make a few turns of the loop end around your hand.

This, however, is not always advisable, especially if your dog happens to be a male in heat with amorous designs on the poodle down the street!

A quick tug on the chain produces the key you require for easy insertion into the keyhole.

It is advisable to make sure no one is home to suddenly open the door with embarrassing results!

To crack the nut, the handles are carefully and slowly brought together. For most nuts a modest amount of pressure will suffice.

Every now and then, certain nuts (notably Brazil nuts) resist being cracked. If both hands must be employed, be sure no one is nearby, since the sudden explosion is like flying shrapnel!

## THE SAFETY MATCH

The safety match is a small wooden stick with flame producing chemicals at the tip.

**MATCHSTICK**　　**HEAD**

**MATCHBOX**

MATCHLESS SAFETY MATCHES

**SCORE**

What makes it a "safety" match is that it will only light when rubbed against the specially treated "score" on the match box.

## THE DESKTOP TAPE DISPENSER

The dispenser is a heavy molded metal or plastic container into which a roll of tape is inserted. It is heavily weighted so that it will stay firmly in place allowing for convenient one-handed use.

**TAPE**

**SERRATED CUTTER**

**WEIGHTED DISPENSER**

Grasping the tape carefully between index finger and thumb, it is pulled across the sharp serrated cutter. A swift downward pull cuts off a piece of the desired length.

## DENTAL FLOSS

Dental floss is basically a waxed or unwaxed string that comes in a plastic spool dispenser.

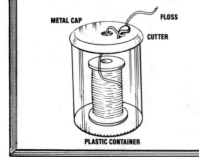

**METAL CAP**　　**FLOSS**

**CUTTER**

**PLASTIC CONTAINER**

To ready for use, a length of floss is wrapped tightly around the middle finger on each hand.

To use, one merely has to firmly strike the match head against the matchbox strip. (Not too firmly! There are often weak spots in the match stick!)

If a weak spot causes the match stick to break and fly off, make sure you follow its flight path. A lost safety match can lose its safeness mighty fast!

**CAUTION**

Serrated Cutter Problem #1: Cutter too dull. Tape won't cut, resulting in the heavy dispenser falling off desk!

Serrated Cutter Problem #2: Cutter too sharp. Tape cuts easily, but so do your fingers, resulting in blood and agony!

Next, guided by the index fingers, the floss is pressed between the teeth to dislodge any rotting, decayed food particles stuck there.

Never flip the floss! You could launch smelly food and other disgusting matter on the walls and furnishings creating an unpleasant mess!

# IF YOU'RE TIRED OF READING INANE INTRODUCTIONS

**IF** you've been training your cat to go in its box for the last 14 years and the little flea-bag still takes a wizz wherever it feels like ...

**IF** you spend most of your time at a wedding reception trying to get the bride and groom to kiss by continuously clinking your glass ...

**IF** your team is down by 40 in the fourth quarter and you're frantically trying to get a Wave started in the crowd ...

**IF** you've been blaring your car's horn for five straight minutes and traffic still hasn't moved ...

**IF** you're into your second hour of trying to figure out who had what instead of just splitting the restaurant check evenly among the ten of you ...

**IF** you religiously keep a diary of everything that happens to you at your job at the shoe store because you're convinced it will someday make a great movie ...

**IF** you weigh 196 pounds or more and still buy negligees from Frederick's of Hollywood ...

**IF** it's your lifelong quest to find a pair of good-looking shoes that are comfortable too ...

**IF** you're 46 years old, still live at home with your parents and are determined to save yourself for the right man ...

**IF** you're desperately clinging to the hope that the IRS is summoning you down to their offices to compliment you on the neatness of your tax return ...

# MAD'S BY-THE-NU
# PREDICTING TV TABLOID AN

ARTIST: RICK TULKA

**1 CHILD ACTOR**
is
Gary Coleman begging for work

**2 CHILD ACTORS**
is a
Beverly Hills drug bust

**3 CHILD ACTORS**
is a
new ABC sitcom with too
many—or too few—Dads

**4 CHILD ACTORS**
is the
next "made-to-order"
pop-music sensation

**1 ACTRESS**
is a
new perfume campaign

**2 ACTRESSES**
is an
"on-the-set feud" denial

**3 ACTRESSES**
is the
latest "trendy cause"

**4 ACTRESSES**
is an
expose on Warren Beatty's love life

**1 SOUTHERN REDNECK**
is a
UFO sighting

**2 SOUTHERN REDNECKS**
is a
promo for a fishing show on ESPN

**3 SOUTHERN REDNECKS**
is a
fatal hunting accident

**4 SOUTHERN REDNECKS**
is the
front row at a demolition derby

# JMBERS GUIDE TO D "INFO-TAINMENT" STORIES

WRITER: MIKE SNIDER

**1 FUNDAMENTALIST**

is a letter-writing campaign against "Married ... with Children"

**2 FUNDAMENTALISTS**

is a sex scandal

**3 FUNDAMENTALISTS**

is a Mark Twain book-burning

**4 FUNDAMENTALISTS**

is Jesse Helms' re-election campaign

**1 COLLEGE ATHLETE**

is a recruiting scandal

**2 COLLEGE ATHLETES**

is an academic-cheating suspension

**3 COLLEGE ATHLETES**

is a "point-shaving" conspiracy

**4 COLLEGE ATHLETES**

is a police line-up

**1 PSYCHIC/ASTROLOGER**

is a look at "The powers inside the Reagan White House"

**2 PSYCHIC/ASTROLOGERS**

is another "New Age" California cult

**3 PSYCHIC/ASTROLOGERS**

is the National Enquirer editorial board

**4 PSYCHIC/ASTROLOGERS**

is a Shirley MacLaine book-signing

# AMERICA
## LAND OF
## OPPORTUNITY

ARTIST: GEORGE WOODBRIDGE    WRITER: MIKE SNIDER

...where those who excelled in school can earn half as much as plumbers who didn't!

...where a former Draft Dodger can rise almost to the position of power to send brave volunteers into war!

...where the Presidency is just an entry-level position to a really big-money career!

...where a tycoon undergoing total financial meltdown can sell thousands of copies of his book, "Surviving at the Top!"

...where crucial jobs in transportation are open to all—regardless of criminal record or level of intoxication!

...where a video camera and an expendable loved-one are your ticket to a chance at $100,000!

...where merely acting in a film about something makes you more of an "expert" than people who lived through it!

...where the government will actually pay people to grow a deadly substance it's trying to eradicate!

...where any citizen with a bottomless bank account and five years to spare can have his "day in court"!

...where Congressmen from every state—no matter how small or poor—can line their pockets equally!

...where employment as an armed security guard is open to all—regardless of prior criminal record!

...where public education truly does prepare young children for real life as grown-ups!

Several issues back, we astutely pointed out to you the true UNimportance of words in everyday life. It is not the words that are significant, we explained, so much as the particular context in which the words are used. Judging by the letters we received after publishing this

# MORE SAME WORDS... *DIFFE*

"I PICKED IT THIS MORNING!"

*...is okay when discussing fruits and vegetables.*

*...not okay for just about anything else!*

HE'S GOT HIS M

*...is cute when cuddling a newborn.*

"COLD AND CLOUDY!"

*...is fine when describing today's weather.*

*...revolting when describing your school cafeteria's soup du jour!*

FILL'

*...is expected when pumping gas is your job.*

"SNAP, CRACKLE, POP!"

*...is pleasant when it's the sound made by your cereal every morning.*

*...unpleasant when it's the sound made by your body every morning!*

I'M OUT

*...is bad news when it's your father or mother.*

article, we came to the conclusion that you applauded this amazingly clever and bold observation (although our conclusion could change once we actually get around to reading those three letters)! In any event, using *different* words and *different* circumstances, we now present...

# 'RENT CIRCUMSTANCES!

ARTIST: RICK TULKA    WRITER: J. PRETE

**MOTHER'S EYES**

...a tad disturbing when hiding from a psychotic homicidal maniac!

**EAT MY SHORTS!**

...is funny when Bart Simpson yells it at his Mom and Dad.

...not so funny when you yell it at yours!

**ER UP!**

...insulting when you are applying for a job!

**I'D LIKE A SMALLER CUP!**

...is no problem when buying a soda.

...a big problem when buying a bra!

**OF WORK!**

...great news when it's one of the Senators involved in the Savings and Loan Scandal!

**TWO DOWN AND THREE ACROSS ARE ALL YOU HAVE LEFT!**

...is fine when describing the last clues to a crossword puzzle.

...not so fine when a dentist is describing your last remaining teeth!

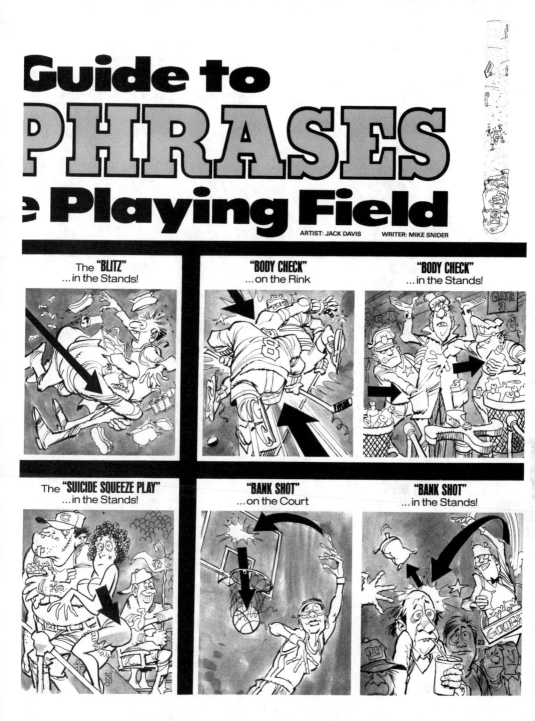

# Guide to PHRASES
## e Playing Field

ARTIST: JACK DAVIS    WRITER: MIKE SNIDER

The "BLITZ"
...in the Stands!

"BODY CHECK"
...on the Rink

"BODY CHECK"
...in the Stands!

The "SUICIDE SQUEEZE PLAY"
...in the Stands!

"BANK SHOT"
...on the Court

"BANK SHOT"
...in the Stands!

23

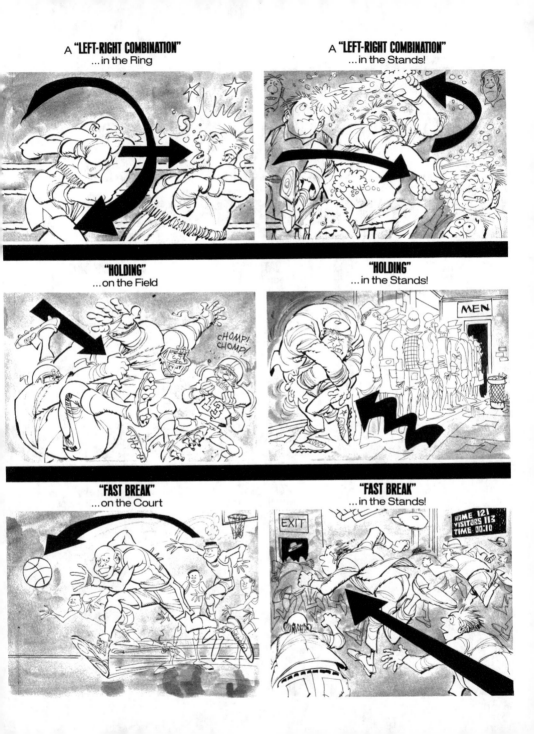

When you need to know about Yo-Yo tricks, you should come to the Yo-Yos here at MAD! We are the official keeper of the list of...

# UNOFFICIAL Y O-YO TRICKS
# EVERY KID KNOWS

ARTIST: PAUL COKER     WRITER: DAN BIRTCHER

**PLUMBING THE DEPTHS**

**BUMPS IN THE NIGHT**

**TEASING THE BEAST-THING**

**FLIRTING WITH DEATH**

**SYMPHONY FOR DRYER**

**CONFUSING THE DRUNK**

Each year, millions of tiny kids are herded into day care centers and Sunday schools where they are commanded to join in the singing of traditional songs and carols before they are old enough to read and understand the lyrics. The result is tragically predictable. They sing the words they think they hear, and form a pattern that often lasts a lifetime. Many preoccupied grownups keep right on singing the same muddled words to the same songs in the same way. This, of course, makes us sound like a nation of idiots as we stand reverently at such somber events as patriotic rallies, church services and even baseball games to fill the air with…

# AMERICA'S TI

## *AS THEY SOUN*

## My Uncle, Liz And Me

*My uncle, Liz and me*

*Eat ham with liberty.*
*Of tea, we sing.*

*Ham that my father fried;*
*Ham when the children cried.*

*On every mountainside,*
*Let's clean 'til Spring.*

## The Star Strangled Grandma

*No way can you see through this song's early light*
*What had sounded like hail at the night light's loud screaming.*

*Who brought tripe and Mars bars to the last Eastern flight*
*On the rampage with scotch while the gals were all steaming.*

*And our pockets were bare*
*When they first hit the air*
*As they proved we were right and our bags were still there.*

*No way does that star strangled Grandma smell Dave,*
*For the mandolin is free,*
*And our home is a cave.*

# RADITIONAL SONGS

ARTIST: PAUL COKER   WRITER: TOM KOCH

## D TO FIVE-YEAR-OLDS

### That Marine! Him!

*From the Halls of Minneso-ota*
*To the doors of misery,*

*We will ride on grumpy ca-attle*
*In Iran and Italy.*

*If the Army or the Navy*
*Ever look at magazines,*

*They will find the creeps with garden tools*
*Have been smashed to smithereens.*

### America, The Boot Is Full

*Your boot is full of spacey guys,*
*And candles made by Jane,*

*From curdled mounds of macramé*
*Above the flutes in Spain.*

*America! America! Go shed your grapes on me.*

*Your clown's no good at motherhood.*
*We'll see what we shall see.*

*Every year around Christmas, magazines are filled with articles about how millions of people suffer from Christmas depression (brought on, no doubt, by those very same articles!). Unlike*

# WHY WE GET THE

ARTIST: GEORGE WOODBRIDGE

## Valentine's Day

... is the time of the year when our loved ones show their affection towards us by giving us a 20 lb. box of chocolate that's been sitting in a warehouse all year long.

## President's Day

... is the time of the year when greedy store owners honor a President who never told a lie by running deceptive ads, and a President who freed the slaves by keeping American consumers in continual debt.

## Arbor Day

... is the time of the year when politicians who have passed legislation that's destroyed rivers and forests show their concern for ecology by planting a tree at a shopping mall.

## Memorial Day

... is the time of the year when television announcers tell us to drive carefully so that we can watch race-car drivers kill themselves during the Indianapolis 500.

*other magazines, though, MAD would <u>never</u> print depressing articles about Christmas. No, we'd rather run a depressing article about **<u>every</u>** holiday! So get ready as we give you a rundown of…*

# HOLIDAY BLAHS

WRITER: BARRY LIEBMAN

## St. Patrick's Day

…is the time of the year when we show our respect for Irish-Americans by getting stinking drunk in their honor and throwing up our guts at their parade.

## Mother's and Father's Day

…are the times of the year when every piece of junk that can't be unloaded on anybody at any other time is advertised as being "perfect for both Mom and Dad."

## Labor Day

…is the time of the year when we celebrate our last remaining days of vacation by going out and enduring endless traffic jams, or staying in and enduring twenty hours of Jerry Lewis.

## Columbus Day

…is the time of the year when we commemorate a man who lost two boats and ended up totally off-course by keeping the post office closed.

# Halloween

... is the time of the year when stories of ghosts, goblins, and things that go bump in the night pale next to stories about psychos poisoning Trick or Treat candy.

# Election Day

... is the time of the year when we officially give someone who has spent $20 million to get a $100,000 job the chance to manage our money.

# Veteran's Day

... is the time of the year when we show our appreciation to all the old soldiers who hated marching in 10-mile hikes by allowing them to march in 10-mile parades.

# Thanksgiving

... is the time of the year when we honor the notion of sharing by recounting how the Indians fed the same people who would eventually steal their land away from them.

# Christmas

... is the time of the year when parents have to explain why the same Santa who's so worried about kids being naughty or nice is urging them to smoke and drink in cigarette and liquor ads.

# New Year's Eve

... is the time of the year when all the restaurants and night clubs show their holiday spirit by handing out noise-makers and raising their prices 400%.

# THE ASTOUNDING AERONAUTIC ADVENTURE

ARTIST & WRITER: DUCK EDWING

**GRENADE HOCKEY**

FATAL DISTRACTIONS DEPT.

With violence in sports attracting such a wide audience, it won't be

# MAKING
# MO
# DANGE

ARTIST AND WRITER:

**TAG TEAM BRIDGE**

**BOBBING FOR PIRANHA**

**.12 GAUGE PING PONG**

BAVOOM!  CHA-CHUNK!

CHUNK!

SPAK!

**PHONE BOOTH CROQUET**

PHONE    TELEPHONE

too long before other activities join the new trend towards...

# GAMES
# RE
# ROUS

TOM CHENEY

**BLINDMAN'S BLENDER**

**BOULEVARD BADMINTON**

**VERTICAL SKATEBOARDING**

**DEMOLITION CHESS**

T.N.T.

Everyone does something they take pride in, something they love to do while the whole world

# ONLY WHEN Y

...can you trip over your own big feet and
not look back for some imaginary obstacle!

...do you fancy yourself the next Tom Cruise!

...can you do a quick deodorant check!

...will you pass the Church collection
plate without putting any money into it!

...do you dare check your zipper without using
the famous "decoy belt-straightening maneuver"!

looks on. But there are other things people are not so proud of—vile things best performed ...

# YOU'RE SURE

# NO ONE

# IS WATCHING...

...do you rehearse important
phone conversations out loud!

...can you do anything with the hand you sneeze
on because you didn't have a handkerchief!

ARTIST: PAUL COKER     WRITER: MIKE SNIDER

...do you take a big swig of
milk right out of the carton!

...do you sneak a peek at the bill before offering to pay it!

When you're shopping, there are certain things a salesman might say to you that should tip you off that he's about to give you the proverbial 1–2 shaftaroony! For example, "I'm about to give you the proverbial 1–2 shaftaroony!", although most salesmen are more clever and use subtler techniques. In any case, whatever he's recommending you buy, the thing to do is select another model—or better yet, another salesman! But really, pal, take it from us, if you want a really great deal on an unbeatable MAD article, then you must check out...

# SALESMEN'
## *THAT*

## When Buying a Microwave Oven

The **nice thing** about this one is that you can cook with the **door open** to tell when the **food's done!**

This is the **latest** in **microwave technology.** Instead of the tray inside turning, the **entire unit shakes** as it heats!

There's no **complicated timer!** The built-in smoke detector **shuts it off!**

## When Buying a Watch

The **crystal comes out** when you touch it so you can see the **time** in daylight without an **annoying reflection!**

The watch **gains five minutes** a day, so you're **never late for anything!**

**Rolex, Relix**—what's **the difference?**

**ARTIST: TOM BUNK**

## When Buying a Computer

The company says the **battery life** for this **laptop** is only **45 minutes** to protect themselves. You can figure it's **actually** good for **five or six hours!**

Maybe **YOU** haven't heard of **Slapdash Computers** but it's the **computer of the pros!**

Sure the **space bar** is in the **back** of the **machine**, but you'll be **amazed** at **how fast** you get **used to it!**

## When Buying a Camera

This is **much** better than any **name brand.** Besides, I hear **Nikon, Canon** and **Minolta** are **getting out** of the **camera business!**

**Sure** it takes a couple of **pounds** of **pressure** to push the **exposure button.** That feature is going to **save you** dozens of accidentally **wasted shots!**

This fully loaded **$19.00 camera** is made by a **major manufacturer** who's name I'm **not allowed to mention!**

# S CLAIMS AND COME-ONS
## *SHOULD SET YOU RUNNING*

### When Buying a Backpack

If it was **waterproof**, any stuff you spilled inside would **never** leak out and **dry**!

The **color comes off** on your **clothes** so it looks like a **matched ensemble!**

The straps are only held by a **single thread** so you don't **overload** the bag!

WRITER: DICK DEBARTOLO

### When Buying an Air Conditioner

Sure it **sounds loud** here in the **showroom,** but late at night in your **bedroom,** you'll **never notice** the **noise!**

And the **best thing** about this **air conditioner** is that it's built in **Sri Lanka,** the **QUALITY CAPITAL** of the world!

A **thermostat** on an **air conditioner** is **nothing** but a **needless frill!**

### When Buying a VCR

A **tape counter?** Why **pay extra** for something **no one uses?**

It's **so simple** to program, there is **NO instruction book!**

The **cabinet** is **supposed** to be that **hot** when the machine is on! It **pre-heats** the **video tape!**

### When Buying a Color TV

They don't use **real wood** for the cabinet any more because **plastic** looks more **natural!**

Surprisingly enough, the manufacturer did a survey and **not one customer missed** having a **volume control!**

You can't really **judge** a **TV** just by its **features, performance** and the **way it works!**

Ever wonder about the correlation between seemingly unrelated events—
between say, the number of crimes per 1000 households and the number of

# CAUSE OR CO

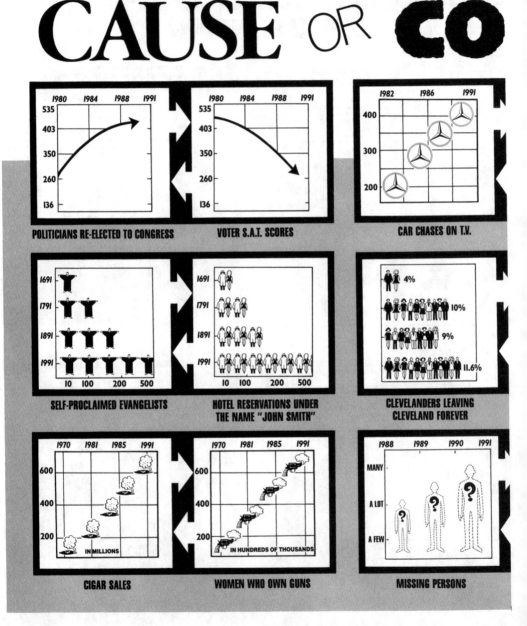

POLITICIANS RE-ELECTED TO CONGRESS

VOTER S.A.T. SCORES

CAR CHASES ON T.V.

SELF-PROCLAIMED EVANGELISTS

HOTEL RESERVATIONS UNDER
THE NAME "JOHN SMITH"

CLEVELANDERS LEAVING
CLEVELAND FOREVER

CIGAR SALES

WOMEN WHO OWN GUNS

MISSING PERSONS

homes that display plastic snowmen? Is there a connection?? *Ummm...*no.
But other statistical pairs *do* suggest definite links. You decide! Are they...

# INCIDENCE??

ARTIST: GEORGE WOODBRIDGE    WRITER: DAN BIRTCHER

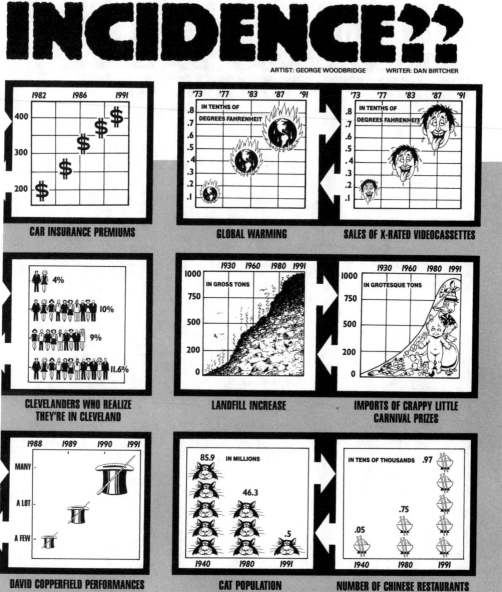

**CAR INSURANCE PREMIUMS**

**GLOBAL WARMING**

**SALES OF X-RATED VIDEOCASSETTES**

**CLEVELANDERS WHO REALIZE THEY'RE IN CLEVELAND**

**LANDFILL INCREASE**

**IMPORTS OF CRAPPY LITTLE CARNIVAL PRIZES**

**DAVID COPPERFIELD PERFORMANCES**

**CAT POPULATION**

**NUMBER OF CHINESE RESTAURANTS**

Thinking about what career to get into? Wondering whether or not you'll fit in? Well, here's the seventh in a series of tests designed to help you choose your future line of work. Mainly, discover your true abilities by taking...

# MAD'S APTITUDE TEST NUMBER SEVEN
# WILL YOU MAKE A GOOD FLIGHT ATTENDANT?

ARTIST: GEORGE WOODBRIDGE    WRITER: FRANK JACOBS

1. You have a burning desire to become a Flight Attendant. This indicates that:
   A. You're turned on by visiting exotic places like Altoona, Fresno and Wheeling.
   B. You enjoy exercising total power over several hundred strapped-in, uncomfortable, nervous people.
   C. You have a high tolerance for monotony and tedium.
   D. Any of the above.

2. You see a passenger struggling to fit a bulky suitcase into an overhead compartment. Your clear-cut duty is to:
   A. Tell him he's blocking the aisle.
   B. Inform him that the suitcase is too large for carry-on luggage, and that he must remove it from the plane, go back to the ticket counter and check it through as luggage.
   C. Attend to more urgent duties, such as getting it on with the wealthy-looking dude you spotted sitting in First Class.
   D. Any of the above.

3. From the appearance of this Flight Attendant, you should be able to tell that she:
   A. Has just taken a look at the meal being served to the coach passengers.
   B. Has just taken a look at a toilet after it's been used by over 100 people on a 9-hour flight.
   C. Has just taken a look in the mirror at *herself* after a 9-hour flight.
   D. Any of the above.

4. If you are married, being a Flight Attendant can be advantageous because:
   A. The complaints and arguments you get at home prepare you for the abuse you get from passengers.
   B. You can carry on affairs in a dozen different cities without your mate getting wise.
   C. Returning to your mate, you can blame your lack of interest in sex on jet lag.
   D. All of the above.

5. Complete this sentence: A Flight Attendant must be trim and agile so that she _____.
   A. Can dodge elbows in the groin while hurrying up the narrow aisles.
   B. Can make a fast get-away after bringing a passenger an airsickness bag.
   C. Can elude the groping for her body by the Captain or other members of the Flight Crew.
   D. All of the above.

6. During the In-Flight Movie, you spy two passengers making passionate love. What should you do?
   A. Turn on the "Fasten Seatbelts" sign, figuring why should they be having more fun than you.
   B. Stand there and watch, figuring you may learn what you've been doing wrong.
   C. Bring the Captain or other members of the Flight Crew back so that they can learn what *they've* been doing wrong.
   D. Any of the above.

7. Although most flights are routine, a good Flight Attendant must always be prepared for the unexpected. Which of these offers the greatest challenge to your self-composure and ability to adjust to the extraordinary?
   A. A coach passenger at mealtime asking for seconds.
   B. An entire cabin paying close attention to your "What To Do In Case Of Forced Landing" demonstration.
   C. A passenger finding an article of interest in the monthly airline magazine.
   D. Any of the above.

8. Towards the end of the flight, you suddenly hear angry cursing followed by a piercing scream. From experience, you know that it is
   A. A passenger attempting to cross his legs while sitting in coach.
   B. A passenger attempting to get an audible sound from his rented headset.
   C. Another Flight Attendant exhibiting the first tell-tale sign of "In-Flight Burn-Out."
   D. Any of the above.

9. You overhear a passenger refer to you as "nothing more than a Flying Waitress!" What should be your immediate comment?
   A. "It's nice to hear something complimentary for a change!"
   B. "Waitresses get tips and respect. I should be so lucky!"
   C. "Is that better or worse than a 'bleeping gofer'?"
   D. Any of the above.

10. After eight or ten years, you will finally gain Seniority. This is desirable because:
    A. You will now have first choice of flights, meaning you can pick Altoona, Fresno *OR* Wheeling.
    B. You can now palm off arduous jobs like drink-cart pulling on the newcomers.
    C. You no longer have to concern yourself with things like "ambition" and "career potential" because for you they are no longer relevant.
    D. All of the above.

## SCORING

*If you answered "D" to all questions, you have the ability to make a good Flight Attendant.*

The average five-year-old thinks he's made a brilliant discovery when he smugly announces that any story beginning "Once upon a time..." is a fairy tale that didn't happen. Well, the average five-year-old is wrong! Many things dismissed as fantasy were very real in years gone by. Let MAD give you the straight poop on the way it was...

# Once Upon A Time...

ARTIST: SERGIO ARAGONES    WRITER: TOM KOCH

....**THERE WAS ONLY ONE TYPE OF COCA-COLA,**    **AND IT ONLY CAME IN ONE SIZE BOTTLE**

**—AND EVERYBODY SEEMED SATISFIED**    ...**AND KIDS LEARNED**

**ALL ABOUT KINKY SEX FROM THEIR FRIENDS ON THE STREETS—NOT FROM GERALDO**

**RIVERA ON TV**    ...**AND BASEBALL PLAYERS PLAYED FOR LESS MONEY**

**THAN THEY NOW GET FOR SIGNING AUTOGRAPHS AT CARD SHOWS**

...AND RADIO STATIONS KEPT THE SAME CALL LETTERS FOREVER, EVEN IF THEY DIDN'T SPELL

A TIME...THERE WASN'T ONE TENNIS TOURNAMENT IN THE WHOLE WORLD NAMI

COMPANY ...AND A KID COULD RIDE

FOR EACH ACTIVITY ...AND YC

ITEM BEFORE YOU KNEW WHETHER OR NOT YOU COULD AFFORD IT.

TO SELL $8.95 WALL CALENDARS BECAUSE MOST OTHER BUSINESSES IN TOWN GAVE THEM AV

PRIZED BASEBALL CARDS IN AN OLD CIGAR BOX—NOT A SAFETY DEPOSIT BOX

ANYWHERE ABOUT WHETHER OAT BRAN WAS GOOD OR BAD FOR YOU. IT WAS JUST FED TO L

**ANYTHING CUTE.**

**YES, ONCE UPON**

...D AFTER A CIGARETTE MANUFACTURER OR A FOREIGN CAR MAKER OR A PHONE

A BIKE OR PLAY TENNIS OR EVEN KICK A BALL WITHOUT HAVING TO WEAR A SEPARATE OUTFIT

...OU DIDN'T HAVE TO WAIT FOR THE CASHIER'S SCANNER TO READ THE BAR CODE ON A GROCERY

**...ONCE UPON A TIME...GIFT SHOPS DIDN'T EVEN TRY**

**...WAY FOR FREE**

**...AND KIDS KEPT THEIR MOST**

**...AND THERE WASN'T A SINGLE ARGUMENT**

**...IVESTOCK AND FORGOTTEN.**

# I SENT A LETTER THROUGH THE MAIL ...

(With Post Apologies to Henry Wadsworth Longfellow)

*I sent a letter through the mail;*
*It wound up ... well, that's quite a tale;*
*I dropped it in a box, you see,*
*On Saturday, 'round half past three;*
*Through Sunday in that box it lay*
*(and Monday was a holiday),*
*Till late on Tuesday, by some luck,*
*Arrived a Postal Service truck,*
*Which hauled the mail and dumped it in*
*A postal worker's sorting bin.*

*My letter now was on its way—*
*To Little Rock through San Jose,*
*Then on to Boise, Idaho,*
*By way of downtown Buffalo,*
*Proceeding then to Bangor, Maine,*
*And, somehow, Barcelona, Spain,*
*Until, at last, it came to earth*
*In Texas, somewhere near Fort Worth;*
*Small wonder that it's got me down—*
*I mailed it to a friend cross-town.*

**WRITER: FRANK JACOBS**

# THE MAD BATHROOM COMPANION

## NUMBER TWO

By "The Usual Gang of Idiots"

Edited by Nick Meglin & John Ficarra

Introduction by Gene Shalit

# Introduction

**_MAD_** first appeared in the fall of 1952. Parents said it was the fall of civilization. They warned it would cause their children's ruination and a ruined nation. Turns out they were right. _MAD_ was followed by baby boomers, rock 'n' roll, the Me generation, umpires who can't call balls and strikes, a country infested by movie critics, the loss of couth, Generation X, and wrestling. It's all _MAD_'s fault, and I was there at the start.

_Fade to flashback._

The first kid each month who came into my father's drugstore to buy the new issue of _MAD_ got a used copy, heh-heh. I had already grabbed it, read it, and sneaked it back onto the rack. Before _MAD_ came along, I would never have done such a thing. I didn't even do it with _Good Housekeeping_. But there was something magnetic about _MAD_, and I was an iron filling.

We kids called it a sensation. Parents called it subversive. Maybe because we read it undercover—namely, under the covers. All we needed to have a perfect night was a copy of _MAD_ and a flashlight. At school, we hid copies behind arithmetic books and Latin texts. (That's how long ago this was—we still called it arithmetic, and schools still taught Latin.) Teachers, puzzled by grins and stifled laughter, probably wondered what was so funny about the square of the hypotenuse or Caesar dividing Gaul.

At first, _MAD_ cost ten cents. That was serious money. In my father's store, a dime could get you a double-dip ice cream cone, a twelve-ounce Pepsi plus a donut, two telephone calls, a buttered roll and coffee, or a pack of Wings cigarettes. So a dime was not trivial, and neither was _MAD_. It was "hep." It was "swell." It had "zip." It was "hot spit"—can you think of a higher compliment? _MAD_ told people off, stuffed the stuffy, poked pomposity, and thumbed its nose at the phony—all with bull's-eye satire. We didn't know from "satire." All we knew was that it made us laugh and say, "Hey, looka _this_!"

Roger Ebert remarked in his introduction to _MAD About the Movies_ that _MAD_ Magazine inspired him to become a movie critic. For the record, _MAD_ did not make me want to be a reviewer. _MAD_ made me want to write like Frank Jacobs and draw like Jack Davis or Mort Drucker. But in a funny way, it brought me to the attention of NBC. Larry Grossman, the network's advertising VP, hired me to create a newspaper campaign for the radio network's revolutionary new idea—a call-in talk show. A man named Brad Crandall, who had an encyclopedic memory and an opinion about everything, took on all callers. I believe this was the very first program to allow the home audience to talk to the guy on the air while he was on the air. (Okay, maybe you think it wasn't the first. Who cares? No, I don't wanna bet. Will you please shut up and let me get on with this? Thank you.) I envisioned the ads as a series of one-panel cartoons kidding the program. So I called Jack Davis (whom I did not know) about doing the drawings. True to his art, Jack's first response was, "You bet!" I was so happy that I seem to recollect sending him a small fortune. (The small part I'm sure of.)

Jack's drawings with my lines were so funny that we were a big hit. The program's slogan was "Express Yourself," so Jack drew a wooden crate with an arm sticking out between the slats and carrying itself. (Maybe you had to be there.) In another, a cleaning woman in an empty studio is sweeping up parts of words and scraps of the alphabet that litter (or letter) the floor. (I guess you *really* had to be there.) Jack got paid, and NBC gave me a pat on the back, a hearty handshake, and what looked like change from a ten. They assured me that psychic nourishment was more important than cash. (When I went to the supermarket and asked for a psychic nourishment's worth of corn flakes, they dialed 911.)

Suddenly satiric coloring books were in vogue (not really, and not in *Harper's Bazaar*, either). I wrote *The Khrushchev Coloring Book*, a sophomoric roundelay rescued by Jack's pen. Some [*danger, redundancy ahead*] stupid general banned it from the PX on his base, igniting a media uproar over freedom of the press. Sales zoomed and Jack pocketed several hundred dollars, enough to buy him a new house in Westchester. (All right, so it wasn't in a swank neighborhood.)

*MAD* and I touched gloves again in 1985, when Doubleday published my best-selling anthology of great American humor, *Laughing Matters*. One of the first classic pieces I sewed up was by Frank Jacobs and Mort Drucker, *MAD*'s hilarious knock-off of the Broadway musical *Fiddler on the Roof*. They called it *Antenna on the Roof*, so I knew it would get a great reception.

Which is more than you can say about this introduction.

**—Gene Shalit**

# A MAD LOOK AT TARZA

ARTIST: JACK DAVIS

KEEP OFF THE TREES

Kenya Park Authority

AHWEEHAROOEEEE!

# N...TODAY

WRITER: DON EDWING

Modern science has come up with a fantastic new gimmick: a strip of paper...chemically treated so when you rub it with your fingernail, an aroma is released. These so-called "Scratch 'n' Sniff" strips are being used by perfume makers to provide samples of their products, and by publishers to create scented books and magazines. Now people who've lived in Kansas all their lives can experience the smell of the ocean, city dwellers can enjoy the fragrance of a cow pasture, and millions of men can thrill to the erotic odor of Farrah Fawcett's armpit without even dating her. We here at MAD are so excited over this big scientific development that we have gone to great effort and expense to imprint these 3 pages with various aromas so that we can share with our readers the thrill of this great invention. Herewith is a selection of

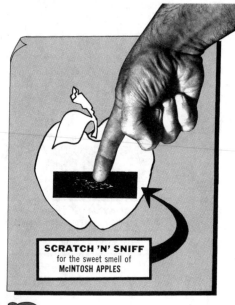

**SCRATCH 'N' SNIFF**
for the sweet smell of
**McINTOSH APPLES**

# MAD
# "SCRATCH 'N' SNIFF"
# STRIPS

**TO THOROUGHLY ENJOY STRIPS** ✱ **SCRAPE THE BLACK RECTANGLES FIRMLY WITH YOUR FINGERNAIL** ✱ **HOLD PAGE APPROXIMATELY 3 to 4 INCHES FROM NOSE** ✱ **INHALE DEEPLY**

**SCRATCH 'N' SNIFF**
for the wholesome, invigorating smell of
**CLEAN CITY AIR**

ARTIST & WRITER:
HENRY CLARK

**SCRATCH 'N' SNIFF**
for a soothing aromatic sniff of
**SAFE CIGARETTE SMOKE**

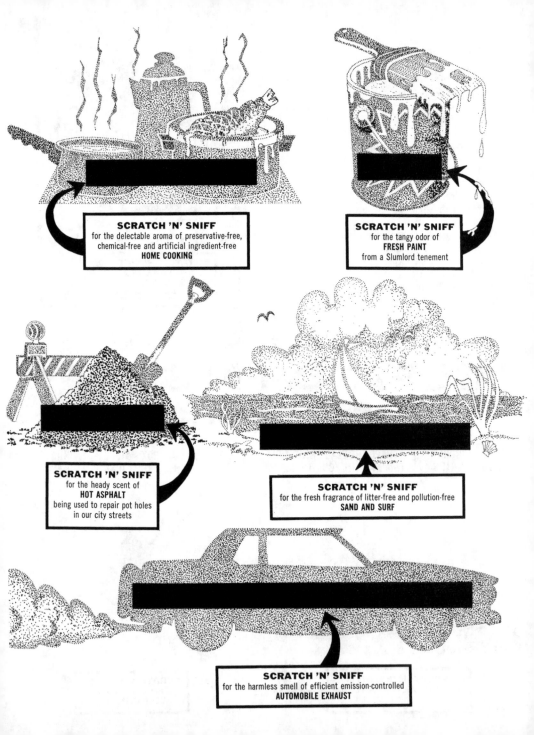

**SCRATCH 'N' SNIFF**
for the delectable aroma of preservative-free,
chemical-free and artificial ingredient-free
**HOME COOKING**

**SCRATCH 'N' SNIFF**
for the tangy odor of
**FRESH PAINT**
from a Slumlord tenement

**SCRATCH 'N' SNIFF**
for the heady scent of
**HOT ASPHALT**
being used to repair pot holes
in our city streets

**SCRATCH 'N' SNIFF**
for the fresh fragrance of litter-free and pollution-free
**SAND AND SURF**

**SCRATCH 'N' SNIFF**
for the harmless smell of efficient emission-controlled
**AUTOMOBILE EXHAUST**

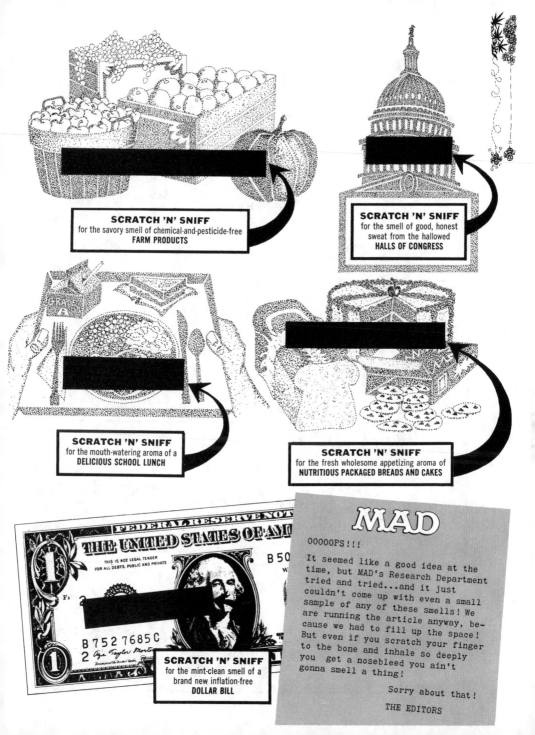

**SCRATCH 'N' SNIFF**
for the savory smell of chemical-and-pesticide-free
**FARM PRODUCTS**

**SCRATCH 'N' SNIFF**
for the smell of good, honest
sweat from the hallowed
**HALLS OF CONGRESS**

**SCRATCH 'N' SNIFF**
for the mouth-watering aroma of a
**DELICIOUS SCHOOL LUNCH**

**SCRATCH 'N' SNIFF**
for the fresh wholesome appetizing aroma of
**NUTRITIOUS PACKAGED BREADS AND CAKES**

**SCRATCH 'N' SNIFF**
for the mint-clean smell of a
brand new inflation-free
**DOLLAR BILL**

## MAD

OOOOOPS!!!

It seemed like a good idea at the time, but MAD's Research Department tried and tried...and it just couldn't come up with even a small sample of any of these smells! We are running the article anyway, because we had to fill up the space! But even if you scratch your finger to the bone and inhale so deeply you get a nosebleed you ain't gonna smell a thing!

Sorry about that!

THE EDITORS

# ONE DAY IN EGYPT

## JOGGER-NUTS DEPT.

Remember how, in the past, the only people who did any running were football players, purse-snatchers and guys discovered in the wrong bedroom? Well, nowadays, it seems as if everybody's running. Some folks say it's because there's a new emphasis on health. We can't buy that. People have always been running for their health. Did you ever see what happens to football players or purse-snatchers or guys discovered in the wrong bedroom when they got caught?! So whatever the reason, everyone is running today, and that means it's time for us to bring you—

# THE MAD RUNNING PRIMER

ARTIST: JACK DAVIS          WRITER: LARRY SIEGEL

## Chapter One
### THE EARLY MORNING RUNNERS

See the people run.
Run, people, run.
Why are they running so early?
Because at this time of day,
The human body is most receptive
To physical stimulation.
Because the bracing dawn air
Is ideal for imbuing the human body
With the glorious spirit of life.
And besides, at 5:30 A.M.,
There's very little in the human body
To throw up!

## Chapter Two
### THE CAMARADERIE OF RUNNING

Here is another group of runners.
Why do runners like to run in groups?
Because they are convivial people.
Because they have things to say
To one another as they run.
Important things like,
"Ugh!" "Gasp!" "Puff!"
"Wheeze!" "Aargh!" "Pyucch!"
And the ever-popular,
"How much #$%&in' longer
Do we have to go?!"

## Chapter Three
### THE MAGIC AURA OF RUNNING

See yet another group of runners.
See the radiant glow on their faces.
See their muscles ripple and bulge.
See their bodies glisten with healthy sweat.
You can't escape the charisma of runners.
You can't escape the exhuberance of runners.
See the man in the middle of the group
Gasp for air and fall to his knees.
You can't escape the smell of runners!

## Chapter Four
### RUNNING FOR HEALTH

See how healthy this runner is.
Not long ago he was a 200-pound mass
Of disgusting flab.
Then he started running.
He's been running 15 miles a day
For over a year.
Now he's a 200-pound mass of coiled steel.
"Wait a minute!", you say.
"If he's been running 15 miles a day
For over a year, how come he *still*
Weighs 200 pounds?"
That's because although he's lost 40 pounds,
He's also acquired two 20-pound foot blisters!

## Chapter Seven
### FAMILY RUNNING

See the married couple
Running with their 4-year-old child.
The married couple has been running
Together for over five years.
Running is their whole life.
They are running fanatics.
When they are not working or sleeping,
They are running, running, running.
They plan budgets while they're running.
They discuss problems while they're running.
They have fights while they're running.
They do *everything* while they're running.
In case you're wondering
How they had their child,
You can read all about it
On pages 78 through 85
In the upcoming edition of
"The Guinness Book Of World Records".

## Chapter Eight
### EXERCISING IN THE CITY

See the man in jogging clothes.
See how he has trouble breathing.
Notice how his heart is pounding.
See the pain on his face.
For over an hour, he's been running.
This is known as exercising in the city.
See the man in the Gucci clothes.
See how *he* has trouble breathing.
Notice how *his* heart is pounding.
See the pain on *his* face.
For over an hour he's been attacked
By pollution, traffic, and muggers.
This is known as *living* in the city.

## Chapter Five
### PROLONGING YOUR LIFE

See this man.
He once had a heart attack.
Now he's in terrific shape.
Now he's probably prolonged
His life about 20 years.
Now he has wonderful things
To look forward to.
Like his daily chest-pounding,
Lung-throbbing, pulse-hammering,
Throat-wheezing 12 mile runs.
Well, we have good news
And bad news for him.
The bad news is: He may *still*
Get another heart attack.
The good news is: If he gets it
While he's running,
He'll probably never know
The difference.

## Chapter Six
### THE BOREDOM OF RUNNING

There's only one thing
More boring than running.
And that's listening to runners
Talk about running.
See the runners passing that milkman.
Their conversation is putting him to sleep.
See the runners passing that policeman.
Their conversation is putting him to sleep, too.
Listen to what the runners are saying.
They're talking about their new running shoes.
They're discussing their new jogging outfits.
Their boasting about their stamina.
They're saying... Yawn...
ZZZZZZZZZZZZZZZZZZZZZZZZZZZZZZZ...

## Chapter Nine
### THE HIGH OF RUNNING

See the look of supreme joy
On this runner's face.
See how he is at peace with himself,
His God, and his world.
See how he is enveloped in rapture.
See how he exudes pure bliss.
This is known as the "high" of running.
When do runners experience this "high"?
Whenever they run ten brisk miles
In the solitude of a brightening dawn
In a lush, green park
Without once stepping in doggie-doo.

## Chapter Ten
### MARATHON RUNNING

See the huge crowd of runners.
There are over 1,000 of them.
What are they doing?
They are running in a Marathon Race.
Watch them today as they aim
For the biggest thrill in their lives:
To run 26 long torturous miles.
Then watch them tomorrow in their cars
As they battle each other for parking spots
In front of office buildings so that, God forbid,
They shouldn't have to walk a block to work.

# WHY GO TO THE UNNECESSARY EXPENSE AND BOTHER OF INSTALLING ALARMS OR OTHER
# SURE-FIRE BURGLAR DET

SHARPSHOOTER

★ MEMBER ★

KILL KILL KILL KILL KILL KILL KILL KILL KILL KILL KILL KILL KILL KILL KILL KILL KILL KILL KILL KILL KILL

NATIONAL GUN-LOVERS ASSN.

Dear Thief:-
We spent $100 on our stereo set, and $800 on our burglar alarm! The guy next door spent $800 on his stereo set, and $100 on his burglar alarm!

P.S. The guy across the street doesn't even <u>have</u> a burglar alarm!

THE HEAT IS OFF!!
THERE'S NO HOT WATER!
THE PHONE IS OUT!!
THE BASEMENT IS FLOODED! —
I'M JUST WAITING FOR THE NEXT ✱✺&$ TO SET FOOT IN THIS HOUSE!

## NOTICE

SOME OF THE ITEMS IN THIS HOUSE HAVE BEEN ENGRAVED WITH FEDERAL IDENTIFICATION NUMBERS. OTHERS HAVE MERELY BEEN WIRED TO EXPLODE WHEN TOUCHED! SO LOTS OF LUCK!

RESIDENCE OF MADAM OLGA

THE WITCH WHOSE BLACK POWERS CAN KILL WITH A MERE THOUGHT

Dear Mailman,
We found bloodstains all over our mail. They must be yours. Next time you put the mail into our slot, please be sure to keep all parts of your body well clear of the opening.
The Lipkins

P.S. Any sign of that book we sent for: "The Care And Feeding Of Wild Jungle Cats"?

# ERRENTS FOR THE WARY HOME OR APARTMENT DWELLER

WRITER: DICK DE BARTOLO

# OUS LAST WORDS

WRITER: PAUL PETER PORGES

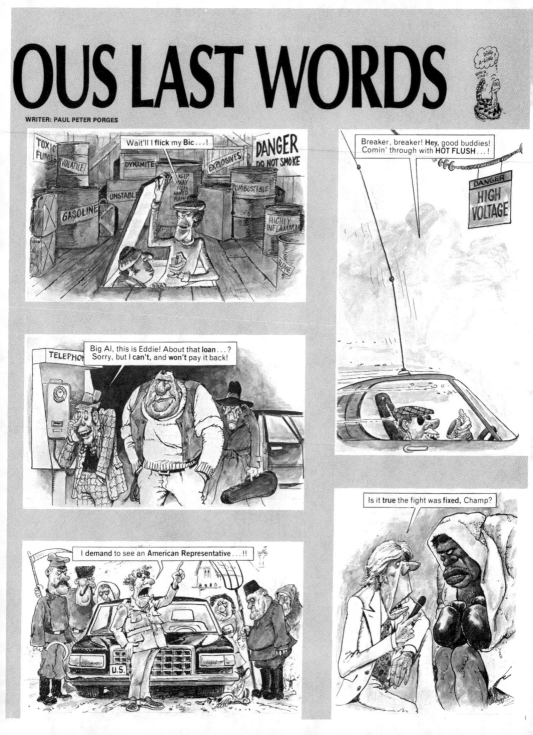

# MAD NOVELTY ITEMS FOR PRACTICAL-JOKER JOCKS

ARTIST: JACK DAVIS   WRITER: PAUL PETER PORGES

## LOADED, NON-FLIPPING TOSS-UP COIN

## SILLY-PUTTY HOCKEY PUCK

## FUNNY FALSE TEETH MOUTHPIECE

## SHREDDING CHEERLEADER POM-POMS

## NON-BOUNCING BASKETBALL

## TRICK STARTER GUN

FOOLED YA!

## HUMOROUS PIT-STOP FLASH CARDS

GO TO JAIL! DO NOT PASS! GO!

## NO-EXIT FOOTBALL JERSEY

## BLACK-SPOT FAKE GOLF HOLE

## REFEREE'S SOAP BUBBLE WHISTLE

# A COLLECTION OF 18 MAD EXCUSE

# WHY DON'T YO

ARTIST: PAUL COKER

You were too depressed by the latest death of a famous Rock Star!

Your father used the last piece of looseleaf in the house as a "pooper scooper" when he walked the dog!

Your analyst was called away on an emergency, and you had to wait in his office the whole evening!

You had to register for the Draft! (Don't try this excuse if you go to an "All Girls' School" idiot!)

You were taking Karate lessons so you can ride in the subways again!

You made an evening appointment at a beauty shop for a Bo Derek cornrow hair-styling . . . and you didn't know how long it takes!

# S THAT TEACHERS JUST MIGHT BUY WHEN THEY ASK...
# U DO YOUR HOMEWORK?

WRITER: JOHN FICARRA

On the way home from school yesterday, you were mugged, and they got all your books!

The battery in your pocket calculator went dead, and all the stores were closed!

You dozed off while meditating, and the next thing you knew, it was morning!

You were out all night, looking for your little Brother, who ran away from home again!

You had to attend your weekly Alcoholics Anonymous meeting!

The air pollution was so bad that your eyes kept tearing, and you couldn't read a thing!

It was your turn to wait in a gas line with the family car!

Last night was the concluding episode of a 22-part Educational TV Series, and you saw the first 21 parts!

You went into one of those "24-hour Banking Centers," and wound up getting locked in the place all night.

You had to be in Court to testify in the custody battle your parents are having over you and your brothers!

You have to work at night so that your family can afford to pay the home heating bills!

You look upon homework as an intrusion upon your "space"!

# AN AL JAFFEE
# SNAPPY ANSWERS TO
# STUPID QUESTIONS
## Fishing Incident

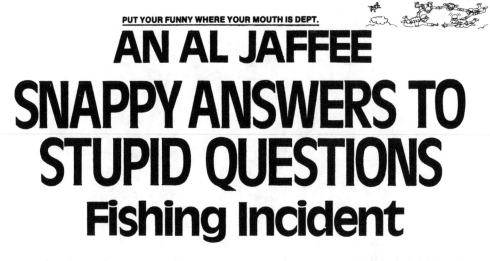

# YOU'RE A GENIUS IF... BUT YOU'RE AN IDIOT IF...

ARTIST: PAUL COKER, JR.
WRITER: ED DANKO

**YOU'RE A GENIUS IF...** **BUT** **YOU'RE AN IDIOT IF...**

... you invent an automobile engine that runs on water.

... you think the oil cartel will ever let you market it.

**YOU'RE A GENIUS IF...** **BUT** **YOU'RE AN IDIOT IF...**

... you create a new highly-destructive nuclear weapon.

... you advocate using highly-destructive nuclear weapons.

**YOU'RE A GENIUS IF...** **BUT** **YOU'RE AN IDIOT IF...**

... you invent a method of transmitting pictures through the air.

... you sit around all day long ... watching too much television.

**YOU'RE A GENIUS IF...** BUT **YOU'RE AN IDIOT IF...**

. . . you fly a kite during a thunderstorm . . . and discover that lightning is electricity.

. . . you fly a kite during a thunderstorm . . . and discover that lightning can kill you.

**YOU'RE A GENIUS IF...** BU

. . . you develop an amazing car bumper that can withstand a 75-mile-an-hour head-on crash.

**YOU'RE A GENIUS IF...** BUT **YOU'RE AN IDIOT IF...**

. . . it only takes you two years to complete a four-year course in Ancient Babylonian Astrology.

. . . you think you'll ever get a good job with a college degree in Ancient Babylonian Astrology.

**YOU'RE A GENIUS IF...** BU

. . . you invent a device that records one TV program while you're watching another one.

**YOU'RE A GENIUS IF...** BUT **YOU'RE AN IDIOT IF...**

. . . you design and build the first supersonic jet airliner.

. . . you allow a supersonic jet to land at your local airport.

**YOU'RE A GENIUS IF...** BU

. . . you write a great document proclaiming all men are equal.

JT YOU'RE AN IDIOT IF...

. . . you believe that the rest of your car can withstand a 75-mile-an-hour head-on crash.

YOU'RE A GENIUS IF... **BUT**

. . . you negotiate a pact with your enemies which eliminates all types of nuclear weapons.

YOU'RE AN IDIOT IF...

. . . you trust your enemies enough to actually give up all of your nuclear weapons.

JT YOU'RE AN IDIOT IF...

. . . you think today's TV pro-grams are really worth going to all that trouble and expense.

YOU'RE A GENIUS IF... **BUT**

. . . you accidentally mix two chemicals together, and make a valuable scientific discovery.

YOU'RE AN IDIOT IF...

. . . you accidentally mix two chemicals together and blow up your scientific laboratory.

JT YOU'RE AN IDIOT IF...

. . . you actually believe in your heart all men are equal.

YOU'RE A GENIUS IF... **BUT**

. . . you make a million bucks publishing a trashy magazine.

YOU'RE AN IDIOT IF...

. . . you waste your hard-earned money on that trashy magazine.

Hey, there, all you ulcerated and unnerved Madison Avenue executives! Here is our alternative to basket-weaving and bead-stringing: mainly our easy-to-follow pattern for...

# THE MAD A

**A** — 1 STEAK SAUCE

**B** — IN B MUSHROOMS

**C** — HI FRUIT DRINK

**D** — CON ROACH KILLER

**I** — MAGNIN

**J** — WAX

**K** — KELLOGG'S SPECIAL

**L&M** — FILTER KINGS

**R** — TOYS US

**S** — TRIPLE TRADING STAMPS

**T** — SPEC- THROAT LOZENGES

**U** — HAUL

**V** — 8 VEGETABLE JUICE

**1** — A DAY VITAMINS

**2** — ALKA ANTACID

**3** — MUSKETEERS BARS

**4** — WAY NASAL SPRAY

**5** — DAY DEODORANT PADS

# D-MAN'S SAMPLER

ARTIST & WRITER: HENRY CLARK

| | | | |
|---|---|---|---|
| **E**<br>F. HUTTON | CHANNEL<br>**F**<br>VIDEO GAMES | BIG<br>**G**<br>CEREALS | PREPARATION<br>**H** |
| SHAKE<br>**N**<br>BAKE | JELL<br>**O** | PROPA<br>**P**<br>H | **Q**<br>TIPS |
| COMPOUND<br>**W** | BRAND<br>**X** | K<br>**Y**<br>JELL | LA-<br>**Z**<br>-BOY RECLINERS |
| FLAGS<br>AMUSEMENT PARKS<br>**6** | **7**<br>UP | **8**<br>O'CLOCK COFFEE | **9**<br>LIVES CAT FOOD |

# ONNA BLAME...?

WRITER: LOU SILVERSTONE

Big City Banks that refuse to bail out bankrupt cities . . .

**OR**

. . . City Governments that have driven the middle class and many industries away with their corrupt practices, their political patronage and their ridiculous unrealistic taxes.

Advertising Agencies who continue to publicize cigarette smoking as the "cool". . ."manly". . ."in" thing to do . . .

**OR**

. . . the Morons who keep puffing away despite all the clear and irrefutable evidence that cigarette smoking can kill.

Young People who drop out of Churches or Temples . . .

**OR**

. . . our so-called Religious Leaders who resort to raising funds by running Bingo Games . . . or holding Gambling nights (usually operated by Gangsters) in our Houses of Worship.

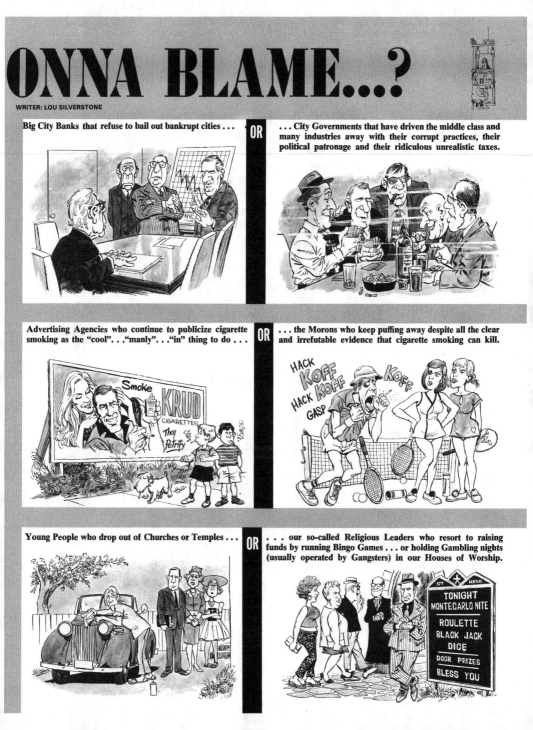

**Dogs who make your sidewalk or lawn their personal John . . .** **OR** **. . . stupid, lazy Dog-Owners who don't care where their mutts "do", as long as it's on somebody else's property.**

**The All-American Heisman Trophy-winner who bombs out his first year in Pro Ball . . .** **OR** **. . . the PR Guys and the Sportswriters and the Sportscasters and the Magazines and Newspapers who gave him that "big build-up."**

**The Executives at the TV Networks who dream up all those ridiculous, moronic shows . . .** **OR** **. . . the Schmucks who sit glued to their TV sets no matter what's on.**

**Manufacturers who produce ecology-destroying products like plastic containers and throw-away bottles and spray cans . . .** **OR** **. . . self-indulgent Consumers who keep on buying them.**

# ONE DAY FIVE THOUSAND YEARS AGO

Parents love reading "Mother Goose" to their kids. The problem is that those old Nursery Rhymes don't prepare youngsters for their future careers. Wouldn't it be a great idea if career-oriented mothers and fathers were

# MAD'S
# CAREER-ORII
# MOTHER GO

ARTIST: PAUL COKER, JR.   WRITER: FRANK JACOBS

## MARY HAD AN LTD
### as told by an
### AUTO MECHANIC

Mary had an LTD;
She drove it for a week;
And ev'rywhere that Mary went
She heard an awful squeak.

She drove it to a shop run by
A fine mechanic, who
Declared that he would find the squeak
Before the week was through.

The squeak is gone and Mary's broke;
Nine hundred was the ticket.
He'd put a new transmission in—
And taken out the cricket!

## JACK AND JILL
### as told by an
### ECONOMIST

Jack and Jill
  Climb down their hill
With water for the nation;
  Already, twice,
  They've raised their price
To keep up with inflation.

Jack and Jill
  More buckets fill;
They work until they totter;
  But though they're beat,
  They can't compete
With cheap, imported water!

supplied with verses dealing with their particular jobs
and professions? Then they could inspire their kids with

# ENTED
# OOSE

## AS I WAS GOING TO ST. IVES
### as told by a
### DOCTOR

As I was going to St. Ives
I met a man who had the hives,
A woman with a fractured hip,
A dozen children with the grippe,
Two cyclists in a head-on crash,
A tourist with a dreadful rash,
Six barefoot girls with broken toes,
A shepherd with a twisted nose;

How many people did I tell to call my nurse
for an appointment during office hours after
I returned from playing golf at St. Ives?

## LITTLE MISS MUFFET
### as told by a
### GOSSIP COLUMNIST

Little Miss Muffet
Is sharing her tuffet
With Bo-Peep and Solomon Grundy;
They say Georgie Porgie
Was seen at an orgy
With Old Mother Hubbard last Sunday.

Seems Little Boy Blue
Gets it on in the shoe
"Cause he's heard the Old Woman is kinky;
And as for Jack Sprat,
Well, his wife left him flat
And is living with Wee Willie Winkle.

## TOM, TOM, THE PIPER'S SON
### as told by a
### PSYCHIATRIST

Tom, Tom, the piper's son,
Stole a pig and away he run;
His parents sent him here to me
To get intensive ther-a-py.

Tom, Tom, it's very clear,
Shows great progress in just a year;
I'm pleased to say that now he feels
Much more at peace each time he steals!

## HUMPTY DUMPTY

### as told by a
### LAWYER

Humpty Dumpty sat on a wall;
Humpty Dumpty had a great fall;
"The bricks of the wall," said his lawyer,
  "were loose;"
"We've got a good case, so we'll sue
  Mother Goose!"

Humpty's lawyer got a big trial;
Humpty's lawyer won it with style,
Took Mother Goose for a million, did he,
Of which he got half, which is not a bad fee!

## LITTLE BOY BLUE

### as told by a
### BOOKIE

Little Boy Blue,
Come bet the Rams;
They're playing the Cowboys,
Put down 50 clams!

Little Boy Blue,
The Chiefs will win;
They'll murder Miami,
So send it all in!

Little Boy Blue,
The Bears are hot;
They'll ruin the Raiders;
It's sure worth a shot!

Little Boy Blue,
You lost your bets;
Do you want the spread
Monday night on the Jets?

## TWEEDLE-DUM AND TWEEDLE-DEE

### as told by a
### FASHION DESIGNER

Tweedle-Dum and Tweedle-Dee
Created women's clothes;
And ev'ry fashion they designed
  The women always chose.

They introduced a seaweed belt,
  A skirt of styrofoam;
They fashioned fancy dresses made
  Of hamster fur and chrome.

They came out with a burlap blouse,
  A yak coat long and shaggy,
A pair of slacks made out of straw,
  A gown shaped like a Baggie.

"It's plain to see," said Tweedle-Dum,
  "We've got the magic touch!"
"It's also clear," said Tweedle-Dee,
  "We don't like women much!"

## TAFFY WAS A HITMAN

### as told by a
### MAFIA DON

Taffy was a hitman;
Taffy made good bread;
Taffy pulled a double-cross
And killed his Capo dead.

Taffy had an alibi,
But his mob could tell
Taffy's tale was full of holes;
Now Taffy is, as well!

# THE BIG ONE THAT GOT AWAY

ARTIST & WRITER: DON EDWING

# JUSTICE ONCE

ARTIST AND WRITER: SERGIO ARAGONES

# A
# COLLECTION OF MAD

ARTIST: BOB CLARKE

# X-RAYvings

WRITER: DON EDWING

# AN AL JAFFEE
# SNAPPY ANSWERS TO
# STUPID QUESTIONS
## Jogging Incident

ARTIST & WRITER: AL JAFFEE

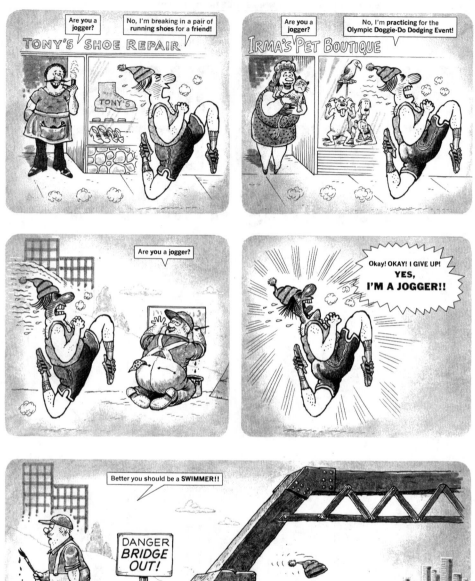

# ONE FINE DAY DOWNTOWN

# HOW CAN Y

ARTIST: PAUL COKER, JR.

. . . The Druggist who does both urine analysis . . . and sundaes!

. . . the Wildlife Guide who is covered with poison ivy sores!

. . . the law-and-order Mayor who double-parks his imported $28,000 official car!

. . . the Investment Expert who brown bags his lunch, and wears 1960 type narrow ties and shoes that need re-soling!

. . . the exclusive Men's Shop Clerk who wears a dark blue suit with brown shoes and white anklet socks!

# OU TRUST...

WRITER: PAUL PETER PORGES

. . . The Ecologist who litters the streets with his pamphlets urging us to save our pulp woods!

. . . the Airline pilot whose pre-flight check consists of kicking the tires, and who hangs a rabbit's foot on his instrument panel!

. . . the Suicide-Prevention Line that's always busy!

. . . the Little League Coach who has 3 sons, 4 nephews and his kid sister on the team!

. . . the Diet Doctor who weighs over 300 pounds and wheezes when he talks!

# YOUR MAD HOROSCOPE

**TODAY'S BIRTHDAY:** There is a party planned for you tonight. Act surprised!

## ARIES
### March 21—April 19

Stars from a far-off galaxy are sending you urgent messages today. Unfortunately, they're sending them via the US Post Office, and there's no way the messages are going to arrive in time to do you any good. Meanwhile, recognize that you can't do everything yourself, then do nothing and blame others for foul-ups.

## TAURUS
### April 20—May 20

Problems at work. The President of your company wants very much to have you fired. Your immediate supervisor, however, strongly disagrees. He wants to have you killed! Door-to-door work is your best bet, but beware! As your efforts meet with big frustration, your wife meets with a bigger man! Lift from the knees.

## GEMINI
### May 21—June 21

A full moon will enter your life soon. Normally, this is a good sign. However, in your case, the full moon will be hanging out of the back of a car window. What exactly this all means is still unclear but, if you stay kind and unassuming, chances are excellent' others will seek to take advantage of your naive nature.

## MOON CHILDREN
### June 22—July 22

Forego immediate satisfactions for a far-off goal, and just hope you don't die in the meantime. A few hassles await you in the upcoming weeks. While they will be minor, they will be enough to make you snap. Critical information may be incorrect, so you might want to disregard anything read in this horoscope column.

## LEO
### July 23—August 22

Trouble brought on by a falling star may make you wish that you were someone else. This is foolish on your part. Everyone knows that when you wish upon a star, makes no difference who you are. Combine work and love as much as possible, but be careful not to show up at the office in a Frederick's of Hollywood close-out.

## VIRGO
### August 23—September 22

Your moon is now in the House of Cards and it is difficult to tell what this means. Poke around, but don't bet on it being a good deal. A close pair of friends who may appear straight are really practical jokers attempting to ace you out. Tell them to "Go fish!" Stand pat, call their bluff and let the chips fall in the soup.

## LIBRA
### September 23—October 23

Terrific news makes you look and feel wonderful. Unfortunately, no terrific news is headed your way for a long, long time. Instead, you enter a period of severe turmoil, followed by partial clearing and seasonal temperatures. Love with Virgos and Libras is exciting — especially if at the same time and on a big waterbed.

## SCORPIO
### October 24—November 21

Family vacations are well worth the money. However, that shirt you recently bought looks like it fell off the $2.00 clearance rack. Opposites attract, so don't be so damn witty and clever or you could wind up married to a real moron. Nothing goes as planned today, unless you planned on a day of nausea and scratching.

## SAGITTARIUS
### November 22-December 21

Your displaying of your writing, painting or musical talent will bring you instant recognition—everyone will immediately recognize that you have none! Newly enacted state statutes may force you to reconsider a current stable love. You are at the right place at the right time, but no one else is. Forget it. Go home.

## CAPRICORN
### December 22—January 19

Your request to be transferred to another department could have startling results — especially if you are currently out of work! Instead of worrying about things you can do nothing about, worry about the fact that you can do nothing about your worrying. Be sure to have lots of patients today, even if you're not a doctor.

## AQUARIUS
### January 20—February 18

Distant stars are signaling you that now is a very good time for some big career, financial and lovelife moves. However, these are the same stars that told you to buy Chrysler stock and to bet on Jimmy Carter in the last election. It is now clear that these stars are real schmucks, and you would be wise just to ignore them.

## PISCES
### February 19—March 20

Feeling self-indulgent? Go ahead, pamper yourself, but be prepared for some flack from those who do not understand the tremendous desire and need to occasionally wet one's pants. Look for a letter in the AM to bring you bad news, and look for those misplaced coldcuts underneath your living room sofa.

**WRITER: JOHN FICARRA**

The world is infested with rude, thoughtless clods whose self-indulgent behavior makes life miserable for the rest of us. So far, these insensitive slobs have been kept in check by official signs warning them to curb their dogs, keep off the grass, refrain from smoking, etc. Such signs have made a small beginning in civilizing these chronic public nuisances, but much work remains to be done. Since even the most uncouth jerk is shamed into obeying boldly-lettered rules posted in parks and other public places, why not extend the system? There's a good chance that we'd be less aggravated by self-centered pests if they were all constantly reminded, warned and threatened by these...

# SIGNS WE'D LIKE TO SEE

ARTIST: BOB CLARKE          WRITER: TOM KOCH

**CHANGE THE SPRINGS ON YOUR LIVING ROOM SOFA**

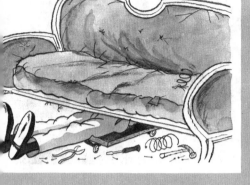

**INSPECT YOUR NEW REFRIGERATOR EVERY DAY FOR DENTS OR SCRATCHES**

**POLISH AND WAX SOMETHING TO A HIGH SHINE**

# THANKS TO THE GASOLINE SHORTAGE
## TO GIVE UP DRIVING ALTOGETHER.

# THINGS YOU C
# REMEMBER YOU

ARTIST & WRITER: PAUL PET

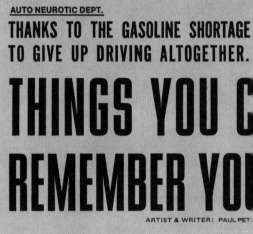

**CHANGE YOUR OIL**

**BRING TWO FOLDING CHAIRS TO YOUR DRIVE-IN MOVIE**

PORGES

## DO A JACKRABBIT START AND ACCELERATE FROM 0-TO-5 MILES PER HOUR IN A SUPERMARKET AISLE

## PUT SEATBELTS ON YOUR NEW BARKER LOUNGER, AND THEN NEVER USE THEM

...RTAGE, SOMEDAY WE MAY HAVE ...THER. HERE, THEN, ARE SOME

# ...I CAN DO TO
# ...OUR CAR BY

PAUL PETER PORGES

## LET SOMEBODY BACKSEAT-NAG YOU ON A TANDEM BIKE

## EAT SOME JUNK FOOD OFF A TRAY HANGING OUTSIDE YOUR WINDOW

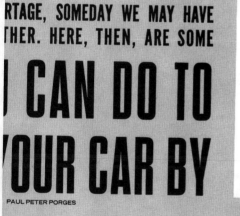

## GET YOURSELF A PORTABLE C.B. AND A NEW C.B. HANDLE

Footsore Fred here!

Strolling Sam, over and out!

Gasless Gus says ten-four!

Breaker! Breaker! This is No-Car Carla!

PORGES

Have you ever wondered *why* it rains every time you wash your car? Are you puzzled *why* the warranty on your TV runs out the day before your picture tube blows? The answer is obvious! We are all at the mercy of mysterious, unstated laws that have the power to make the young feel old, the wise look foolish and the strong turn into mush! In other words, we're all subject to

### THE WAITING PRINCIPLE

Whichever line you pick to stand on, the other one moves faster.

### WAITING PRINCIPLE COROLLARY

The moment you move to the faster line, it will start to move slower.

### THE WINDFALL THEOREM

Any unexpected gift of money is immediately equalled in amount by an unexpected expense.

### THE GYM-GOER'S MAXIM

The bulges on your body that you want most to get rid of are the ones least affected by exercise.

### THE POSSESSION RULE

The more cherished the keepsake, the greater the chance it will be smashed beyond repair by your cleaning lady.

### THE BICUSPID PRINCIPLE

The more excruciating the toothache, the more likely it will occur on the Friday evening before a long week-end.

# D LAWS

ARTIST: PAUL COKER
WRITER: FRANK JACOBS

### THE SINGLES LAW

No matter when you arrive at a party, the best-looking girls have been taken.

### THE TV EQUATION

The better the show, the greater the need to go to the bathroom.

### THE SATURDAY NIGHT THEOREM

When two girls come on to you and your buddy, the uglier one will go for you!

### THE 1ST LAW OF AIR TRAVEL

The earlier you arrive at the airport for your flight, the later your flight will depart.

### THE 2ND LAW OF AIR TRAVEL

The amount of time saved by your plane arriving early at your destination is equal to the amount of extra time you have to wait for your luggage.

### THE 3RD LAW OF AIR TRAVEL

The number of taxis at an airport is in inverse proportion to the number of flights arriving.

### THE CAR OWNER'S AXIOM

Any repair bill below the mechanic's estimate indicates there was nothing seriously wrong with your car in the first place, and you're being cheated.

### THE ESCAPE-THE-COLD AXIOM

The more you look forward to a Winter vacation in the sun, the more certain it is there will be more rain those 2 weeks than anyone there can remember.

### THE LAW OF CONSULTATION

The chance of any two doctors giving a different diagnosis for the same symptoms becomes a virtual certainty when both doctors are "Specialists."

### THE 1ST LAW OF HOME REPAIR

The most essential part of any article you repair is always discovered on the floor, after you put it back together.

### THE 2ND LAW OF HOME REPAIR

The one tool essential to the completion of a project is the very same one borrowed by your neighbor last Spring.

### THE 3RD LAW OF HOME REPAIR

The more irreplaceable that one tool, the more likely it is your neighbor moved away last month.

### THE LAWYER'S FORMULA

The fee charged by a lawyer increases in direct proportion to the length of the name of the law firm he works for.

### THE RESTAURANT CONSTANT

The desire for a certain dish on the menu is in direct proportion to the probability that they'll be out of it.

### THE PRIME TIME PRINCIPLE

The higher the quality of two TV shows, the greater the probability they will be aired at the same time.

# EARLY ONE MORNING DOWNTOWN

UNDERPLAY-BY-PLAY DEPT.

SINCE, LIKE US, YOU'RE PROBABLY UP TO HERE WITH THOSE TIRESOME CAN

# MAD'S Candid Sn
# Insignificant Mo

**DELAYED START OF INTERNATIONAL WATER POLO MATCH BETWEEN SAUDI ARABIA AND THE SUDAN**

**SIMPLE POP FLY DURING SING SING ANNUAL INTERMURAL BASEBALL GAME**

**ONE-MAN SCRAMBLE FOR FOUL BALL DURING LATE SEASON BLUE JAYS—MARINERS GAME**

**WINNER'S VICTORY LAP AT THE 1975 AKRON DEMOLITION DERBY**

# apshots Of Some ments In Sports

FANS DISAGREEING WITH REFEREE'S CALL
AT SOUTH AMERICAN SOCCER CHAMPIONSHIP

BIG UPSET DURING ANNUAL OKEFENOKEE
SWAMP GATOR-WRESTLING CHAMPIONSHIP

ARTIST & WRITER: PAUL PETER PORGES

BANTAMWEIGHT CONTENDER MISTAKINGLY USING
HEAVYWEIGHT'S MOUTHPIECE AT GOLDEN GLOVES

JUMP BALL AT THE ANNUAL BROOKLYN
CO-ED INTERFAITH BASKETBALL GAME

**GOLF PRO IN ROUGH DURING AMAZON OPEN**

**U.S. BOBSLED TEAM TAKING A COFFEE BREAK**

**DISTRACTED NET JUDGE DURING FINALS AT THE WARSAW LAWN TENNIS INVITATIONALS**

**RELEASE OF PIGEONS AT CEREMONY OPENING THE XVIII OLYMPIC GAMES**

**DELAYED CALL GIANTS-DOLPHINS COIN TOSS**

**INTRODUCTION OF ICE HOCKEY'S OLD TIMERS**

My object all sublime
I shall achieve in time—
To let the punishment
fit the crime,
The punishment
fit the crime;
And make each prisoner pent
Unwillingly represent
A source of innocent
merriment,
Of innocent merriment!

This is the introductory verse to an amusing song performed by the title character in "The Mikado." In it, Gilbert and Sullivan then proceed to list their pet hates and the punishments they'd like to see meted out. But since 'The Mikado' was written in 1885, those pet hates are now outdated. Which is why MAD feels it's time for

# A "Let The Punishment Fit The Crime" Up-Date

ARTIST: JACK DAVIS     WRITER: MICHAEL J. SNIDER

Our project's aimed at each
Deserving social leech;
We'll make the penalty
fit the breach,
The penalty
fit the breach;
For ev'ry reprobate
We'll coldly calculate,
And give a specially-
fitting fate,
A specially-fitting fate!

The Nuclear Power Apologists who
call all our fears unbased:
Their attics and basements
Will serve as encasements
For radioactive waste!

The greedy Professional Athlete
whose salary hikes never cease:
A turnstile he's chained to
So he can explain to
Fans why admissions increase!

The Reckless Driving Highway Clod
who has to be finally checked:
His tapes, we will loot them
He'll learn pain and grief well
On some cloverleaf hell
Where all the exits connect!

The Disco Freak in public places
whose giant tape-player blares:
His tapes, we will loot them
And then substitute them
With hymns and Irish folk airs!

Our project so decreed
Is all but guaranteed
To make the penalty
fit the deed,
The penalty
fit the deed;
And ev'ry crime will be
An opportunity
To try a little
frivolity,
A little frivolity!

The Sidewalk Roller Skating Creep
who knocks you right off your feet:
We'll force him to travel
O'er pot holes and gravel
While cab-dodging in the street!

Our project will suffice
To make them pay the price,
To make the penalty
fit the vice,
The penalty fit the vice;
What better way to go—
To stem the shameful flow—
Then make their come-uppance
a propos,
Their come uppance apropos!

The rabid White Supremacist
whose tolerance really rots:
We'll gather their legions
And ship them to regions
Like Harlem and Hough and Watts!

The Over-Spending Bureaucrat
whose budget's destined to bust:
His debts, we've enacted
Will all be contracted
To "Mafia Loan & Trust"!

The preaching Religious Fanatics
who babble, chatter and stare:
They'll all be sequestered
And thoroughly pestered
By Madalyn Murray O'Hair!

The Punk Rock Band whose musical
talents obviously don't exist:
They're helped by obtaining
Remedial training
In Beethoven, Brahms and Liszt!

The sneaky Real Estate Promoters
who change swamps into gold:
We'll only let buy land
Around Three Mile Island
And sell 'til all of it's sold!

The Fiends Who Write Those TV Ads
that have us all revolted:
They'll all meet their doom
In a huge screening room
(Whose doors are locked and bolted!)

We'll make them watch an endless show
of all they've e'er begat:
Every (yecch!) bathtub ring;
Stupid products that sing;
Clod "Whipple" and "Morris The Cat"!

IN AN EFFORT TO FIGHT INFLATION, BY SCREWING THE OIL CARTELS

# SOME MAD ENERG

ARTIST: BOB CLARKE

### THE WINDMILL-POWERED PENCIL SHARPENER

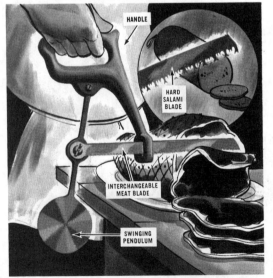

### THE POGO-STICK-ACTIVATED HIGH-SPEED BLENDER

FOOT REST

HANDLE

LOCK-ON LID

BLADES

CONTAINER

SPIRAL SHAFT MOUNTED ON BALL-BEARING BASE

COIL SPRING

### THE PENDULUM-PROPELLED CARVING KNIFE

HANDLE

HARD SALAMI BLADE

INTERCHANGEABLE MEAT BLADE

SWINGING PENDULUM

### THE COMBINATION STOOL & WATER PICK

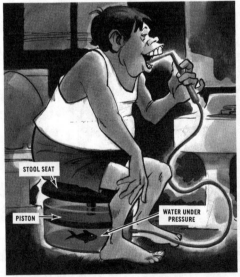

STOOL SEAT

PISTON

WATER UNDER PRESSURE

AND THE UTILITY COMPANIES, YOUR IDIOT EDITORS NOW PRESENT...

# Y-SAVING DEVICES

WRITER: PAUL PETER PORGES

## THE SELF-GENERATING ELECTRIC GUITAR

## THE WIND-UP RUBBER-BAND-DRIVEN POWER TOOL

## THE PUSH-PEDAL-POWERED VACUUM CLEANER

## THE SOLAR-ENERGIZED CORDLESS HOT COMB

# DON MARTIN

presents

# "THE STORY OF MOSES"

## PART I—MOSES .... AS A

## PART II—MOSES .... AS A

## PART III—MOSES .... AS A

# CHILD

## SMALL BOY

## YOUNG MAN

# PART IV—MOSES.... AS AN OLD MAN

Remember what tipping used to be for? It was for a job well done. Now, we tip for *any* job, no matter *how badly* it's done. And we usually *over-tip* for a job that's done the way it *should* be done. Well, here's your chance to change all that. Since you're probably too chicken to leave no tip at all for a bad job, just cut these out, place them in an envelope, and discretely hand out where necessary these . . .

# MAD "NO TIP" CARDS

WRITER: DICK DE BARTOLO

### FOR THE WAITRESS

You forgot the onions on my burger!
You forgot my Coke and French fries, too!
So I'm sure that you will understand when
I forget to leave a tip for you!

### FOR THE BELLBOY

You carried my tiny bag up the stairs,
And made me feel like I'm weak!
You made a deal of unlocking the door,
Like it was something unique!
You showed me just how to turn on the light,
And things that wasted my time!
Now it's my turn to make you feel small, pal—
Have you got change of a dime?

### FOR THE WASHROOM ATTENDANT

Big deal! You handed me a towel
And then turned on the water!
Who asked you!? I'm not crippled yet!
I'm handing you no quarter!

### FOR THE HATCHECK GIRL

I didn't want to check my hat,
My topcoat and my umbrella!
To make things worse, what I got back
Belongs to some other fellah!
So don't expect a tip from me;
Be glad that I'm not a "yeller"!

### FOR THE MAILMAN

All year long you tore up my mail,
And jammed it in my slot!
But now that Christmas time is here,
How careful you have got!
It's obvious you want a tip;
Your hinting did not fail!
I don't know how you'll get it, though—
I put it in the mail!

### FOR THE SHOESHINE MAN

The job you did on my shoes was fine—
That's not what I am knocking;
The tip you're not getting's for the shine
You slopped all over my stocking!

### FOR THE BARBER

You cut off more hair than I wanted!
You sliced me up, drawing blood twice!
As a Barber, you're really a Butcher!
Here's my tip—Get legal advice!
YOU'RE GETTING SUED, DUDE!

### FOR THE CAB DRIVER

YOU DIDN'T MISS ONE POT-HOLE, SAM!
YOU DIDN'T MISS ONE TRAFFIC JAM!
YOU DIDN'T MISS ONE SIGNAL LIGHT!
YOU DID, HOWEVER, MISS MY FLIGHT!
SO THANK YOU FOR A LOUSY TRIP—
I HOPE THAT YOU WON'T MISS MY TIP!

What's going on in Nursery Land these days? Well, Tom, Tom the Piper's Son is stuffing ballot boxes, and Jack and Mrs. Sprat are splitting their votes between the Democrats and G.O.P. In other words, it's voting time for Solomon Grundy and his friends, which is our way of introducing . . .

# MAD'S

## Humpty Dumpty

Humpty Dumpty made an address;
Humpty Dumpty hollered, "Spend less!"
All the conservative voters agreed
That Humpty in office was sure to succeed.

Humpty Dumpty spoke to the poor;
Humpty Dumpty hollered, "Spend more!"
All of the liberal voters concurred
That Humpty by far was the one they preferred.

Humpty Dumpty stays on the fence;
Humpty Dumpty knows this makes sense;
He'll win all the voters up North and down South
By making full use of both sides of his mouth.

## Little Bo Peep

Little Bo Peep
Is fast sleep
And that's the way she'll stay;
Little Jack Horner
Lies flat in his corner
And won't wake up today;
Little Boy Blue
Is dozing, too—
There isn't a soul who's awake;
Why are they snoring?
From hearing those boring
Long speeches their candidates make.

## Sing a Song of Issues

Sing a song of issues,
Of unemployment rates,
Of busing and of housing,
Of greater aid to states;
When the campaign's over,
We can guarantee
We'll make the man the winner
Who looked best on TV.

## The Crooked Man

There was a crooked man,
And he had a crooked laugh,
And he ran a crooked office,
And he hired a crooked staff.

He served a crooked term,
And he did a crooked job,
And he rammed through crooked bills
For a crooked local mob.

Why back the crooked man
When his crooked ways you see?
Because the rival candidate
Is crookeder than he.

# ELECTION-YEAR MOTHER GOOSE

ARTIST: PAUL COKER, JR.    WRITER: FRANK JACOBS

## Wee Willie Winkie

Wee Willie Winkie
Doesn't seem for real,
Takes no contributions,
Never makes a deal.

Wee Willie Winkie
Always comes off clean,
Free from all corruption,
Owned by no machine.

Wee Willie Winkie
Rids himself of sin;
Maybe that's why Willie
Never seems to win.

## Jack and Phil

Jack and Phil
Work on the Hill;
Two Senators are they;
But they pursue
The work they do
In quite a diff'rent way.

Jack's a slob
Who muffs his job,
While Phil achieves perfection;
It should be clear
Which one this year
Is up for re-election.

## Harry is a Congressman

Harry is a Congressman
In Washington, D.C.,
And in his spacious office there
You'll meet his fam-i-ly.

His brother is his right-hand man
(he's never worked before);
His father gets 12 grand a year
(he's paid to shut the door).

His wife works as his filing clerk
(she cannot read or write);
His daughter mans the telephone
(a chimp is twice as bright).

Today when unemployment's high
And folks can't pay their rents,
How nice to know one fam-i-ly's
Found work—at our expense.

## The Other Day Upon the Stair

The other day upon the stair
I saw a man who wasn't there;
He wasn't there again today;
I think he's from the C.I.A.

## Taffy Was a Rich Man

Taffy was a rich man;
Taffy was connected;
Taffy spent five hundred grand
To get his man elected.

Taffy's now Ambassador
And struts around with pride;
Why don't *you* spend five hundred grand
And *you'll* be qualified.

## Tweedledum and Tweedledee

Tweedledum and Tweedledee
Were running for the House,
When Tweedledum smeared Tweedledee
By calling him a louse.

Tweedledee said Tweedledum
Had caused a vicious stink,
Then spread the word that Tweedledum
Was going to a "Shrink."

Tweedledum said Tweedledee
Was vile and full of bunk;
"The problem is," said Tweedledum,
"That Tweedledee's a drunk."

Tweedledee said Tweedledum
Was wrong in ev'ry way,
Then whispered to a columnist
That Tweedledum was gay.

Today I heard that Tweedledee
Was spotted at an orgy;
To hell with both—Election Day
I'll write in Georgie Porgie!

## As I Was Watching NBC

As I was watching NBC,
I heard a newsman telling me
Although returns were barely in
That A would lose and B would win.

As I was watching CBS,
I heard an analyst profess
That his computer could foresee
That C should now concede to D.

As I was watching ABC,
I heard that F would unseat E,
And, from 12 votes in Tennessee,
That H would wind up beating G.

As I turned off my set, I swore,
"What good are voters anymore?
"We might as well get rid of them
"And leave the vote to IBM."

## Despite the Crooks Unbeatable

Despite the crooks unbeatable—
Those creepy clods unseatable—
With dirty deals despicable
That make the voters trickable—

Despite folks made insensible
From views incomprehensible
In speeches unendurable
By party hacks incurable—

Despite campaigns regrettable
With promises forgettable—
Despite the rumors spreadable—
Our system works—Incredible!

DID YOU REALLY THINK THE T-SHIRT CRAZE STARTED ABOUT 5 YEARS AGO? WELL, SURPRISE!

# T-SHIRTS THRO

ARTIST: HARRY NORTH

**NAPOLEON AND JOSEPHINE**

**ADAM AND EVE**

**TARZAN**

**VENUS DE MILO**

**BARON VON RICHTHOFEN**

**MOSES**

**ROBINSON CRUSOE**

IT STARTED ABOUT 5000 YEARS AGO! AND IF YOU DON'T BELIEVE US, JUST LOOK AT THESE...

# DUGH THE AGES

WRITER: DICK DE BARTOLO

Some of the biggest-selling books these days are "The Joy of Sex" and "More Joy of Sex." Now, we ask you: Who in heck needs a book to tell us how much joy and pleasure sex is? We already know that! And if we don't, a book isn't going to help! What we

# SOME "JOY OF

ARTIST: BOB CLARKE

### THE JOY OF ACNE

### Chapter I

Stop feeling that The Almighty has dealt you a terribly unfair blow by filling your face with purple and red beauties! You're lucky, and you should rejoice!

How lucky? Well, just think: Without those little pustules, what would you see when you looked in a mirror? Practically nothing at all. Merely a face that's hardly worth spending any time looking at.

But with acne, you can spend hours peering at yourself because you're so damn interesting. Other people who spend time looking at themselves in mirrors are called "ego-maniacs." But you can do it with a clear conscience, if not a clear complexion.

Now, let's look at the advan-

### THE JOY OF WEEKEND HOMEWORK

### THE JOY OF NOT BEING ACCEPTED INTO COLLEGE

### Chapter One

If you fail to get into college, you may think that your life is over. It's not, as a matter of fact. It's just beginning . . . in a big way.

When your parents call you "stupid" and "bum," don't fight with them. Agree with them. Soon, they'll tire of hurling epithets at you, and will then try to cheer you up by saying things like, "You're really not a bum!" "Actually, you're a bright kid!" But stay with your identification as a dope and a bum. Make them feel that their words have damaged your psyche for life.

Next, they will start to feel responsible for your depressed condition and will kill themselves, trying to make you happy and get rid of their guilts. And that's when you

### THE JOY OF BEING HORNY

do need in these troubled times are books that tell us how to get joy and pleasure from activities and situations that aren't very joyful and pleasurable. And so, as a public service, and to help push more slow-selling magazines, MAD now presents . . .

# . . . " BOOKS WE COULD REALLY USE

WRITER: STAN HART

## CHAPTER ONE

One of the greatest sources of anxiety and anguish for a teenager is what to do on a Saturday night. Questions such as: "Will *HE* call me for a date?" or "Will *anyone* in this *entire planet* call me for a date?" are no longer problems. Because you simply have no time to bother with such questions. Even if someone did call you, he'd probably want to jump on your bones in a drive-in movie or a deserted lovers' lane, thereby causing you another problem: mainly, how you should handle your chastity . . . among other things.

Who needs such problems? By being assigned a heavy load of weekend homework, consider all the agonies you've avoided.

THE JOY OF UNWANTED PREGNANCY

THE JOY OF FAMILY GATHERINGS

## CHAPTER I

To some young girls, the threat of an unwanted pregnancy is a terrible thing to contemplate.

Take heart. There can be joy in it. First, it refutes your parents' claim that you can't do anything right. Kid, you've done it right this time! Next, think about all the old clothes you've been wearing. Aren't you tired of them and also the hassle your parents give you whenever you ask for new threads? Well, now you'll have a complete new wardrobe every couple of months! And don't feel sorry for your folks. Just think of the joy they'll derive being pitied by all their friends. A once-overlooked couple will now be center stage, and you've put them there!

## Chapter One

Just because you can look, but you can't touch is no reason to me miserable. Be happy. Be joyous. After all, aren't you always saying to yourself, "Boy, what I could do with a girl like that!"? Sure you are!

Well, if you had a girl like that, chances are you'd do something awkward, foolish or disgusting. Also, you might find that there's more satisfaction in thinking about making out than making out itself.

So rejoice that you don't have the chance to louse up. your fantasies and dreams. The real world is always a big disappointment. Take the experience of Marvin Farshimmelt, for example. Once,

## CHAPTER ONE

Torture, you say, when your parents drag you to a family gathering?

Wrong! It's a joy . . . if you think about it for a second.

Where else can you reinforce your prejudices that all adults are idiots? Where else can you feel totally justified in loathing members of your family . . . like that dopey Uncle who thinks that a lampshade on a head is still hysterically funny?

Family meetings afford a wonderful opportunity to wallow in self-pity . . . that you're part of a family that has such mindless oafs in it.

Why restrict the awarding of medals to the military? After all, Civilians perform heroic acts while fighting life's daily battles as well! Let's recognize them with

# THIS ISSUE'S PROPOSED
# MAD MEDALS
## . . . TO BE PRESENTED TO DESERVING DOCTORS

### THE MISSING FORCEPS MEDAL

Awarded to Doctors who successfully pass on to their patients the higher costs of Malpractice Insurance while in no way attempting to cut down on the causes of these increased costs, mainly greed and actual malpractice.

### THE FULL CALENDAR CITATION

TODAY'S APPOINTMENTS
The entire city of Chicago

Goes to Doctors who demonstrate the efficiency and diligence necessary to see an unbelievable amount of patients per hour in their offices and on their hospital walk-throughs while managing to collect full fee charges for each.

### THE LITTLE GREEN PILL MEDAL

For prescribing without conscience or trepidation certain extremely expensive name-brand drugs, thus insuring both warm and lasting relationships with pharmacists, and rewarding free vacation trips from drug companies.

### THE GOLDEN SCAPEL AWARD

Awarded to Doctors who have performed surgery above and beyond the call of necessity. These procedures involve the removal of patients' appendixes, tonsils, gall bladders, ovaries, etc., whether they needed to be or not! The motto inscribed on the reverse side of the medal reads, "A removed organ can never become a really diseased organ!"

### THE A.M.A. MEDAL OF HONOR

This decoration represents the medical profession's highest award . . . and can only be presented to those doctors who distinguish themselves with an unbroken record of heroically fighting the battle against Socialized Medicine, Public Health Care, lower fees, and any other profit-cutting ideas that lawmakers and do-gooders periodically come up with.

ARTIST & WRITER: AL JAFFEE

# STUFF WE DON'T GET TO SEE ON THE TUBE

A football player sitting on the bench during a game who's so engrossed in the action that he doesn't smile and give us the "We're Number One!" sign when the TV camera focuses on him.

A private eye who isn't involved in murder, smuggling, etc., but only does what private detectives really do: gather evidence in messy divorce cases.

This should **do** it, Angle! Mrs. Kvetch should be able to get her divorce **easily** with **this** evidence!

What are they doing, Jammy?! Le'me **look**!!

**ARTIST: JACK DAVIS**     **WRITER: LOU SILVERSTONE**

A talk show host who actually read the book by the author he is interviewing.

A diaper commercial that indicates babies do something else besides wet.

An oil company commercial that brags about how much money they're making.

Gee, all I **said** was I **read** his **book**!

My baby stays comfortable in Panders because they're **more absorbant**—and keep him—uh—**drier**! Unfortunately, they **don't** absorb the **smell** of—ulp!

This is Bob "Snake Oil" Hope for Taxico! See that **oil** gushing out of that well? **That's not oil**! That's **money**! Last month, our profits were up **another 130%** to an all-time high of **$70 billion**, and **that ain't hay**!

**Two cops who are partners but don't like each other.**

**A really stupid animal of some kind in a TV series.**

**A small town where the people are friendly to strangers.**

**A preacher who doesn't ask for contributions**

**A doctor who insists upon getting paid.**

**A press conference where a politician answers a question directly.**

# More HOW CAN

. . . the Ski Instructor in a body cast!

. . . the Blind Date who's all dressed up in leather and boots and chains!

. . . the Short-Order Cook with a cold!

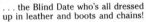

. . . the brand new car with an oil spot the size of a wading pool underneath!

. . . the TV Weatherman who points to Texas and calls it the Ohio Valley!

# YOU TRUST...

ARTIST: PAUL COKER WRITER: PAUL PETER PORGES

... the Boxer who kneels to pray before he knocks his opponent's brains out!

...the Safety Expert whose shoelaces are untied and shirt tails hang loose!

... the Faith Healer who has a hernia, suffers from gout and is nearly deaf!

... the Tennis Pro who plays with an oversize and oddly-strung racquet!

...the Psychiatrist who pops Valiums!

... the Cab Driver who speaks with an accent and reads the city map upside down!

... the Travel Agent who books your trip to Hawaii via Cleveland, Ohio; St. Louis, Missouri and Vancouver, British Columbia!

... the Killer Dog that's afraid of sudden loud noises!

... the Fire Chief who chain smokes while directing a four-alarmer!

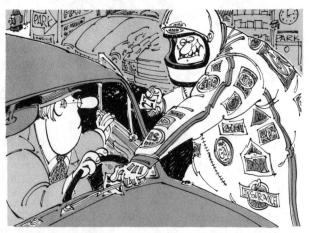

... the Parking Lot Attendant who wears a crash helmet and racing gloves!

# AN EYE-POPPING SCENE ON A CORNER

ARTIST & WRITER: DON EDWING

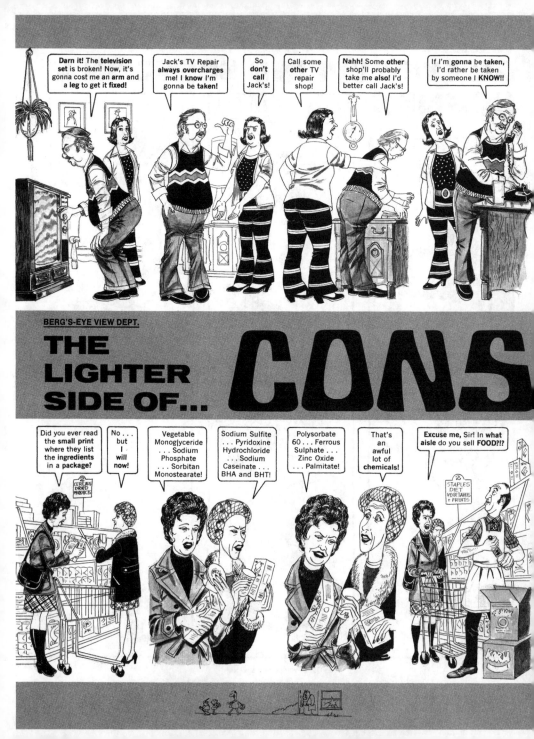

# ONE DAY IN PHILADELPHIA

## GIFT HORSING AROUND DEPT.

In the old days, meaning more than three years ago, manufacturers and retailers would often give a buyer a "FREE GIFT" or "BONUS" with their product or service. If you were purchasing an Electric Drill, for example, the manufacturer might throw in a free set of Drill Bits. But with inflation choking our economy, manufacturers and retailers can no longer afford this practice. Instead, they are hyping as "Free Gifts" the things you'd ordinarily get anyway! Like f'rinstance this article, which we're throwing in as a FREE GIFT for buying the magazine, and contains some MAD examples of

**THIS BOTTLE OF**
*Grepsi Cola*
**Includes A FREE SCREW-ON RE-USABLE CAP**
Which You Can Use to Store Any Unused
G R E P S I   C O L A

**Schlock & Deckle**

**ALL PURPOSE**
**ELECTRIC DRILL**
MODEL PU-2

## INCLUDED AT NO EXTRA COST:
Instruction Booklet
Warranty Card
List Of Service Centers
Assorted Packing Materials Designed To Insure Your Chance Of Receiving The
Schlock & Deckle **ELECTRIC DRILL In One Piece**

**FREE!**
WITH EVERY
**PURCHASE!**
AN
ELECTRONICALLY
PRINTED
CASH REGISTER
RECEIPT!

BUY A DOZEN EGGS AND TAKE THEM HOME IN A
**FREE DECORATOR CARRYING CASE**
IDEAL FOR PROTECTING YOUR PURCHASE DURING TRAVEL!
CONVENIENT FOR STORING EGGS IN YOUR REFRIGERATOR!
ATTRACTIVE TO NOSY PEOPLE WHO MIGHT PEEK INTO IT!

When a friend has a birthday, you send a birthday card. When a couple has an anniversary, you send an anniversary card. But there may be times when you won't be able to find the right card for the occasion. If this happens, we invite you to turn to this selection of

# MAD GRE
## FOR <u>VERY</u> SP

## To a Would-Be Suicide

You cannot learn to tie a noose
  And pills stick in your throat;
You lack the skill to aim a gun;
  You try to drown—and float;
And so I guess it's up to me
  To supervise your fate;
This card's a rolled-up Navy raft;
  Just swallow—then inflate.

## To A Pedigreed Dog Owner

It's clear to me how much you prize
  Your purebred female collie;
Two thousand bucks to buy a dog
  Is quite a sum, by golly!
I'd like to fill your life with joy,
  To lift your spirits, but—
Last weekend, when she was in heat,
  She made it with a mutt.

## *To an Auto Crash Victim*

*You have two badly broken arms;*
  *Your pelvis is a wreck;*
*Your head's in traction for a year*
  *From whiplash of the neck;*
*But though you'll suffer many months*
  *From wounds that will not heal,*
*Just look at it another way—*
  *Think how your car must feel.*

# ETING CARDS
## ECIAL OCCASIONS

ARTIST: PAUL COKER    WRITER: FRANK JACOBS WITH EARLE DOUD

### To A Young Bride

*It seems, my dear, like yesterday*
*You started out in life,*
*And here you are at seventeen*
*About to be a wife;*
*Let's hope the wedding gown you wear*
*Is full and loosely styled,*
*So no one there will get the chance*
*To see that you're with child.*

### To A Confused Person

You comb the land from coast to coast,
    You search the whole wide earth,
In hopes some day that you will find
    A record of your birth;
And so I want to share with you
    What all your friends have known—
You'll never find the proof you seek,
    Because you are a clone.

### To A Mass Murderer on Trial

You know the judge can send you up
    For your remaining years,
And so I send this card to you
    To banish all your fears;
No life in stir awaits you, pal,
    You won't be rotting there;
The Legislature's changed the law—
    They're bringing back the Chair.

ALS Electric Repair

## TO AN EX-BOY FRIEND

What fun we had, the two of us,
  Those nights when we smoked pot,
Until that day you said, "Get lost!"
  And ditched me on the spot;
You treated me like so much dirt;
  I really was disgusted;
Which is my way of telling you
  Who went and got you busted.

## TO AN EX-GIRLFRIEND

*I love the park where first we met,*
  *The whisper of the breeze;*
*I love the grass where once we sat*
  *Beneath the noble trees;*
*I also love the wooden bench*
  *Where first we kissed and hugged;*
*They all remind me how I fled*
  *And left you to be mugged.*

## TO A HEALTH NUT

*You don't eat fish or fowl or meat;*
  *You won't use salt or spices;*
*You've put a ban on cakes and pies,*
  *And eggs provoke a crisis;*
*This card's not meant to put you down;*
  *It's just an explanation*
*Why once again I'm passing up*
  *Your dinner invitation.*

## To A Terrorist

You victimize and kill and maim;
  In short, you go too far;
But nothing I can ever say
  Will change the way you are;
By now, whatever's left of you
  Lies scattered on the floor;
I bet you never opened up
  A letter-bomb before.

One of the newest and fastest-rising sports here in the United States is also one of the oldest and most popular sports in just about every other country in the world. We're referring, of course, to Soccer. Those of you who are familiar with Soccer might as well skip this article . . . because there is nothing in it you don't know! Those of you who are unfamiliar with Soccer might as well skip it, too . . . because there is nothing in it you'll *want* to know! Which leaves us and the Printer to enjoy . . .

# THE MAD SOCCER PRIMER

ARTIST: JACK DAVIS
WRITER: LARRY SIEGEL

## Chapter One

See the men in the funny short pants.
What are they doing?
They are playing a game called Soccer.
It is the most popular game in the world.
What is the foremost rule of Soccer?
That you may kick the ball . . .
Or hit it with your head . . .
But you may never touch it with your hands.
What was potentially the greatest Soccer Team
In sports history?
Probably the 1979 New York Mets.

## Chapter Two

What is the primary idea of Soccer?
To get the ball into your opponent's goal.
How will these men move the ball
Down the very, very large Soccer Field?
Perhaps by dribbling it with their feet.
How else will they move the ball?
Perhaps by passing it with kicks.
When do you think one team will get the ball
Close enough to take a shot at the other goal?
Perhaps by next Thursday.

# Chapter Three

Soccer is considered to be
The fastest-growing sport in the United States.
Here we see two typical American Soccer Teams in action.
There are eleven men on a side in Soccer.
How can we tell that these 22 players
Make up two typical American Soccer Teams?
Because on the field, this is what we see . . .
(And suppose, instead of saying it,
We sing it . . .)

Six Germans running,
Five Ar-gen-tines.
Four Spanish Backs,
Three French men,
Two Turkish Wings,
And a pair o-of Polish Goal-ies!
How come there are no Canadians playing American Soccer?
Because they are busy in Chicago and Boston and Detroit
Playing American Hockey!

## Chapter Four

Look, look, look.
One team has actually maneuvered the ball
Close to its opponent's goal.
Isn't it exciting?
This the first time it has happened today.
And they have only been playing for 78 minutes!
Now, all they have to do is penetrate a defensive wall
Of two Center-Backs, a Right-Back, and a Left-Back . . .
Not to mention the Goalie . . .
And they might get a shot at the goal.
What are the chances of scoring in Soccer?
About the same as Truman Capote's chances of scoring
At the office Christmas Party of Cosmopolitan Magazine.

## Chapter Five

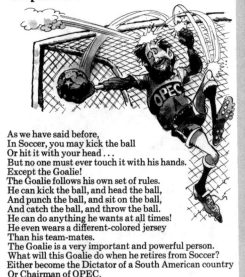

As we have said before,
In Soccer, you may kick the ball
Or hit it with your head . . .
But no one must ever touch it with his hands.
Except the Goalie!
The Goalie follows his own set of rules.
He can kick the ball, and head the ball,
And punch the ball, and sit on the ball,
And catch the ball, and throw the ball.
He can do anything he wants at all times!
He even wears a different-colored jersey
Than his team-mates.
The Goalie is a very important and powerful person.
What will this Goalie do when he retires from Soccer?
Either become the Dictator of a South American country
Or Chairman of OPEC.

## Chapter Six

See the crowd watching an American Soccer game.
A Soccer crowd is a lot like the United Nations.
Why is that?
Because it is comprised of people
Of all different nationalities?
Partly...
But also because they make a lot of noise
And they usually accomplish nothing.
South Americans are fascinated
By the teamwork in Soccer.
Europeans are fascinated
By its finesse.
Asians are fascinated
By its competitive spirit.
Why are Americans fascinated by Soccer?
Because they want to see for themselves
If it's true that Soccer
Is the only sport ever created
That is more boring than Baseball.

## Chapter Seven

See the angry Soccer fans.
They take the game very seriously
And they have very short tempers.
Look, look, look.
The stands have gone berserk.
The Italian fans are beating up on the British fans.
The Brazilian fans are belting the Portuguese fans.
The Indonesian fans are pounding the Egyptian fans.
Isn't this dreadful?!
Isn't it inexcusable?!
It sure is!!
Don't they realize that
Because of this terrible racket they're making,
They just woke up the American fans?!

## Chapter Eight

Soccer is a very strenuous game.
Play very rarely stops.
The only one who calls time is the Referee.
And only if there is serious injury on the field.
Look at the player
Lying motionless in a crumpled heap.
He was killed by angry fans
Who are rooting for the other team.
Why doesn't the Referee call "time"?
Because, compared to what Soccer fans
Usually do to rival players,
Death is not considered a serious injury.

## Chapter Nine

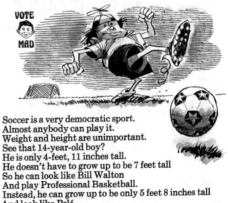

Soccer is a very democratic sport.
Almost anybody can play it.
Weight and height are unimportant.
See that 14-year-old boy?
He is only 4-feet, 11 inches tall.
He doesn't have to grow up to be 7 feet tall
So he can look like Bill Walton
And play Professional Basketball.
Instead, he can grow up to be only 5 feet 8 inches tall
And look like Pelé
And play Professional Soccer.
But supposing he doesn't grow up at all!?
That's okay, too.
He can always look like Paul Williams
And write songs.
Come to think of it,
Who needs Soccer?!?

Remember the good old days of TV commercials when, in order to prove how good his product was, an advertiser used to knock "Brand X"? Well, if you've been watching the tube lately, you know that we don't have "Brand X" to kick around anymore. No sir, nowadays on TV, advertisers kick around the real thing. For example, Lincoln kicks Cadillac, Pepsi kicks Coca-Cola, Pinto kicks all the other cars, and so on. It's all

# COMPARISON
# IN EVERYDA

## CHOOSING A HOUSE OF WORSHIP

Well, Mrs. Farber . . . you've spent an **hour** in **both** of these **Houses of Worship!** And you don't know **which** is which, right? Now . . . which **one** do you prefer . . . ?

Oh, there's **no** doubt about it! I found the one under **that** cloth much more **uplifting!** I mean, I was **real depressed** when I walked in, but **that** one **really raised my spirits!** Yes, I definitely prefer **that** House of Worship!

Are you surprised to see **which** one you chose?

**Wow! A Catholic Church!** *Shriek . . . laugh . . . giggle!* **I don't believe it!** I mean, I've been using **Synagogues** all my life . . . but it's the **Catholic Church** for me from now on! Yes, sir, I **never** experienced a **miracle** like that before!

## SELECTING THE BEST SURGEON

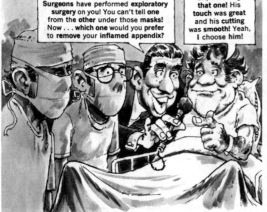

Well, Mr. Gribbs, both of these **Surgeons** have performed **exploratory surgery** on you! You can't tell **one** from the **other** under those **masks!** Now . . . **which one** would you prefer to **remove** your inflamed appendix?

Oh, **definitely that one!** His **touch** was great and his **cutting** was **smooth!** Yeah, I choose him!

Why . . . it looks like you chose **Dr. Finster!**

Over **Dr. Zetts?!** You gotta be kidding! *Chuckle . . . chuckle . . .* I mean, I've been going to Dr. Zetts **all my life!** Why, he removed my **hemorrhoids!** He fixed my **hernia!** His pills always tasted **milder!** But now— well, **I'm switching to Dr. Finster** from here on in!

done through the ever-popular gimmick known as "The Comparison Test." Well, we got to thinking: What would happen if this device were to be carried over into other areas? F'rinstance, let's take a MAD look at

# TESTS Y LIFE

ARTIST: JACK RICKARD    WRITER: LARRY SIEGEL

## PICKING OUT THE RIGHT COP

**Would you care to tell us about the miracle, Mrs. Farber?**

**You bet!** I mean . . . there I was with a **lousy** card with **nothing across, nothing diagonal,** and only **two numbers down!** And then, all of a sudden—**WHAM!** Three numbers down in a row, and **BINGO!** I tell you, that was **some miracle!**

**Well, today's the day! I can't wait for Dr. Finster to remove my appendix and . . . Say! Which comparison test are THEY doing?**

**Oh, that's no comparison test!** Those are two of Dr. Finster's **former patients!**

**Oh, my God! DR. ZETTS! DR. ZETTS!**

**Save your breath! One of THEM is Dr. Zetts!!**

Mr. Fink, as the owner of the **Schlock Hotel,** you'll need **special police protection** for your **Call Girl racket!** After comparing **these two officers,** which one do you think you'd prefer to **work** with . . . ?

**No question about it!** The cop on the **left!** His **attitude** is more satisfying, his **sincerity** just **lasts** and **lasts,** and **most of all,** I **can't resist** the way he holds out his **open hand!**

Well, the officer you just slipped **$500 to** is **Marty Payola,** one of the **crookedest cops in town!** Does that **surprise you?**

**Not really!** Especially since I've been using him in my **Bookmaking operation!**

**Hold it!** You're **under arrest** for **bribing a policeman!**

Unfortunately, **the other** officer is **Mike Square,** the **only HONEST** cop in our fair city!!

**Gi'me a break** officer! I've got a **wife** and **kids** to support! Would **$500** make you **forget** the whole thing?

**You think you** can buy the **only honest cop in town** for a lousy **500 bucks?!?**

Make it **$750!**

**You got a deal!**

**Snap it up,** Mr. Fink. It's getting **late** and we still have to shop for a **JUDGE** this afternoon!

# ONE EVENING AT A BANQUET SALUTING AN OUTSTANDING AMERICAN

**A BIG HAND FOR LITTLE FEATS DEPT.**

If you ever read the "Guinness Book Of World Records," you know that it lists accomplishments like "Coin Snatching," "Custard Pie Throwing" and "Smoke Ring Blowing." They even have records for "Hot Water Bottle Bursting" and "Onion Peeling," and they tell of a man who was struck by lightning 7 times. Well, all this makes entertaining reading, but it doesn't have very much to do with our everyday world. It's time, MAD feels, that we honored those achievements of the ordinary men, women and children living their ordinary lives. In other words, here are some of the marvelous accomplishments that might be recorded

# IF THE GUINNESS BOOK OF WORLD RECORDS DEALT WITH EVERYDAY LIFE

ARTIST: PAUL COKER    WRITER: FRANK JACOBS

## THE GREATEST CONSECUTIVE NUMBER OF BLIND DATES

is 33, experienced by Melvin Sturving of Denver, Colorado. Of the 33, the most disastrous one was the last one, which led to his marriage.

## THE LONGEST TEMPER TANTRUM

was thrown by Billy Winkler, 7, of Kansas City, Kansas, after being refused a third Twinkie by his mother, July 1, 1979. Billy screamed and beat his fists on his Teddy Bear for 8 hours, 4 minutes, breaking the old mark set by Arnie Gink, of Bangor, Maine, who cried and stomped for 7 hours, 27 minutes, after not being allowed to see "Star Wars" for the fortieth time.

## THE MOST PIECES OF JUNK MAIL RECEIVED IN 1 WEEK

is 903 ... by Morton Occupant of Des Moines, Iowa.

## THE MOST DELICIOUS MEAL EATEN ON A DOMESTIC AIRLINE

was enjoyed by Frank Argly on a United Airlines flight from New York City to Los Angeles, July 12, 1977. The food was prepared by Argly's wife, Wanda, and carried on board by him in a paper bag. Argly, incidentally, is the holder of the record for The Only Delicious Meal Eaten On A Domestic Airline, as well.

## THE WORST TASTE IN CLOTHING

was exhibited by Elmo Nurdly, of Buffalo, New York, in June, 1976. Nurdly wore a used 1958 orange and blue warm-up jacket, plaid pants in clashing shades of purple and red, and saddle shoes to his school graduation, his Mother's funeral, his own wedding, and the local Burger King. Naturally, he was barred from entering on each occasion.

## THE MOST EXPENSIVE SIX-BLOCK TAXI RIDE

was taken by Zynam Lupescu, a Rumanian tourist, while visiting New York City. Mr. Lupescu hailed a cab on E. 33rd Street and got out on E. 39th Street 11 hours and 50 minutes later, after being driven all through Brooklyn, the Bronx and parts of Staten Island. Mr. Lupescu paid the meter fare of $171.10 . . . after which he was roundly cursed out by the angry taxi driver for tipping a lousy $15.

## THE LONGEST WAIT FOR A DATE

is 5 hours, 14 minutes, endured by Cecil Terhune of Birmingham, Alabama. On August 3rd, 1970, Terhune came to pick up Betty Sue Fingus, then waited in his Corvair while she changed outfits seven times, experimented with four hair styles, replaced her false eyelashes, manicured her nails, tried five different shades of lipstick, and shaved her legs before she showed up. The evening was spent bowling.

## THE MOST SHORT-LIVED ROCK GROUP

was "The Smelling Salts," made up of three guitar players and a drummer in East Lansing, Michigan. The group was organized at 11:34 P.M., October 3rd, 1974, and disbanded 5 minutes later after two members were arrested on drug charges, and a third named in a paternity suit.

## THE MOST TELE- PHONE RINGS DURING 1 CALL

occurred February 9 1978, when Jasper Wheelock of Austin, Texas, woke up with a 105° fever, and phoned his Doctor. After exactly 278 rings, the call was finally picked up . . . by the Doctor's Answering Service.

## THE GREATEST GENERATION GAP

was experienced by Walter Crunlick, 47, and his son Mark, 17, in 1969. During a 172-day period, the two disagreed violently about 274 political, economic, social, moral, religious and environmental issues. The one issue they agreed on—Korean Fishing Rights —they refused to discuss.

## THE LARGEST CON- SECUTIVE NUMBER OF OUT-OF-FOCUS VACATION SLIDES

is 97, shown to a group of neighbors by Ben and Harriet Zweibach of San Jose, California, following their 2-week trip to Ogden, Utah. Of the 97 slides, 63 were shown upside - down.

## THE LEAST SUCCESSFUL HAIRPIECE

was worn by Byron Emberton, of Fort Smith, Arkansas, who, during a six-hour period on March 10th, 1976, was mocked, laughed at, snickered over, and humiliated by 27 people, including his wife, their 6 children, the UPS delivery man, and their family parrot. Emberton exchanged his hair piece for another . . . shortly thereafter setting the record for "The Second Least Successful Hairpiece."

## THE MOST MONEY SPENT ON A WOMAN WITHOUT MAKING OUT

is $55,897.45, by Preston Urquahr of Baltimore, Maryland, during his crush on Evangeline Steegbarrow. The couple dated 113 times, during which they'd held hands twice . . . both times gloved. Although Miss Steegbarrow was fond of Preston, she'd just never felt right about "starting a relationship."

## THE BEST-FAKED HIGH SCHOOL EXAM

was a 7-page essay on the War of 1812, written in class by Milton Rubischer, 17, of Miami, Florida, on October 22, 1961. Milton received an A+, despite his not having the slightest idea of what the war was all about. His success inspired him to enter into Politics after graduation.

## THE MOST CANS OF BEER DRUNK WITHOUT GOING TO THE JOHN

is 17, by Rufus Mulvaney while watching a crucial ballgame in a tavern in St. Paul, Minnesota, on October 2nd, 1972. After finishing off the 17th can, Mulvaney raced to the John, and came within 3 paces of making it.

## THE LONGEST AMOUNT OF TIME SPENT IN A RESTAURANT WITHOUT SEEING ONE'S WAITER

is 2 hours, 11 minutes, by Darlene and Henry Undershot at the Blue Gull Bar And Grill in Lincoln, Nebraska. When the waiter finally did show up, he calmly informed the couple that they were too late for "The $6.95 Early Bird Special Dinner."

## THE MOST HOURS SPENT IN PSYCHIATRIC THERAPY WITHOUT PROGRESS

is 1,178, by George Quillcross of Joplin, Missouri. Of these, 1,161 were spent analyzing, with no success, a dream in which Quillcross was totally encased in a giant marshmallow.

## THE WORST COMPUTER FOUL-UP

occurred on November 30th in 1977, when Elvira Fosdick, 91, of Sun City, Arizona, was delivered seven thousand copies of "Gay Sex Magazine." Mrs. Fosdick was prepared to complain to the Post Office when she discovered that her husband, Sid, 94, enjoyed reading them.

## THE LONGEST WAIT FOR A BUS IN MILD WEATHER

is 5 hours, 30 minutes, endured by H. Fenton Tendrill, of Cininnati, Ohio, on August 22, 1978. Tendrill waited at a designated bus-stop as sixteen No. 3 buses, none of them more than half-filled, passed him by. In desperation, Tendrill then lay down in the path of the seventeenth bus . . . which ran him over.

## THE MOST OBSCENE CALLS

is 2,378, received by Francine P. Furdolino, of Austin, Texas. Of these calls, 127 developed into serious relationships.

# IT MAY BE DIFFICULT TO BELIEVE, SINCE NONE OF US SEEM TO HOLD ON TO IT LONG ENOUGH TO STRIKE UP A CONVERSATION WITH IT, BUT

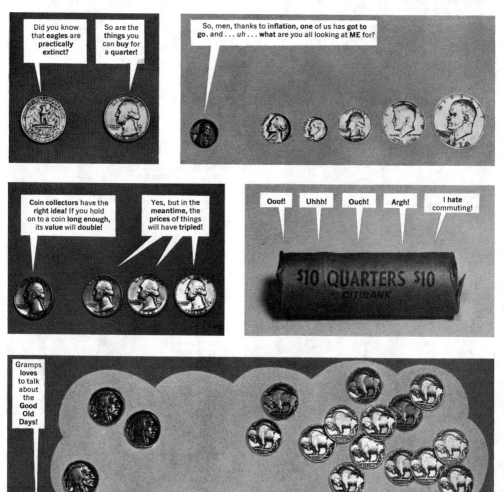

# EY TALKS

ARTIST: BOB CLARKE    WRITER: HENRY CLARK

# A MAD LOOK AT T
# THE ENER

ARTIST: HARRY NORTH, ESQ.

### NIGHT GAMES UNDER "BRING-YOUR-OWN-LIGHTS"

### MONTHLY HEATING OIL DELIVERIES

### STRANDED HIGHWAY FUEL BEGGARS

### GASLESS WEDNESDAYS

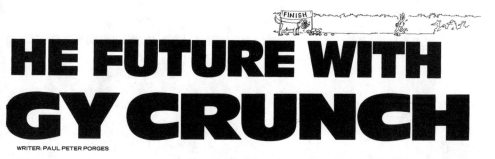

# HE FUTURE WITH
# GY CRUNCH

WRITER: PAUL PETER PORGES

## NON-ELECTRONIC CUE-CARD ROCK CONCERTS

## ELIMINATION OF ELEVATOR SERVICE DURING NON-PEAK HOURS

## NAMES IN ONE LIGHT ON BROADWAY

## HELL'S ANGELS SCOOTER GANG RALLIES

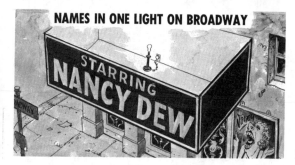

## NON-ELECTRONIC BURGLAR ALARM SYSTEMS

## 12 MPH HIGH-SPEED ROBBERY SUSPECT CHASES

## LIVING HEAT BLANKETS

## COLD SHOWERS AT LATE SEASON FOOTBALL GAMES

## SUBURBAN GASOLINE SNEAKS

## JOG-IN RESTAURANTS

# ONE AFTERNOON WHILE RUNNING AN ERRAND

# A MAD LOOK AT

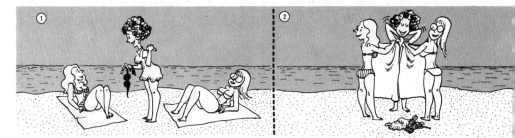

# THE BEACH

ARTIST & WRITER:
SERGIO ARAGONES

# CANDID CLOSE-UPS OF S

HENRI TOULOUSE-LAUTREC CHANGING
THE LIGHTBULB IN HIS PARIS STUDIO

MATHEMATICIAN PYTHAGORAS STUMBLING ACROSS HYPOTENUSE

A PILGRIM MISSING THE FAMOUS LANDING AT PLYMOUTH ROCK

ADMIRAL BYRD BEING CAUGHT BY SUDDEN SPRING THAW WHILE ON SECOND SOUTH POLAR EXPEDITION

THE MARQUESS OF QUEENSBERRY ATTEMPTING TO INTRODUCE RULES OF GENTLEMANLY CONDUCT TO BRAWLERS

# OME LEGENDARY FEETS

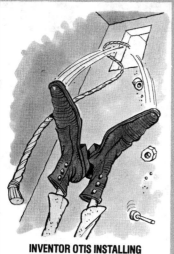

**INVENTOR OTIS INSTALLING THE VERY FIRST ELEVATOR**

**SIGMUND FREUD PRACTICING BEFORE HIS COUCH WAS DELIVERED**

**DAVID'S TRAINER SCOUTING GOLIATH FOR THE UPCOMING MATCH**

ARTIST: BOB JONES     WRITER: PAUL PETER PORGES

**PHARAOH DEDICATING PYRAMID OF CHEOPS' CORNERSTONE**

**HANNIBAL DESCENDING THE ALPS**

Why restrict the awarding of medals to the military? After all, Civilians perform heroic acts while fighting life's daily battles as well! Let's recognize them with

# THIS ISSUE'S PROPOSED

# MAD MEDALS

## . . . TO BE PRESENTED TO DESERVING LAWYERS

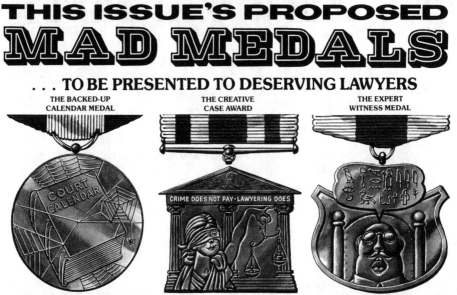

**THE BACKED-UP CALENDAR MEDAL**

For boldly stalling and delaying . . . to drag out court trials, thus generating tremendous incomes for judges, lawyers, court employees, bail bondsmen, etc.—thereby strengthening the solid pillar on which our system of justice depends.

**THE CREATIVE CASE AWARD**

For heroically creating law suits out of nothing, and running up huge fees for clients whether they win or lose, and getting lots of publicity which brings in more clients and may even be useful for future political activity.

**THE EXPERT WITNESS MEDAL**

For bravely seeking and buying expert testimony that supports client's case (even if client is guilty of the most heinous crime) . . . thereby stimulating the economy by providing additional income to doctors, psychiatrists, etc.

**THE ESPRIT DE CORPS MEDAL**

For gallantly sticking it to Insurance Companies by superb acting in front of juries, getting them to make fantastic awards despite the fact that everyone, including jurors themselves, will pay higher insurance premiums as a result.

**THE GULLIBLE JUROR AWARD**

For bravely running for election, thus resolutely helping to fill almost all political offices with lawyers so that legislation, first and foremost, will protect the rights, the privileges and the profits of this noble profession.

ARTIST & WRITER: AL JAFFEE

# ONE MORNING BACK ON MAIN STREET

# A MAD LOO

ARTIST: GEORGE WOODBRIDGE

# K AT DOORS

WRITER: PAUL PETER PORGES

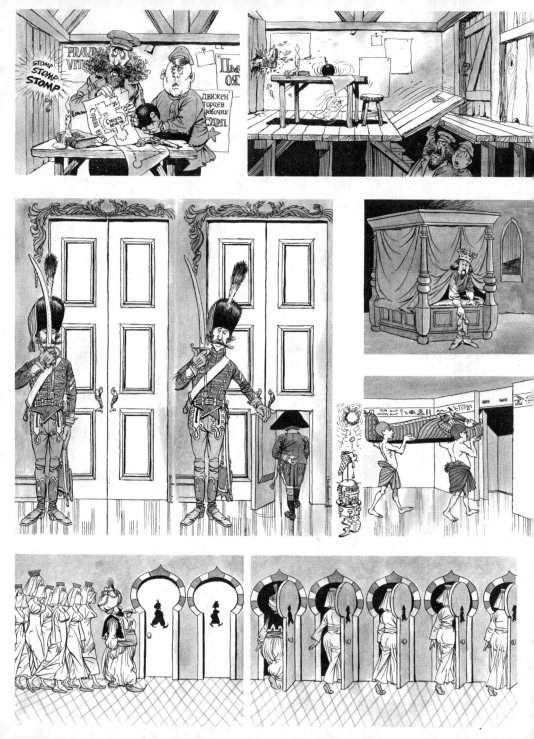

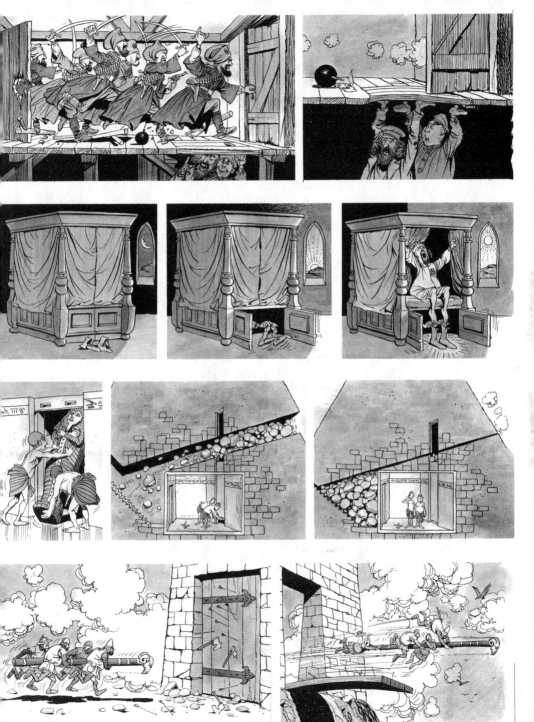

# ONE NIGHT ON SKULL ISLAND

# A MAD PEEK BEHIND THE SCENES
# CAR RENTAL COMPANIES

ARTIST: BOB CLARKE          WRITER: STAN HART

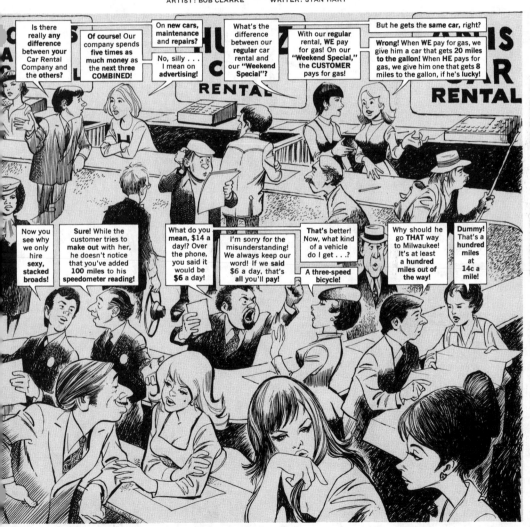

# CANDID MAD HISTORICAL

**GOOD-NATURED HORSEPLAY DURING NAPOLEON'S RETREAT**

**IVAN THE TERRIBLE AS A CHILD**

# SNAPSHOTS OF CELEBRITIES

ARTIST & WRITER: PAUL PETER PORGES

**PAVLOV WITH A NON-SALIVATING DOG**

**ATTILA THE HUN RECRUITING HALF HIS HORDE**

**BARON VON RICHTHOFEN WORKING AT HIS DESK**

**BETSY ROSS AND SOME OF HER OTHER FLAGS**

**MR. REUTERS TRYING TO CATCH A LATE NEWS BULLETIN**

# ONCE UPON A TIME IN THE BLACK HILLS OF S. DAKOTA

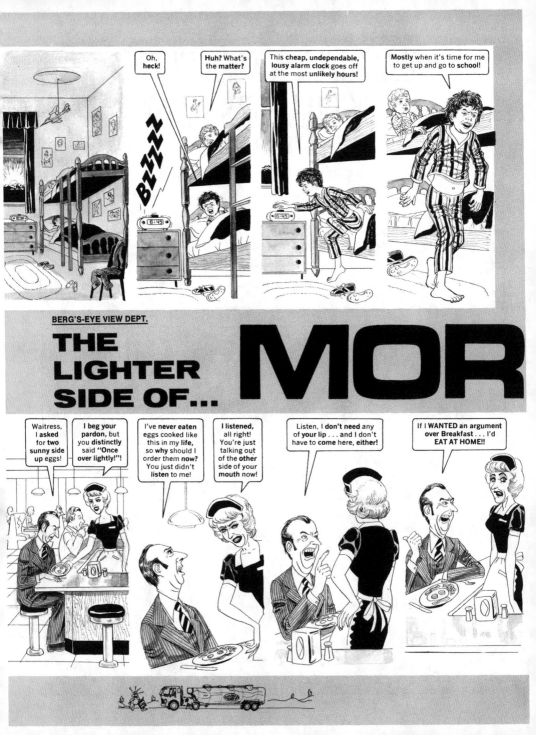

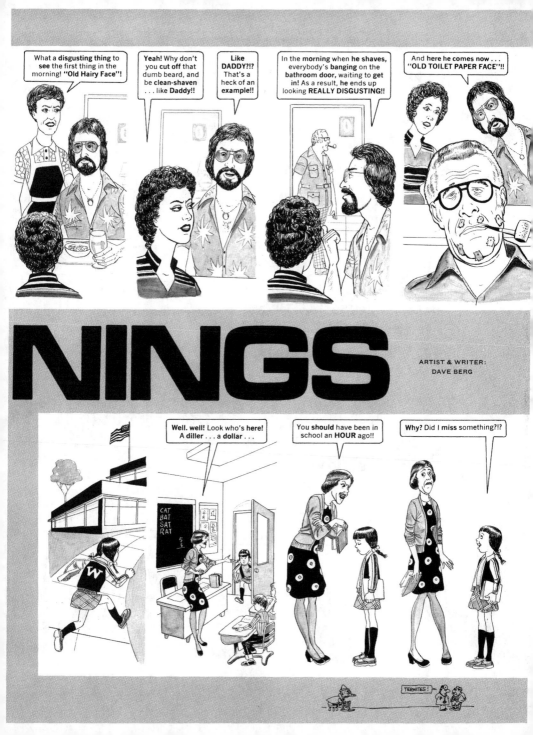

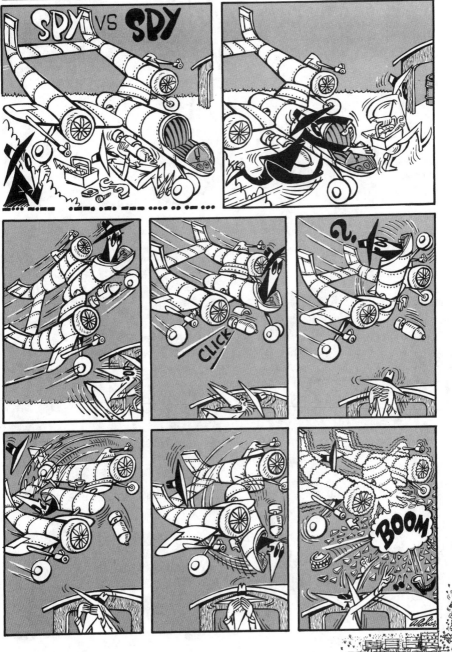

# TIES DIAPERS

REMEMBER! THIS WAS BEFORE "PAMPERS"!

**NAPOLEON**

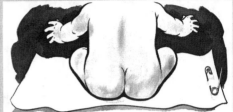

**LADY GODIVA**

**STEVE MARTIN**

**THE GRAND DRAGON OF THE KU KLUX KLAN**

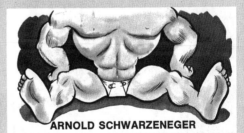

**ARNOLD SCHWARZENEGER**

**YASIR ARAFAT**

**KISS**

# FLOPPY DISK

**The Mystery Of
The Sudden Hot-To-Cold-Switching Shower**

# THE MYS
# OF THE M

**The Mystery Of The Loose Pajama Bottoms**

**The Mystery Of
The Soap-In-The-Eye Vanishing Towel**

**The Mystery Of The Incorrect Timepieces**

**The Mystery Of
The Pasteless Toothbrush**

**The Mystery Of The Forgotten Toast**

# STERIES
# MORNING

WRITER AND ARTIST: PAUL PETER PORGES

### The Mystery Of The Disappearing Butter Patty

### The Mystery Of The Missing Sports Page

### The Mystery Of The Roaming Eyelash

### The Mystery Of The Self-Slamming Front Door

### The Mystery Of The Extra Shirt Button

### The Mystery Of The Bad Weather Phantom Buses

A few years ago, a new group of social activists appeared on the national scene
... the militant anti-smokers. Through their efforts, smoking is now restricted
in many public buildings, restaurants, businesses, elevators and most forms of

# PUBLICALLY PROHIBIT

ARTIST: JACK RICKARD

Giving away the end of a movie to a person or persons
who have not seen the film was federally outlawed in
1982 after Franz Grubernik, of Anaheim, California,
caused a riot in the lobby of the Primo Theater in Los
Angeles by revealing the shocking conclusion to Brian
De Palma's latest suspense thriller, "Pressed To Kill,"
to 350 people at the premier, including Mr. De Palma.

The AMA had little criticism for this piece of government
legislation concerning the Medical Profession. After being
victimized for years by persons attempting to chisel free
diagnoses from them at parties, tennis courts, etc., the
Medical Community welcomed this statute to the books.
Now, people soliciting gratis medical opinions are liable to a
mandatory examination by a Proctologist with cold hands.

Until enactment of this 1982 law, guests who arrived early for
dinner parties were merely considered inconvenient. However, it
was quickly passed after the French Ambassador, his watch still
set on Paris time, arrived six hours early for a party at the
Spanish Embassy, stumbling upon the wife of the British Ambassador, the Mexican Ambassador and the entire Italian Embassy
staff engaged in activities outlawed by the Geneva Convention.

Federal Law HR-79-144, enacted in 1983, prohibits
the showing of grandchildren's photos to strangers
in public buildings or on common carriers without
the express written consent of the strangers. The
penalities provide for fines up to $300 for each
offense, and/or the forced viewing of home movies
of the arresting officer's own family on vacation.

transportation. But now that we have restrictions established for smoking, will we be able to ignore the other bad habits that we drive each other crazy with? MAD predicts that we'll someday wind up with laws and regulations like these

# ED BAD HABITS OF THE FUTURE

WRITER: DENNIS SNEE

First enacted in New York on a trial basis, this popular law thwarted rubbernecks and cheapskates alike in their quest for a free peek at the news. Reading over other people's shoulders is virtually non-existant today, largely due to the harsh penalties imposed by this law. Offenders can be sentenced to as many as thirty days of reading a train schedule through a fat person's legs if convicted.

After a rash of suicide attempts by elevator operators driven to near-insanity by being asked repeatedly if it was hot enough for them, Congress passed this law in 1984. In addition, the law prohibits asking tall people "How's the weather up there?", etc. Only a last minute lobbying effort by The Optimists of America prevented "Have a nice day!" from being included in the long list.

Would-be comics have criticised this 1983 "Punchline Law" since its adoption, but it has discouraged those social bores from killing other people's jokes. The law also makes eviction of drunks and hecklers easier. And violators are now dealt with severely. Sentences range from forced labor in a Gag-Novelty Shop, to mandatory attendence at a Henny Youngman nightclub appearance.

Loss of private phone service and a stiff fine can result if anyone reaches a wrong number and hangs up without (1) expressing regrets for the inconvenience and (2) identifying himself. This 1982 statute also provides additional heavy penalties for wrong numbers made after midnight, or any time when causing persons to wake up, or interrupt a shower or bath or any other activity of a priority nature.

# AN ADVERTISEMENT

Have you ever read an ad and found a house that sounded like a dream only to kill a whole day driving out there to discover that it's really a dog? Then you know what it's like to fall prey to the sneaky Real Estate Ads placed by crafty builders and developers. Well, it needn't ever happen to you again, as MAD now offers a typical ad with the usual come-ons, and then interprets what each gimmick actually means in this Public Service Article that teaches you ...

# HOW TO READ A REAL ESTATE AD

## PREVIEW SHOWING!

# Grandview Acres

A UNIQUE, WOODED, WATERFRONT COMMUNITY IN SCENIC SWAMP HILLS, N.J.

**ESCAPE THE POLLUTION OF THE CITY! LIVE IN AN EXCLUSIVE NEIGHBORHOOD FAR FROM THE CRIME OF THE CITY AND CONVENIENT TO NEARBY SCHOOLS!**

**Incredibly Beautiful Homes... Amazingly Priced From As Low As $39,999 To $54,999!!!**

**INCLUDING ALL OF THESE LUXURIOUS APPOINTMENTS:**

- **2½ Baths**
- **Full Basement**
- **Two-Car Garage**
- **Private Sauna**

**SENSATIONALLY LOCATED TO PROVIDE ALL OF THESE EXCITING FEATURES:**

- **Your Own Cabana Near The Beach**
- **Boating And Sailing In Season**
- **Beautiful View Of N.Y. Skyline**
- **45 Minutes From Midtown Manhattan**

WRITER: ALEN ROBIN          ARTIST: BOB JONES

## ESCAPE THE POLLUTION OF THE CITY!

The trouble is, everyone else is escaping from it, too!

## LIVE IN AN EXCLUSIVE NEIGHBORHOOD

Minority groups, wait till you see that "Welcome Wagon"!

## ● 2½ Baths

There's an extra charge to complete the unfinished half!

## ● Full Basement

Every time the tide comes in, but you can install pumps!

## ● Your Own Cabana Near The Beach

Actually, it's in the water! But that's near the beach!

## ● Boating And Sailing In Season

The season is whenever it rains! Then, you're forced to!

## FAR FROM THE CRIME OF THE CITY

Right smack dab in the middle of the Crime Of The Suburbs!

## AND CONVENIENT TO NEARBY SCHOOLS!

But not the kind that will get your kids into any college!

## • Two-Car Garage

Yours . . . and the one that belongs to your four-year-old!

## • Private Sauna

Poor insulation turns your house into one every Summer!

## • Beautiful View Of N.Y. Skyline

Don't expect too much! It's the "Yonkers, N.Y." skyline!

## • 45 Minutes From Midtown Manhattan

Between 3 A.M. and 4 A.M.! Other times, figure two hours!

# WAIT TILL YOU GET H

...news teams of the major TV Networks are parked on your lawn.

...your home is in the path of the new airport's landing pattern.

...your Wife has volunteered your house as Headquarters for the School Board elections.

...parking regulations on your street have been changed.

...your Son, while away at school, had himself tatooed.

# OME AND FIND THAT...

ARTIST & WRITER: PAUL PETER PORGES

...your do-it-yourself wallpapering job has come unglued.

...somebody spraypainted something against your new car.

...the container of stool specimen you forgot on the bus had your name and address on it.

...a computer has found you and your seven unpaid traffic tickets.

...the weeds in your herb garden can be smoked in skinny cigarettes.

If you walk down a brightly-lit street, that's good! If you walk down a dark street, two things can happen:

| You won't get mugged! | You will get mugged! |
| --- | --- |

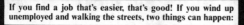

If you find a job that's easier, that's good! If you wind up unemployed and walking the streets, two things can happen:

| You'll walk down a brightly-lit street! | You'll walk down a street that's dark! |
| --- | --- |

# IF YOU
# DOW
# DARK S

ARTIST: GEORGE WOODBRIDGE

If you're able to work again at your old job, that's good! If you're not able to return to work, two things can happen:

| You'll find another job that's a lot easier! | You'll wind up unemployed and walking the streets! |
| --- | --- |

If you're patched up in tolerable shape, that's good! If you're patched up in terrible shape, two things can happen:

| You'll be able to work again at your old job! | You won't be able to work again at your old job! |
| --- | --- |

# EARLY ONE MORNING OUT ON THE BAY

# THE GIFT

ARTIST: BOB JONES    WRITER: FRANK JACOBS

*When Nature made the Elephant,*
*A gift she did bequeath—*
*A trunk which hangs down from the front*
*And picks up things beneath.*

*The Whale was blessed with tail and fin*
*For swimming through the seas;*
*The Walrus with great folds of skin*
*Providing anti-freeze.*

*The Polar Bear was colored white;*
*The Skunk was filled with gases;*
*The Hawk was blessed with wondrous sight*
*Without the aid of glasses.*

*Soft, silky fur was dealt the Seal,*
*The Kangaroo a pocket.*
*And to the sleek Electric Eel—*
*A built-in DC socket.*

And Man, as anyone can see,
  With _his_ great gift is blessed:
A mind to think up ways that he
  Can kill off all the rest.

Why restrict the awarding of medals to the military? After all, Civilians perform heroic acts while fighting life's daily battles as well! Let's recognize them with

# THIS ISSUE'S PROPOSED
# MAD MEDALS

## ... TO BE PRESENTED TO DESERVING POLITICIANS

### THE PERFECT ATTENDANCE MEDAL

Goes to Politicians—not who attend their jobs on Capitol Hill every day —but who attend to the special needs of powerful lobbyists, law partners, friends and family members they have managed to put on the public payroll.

### THE FOREIGN SERVICE CITATION

For distinguished foreign service . . . which in this case means traveling to foreign lands, and being served royally! Taking a wife along earns a bronze cluster, a secretary—a silver cluster, and a sexy movie star—a gold cluster.

### THE DOUBLE-JEOPARDY AWARD

For gallantly and courageously putting in expense vouchers for trips to two difference places. The jeopardy comes in if anyone discovers that the trips happened to occur on the same date to places on opposite sides of the world.

CONGRESSIONAL RECORD

Record shows he was Indicted and Convicted of Bribery, Fraud, Misappropriation of Campaign Funds, Nepotism, Malfeasance in Office, and Abuse of Franking Privileges. Re-elected for his 16th Term in The House of Representatives.

THE BEST DAMN POLITICIAN MONEY CAN BUY

### FREE SPEECH AWARD

PERSONAL APPEARANCE EXPENSE VOUCHER
TAXI, WASHINGTON TO SAN FRANCISCO, 12 ROOM HOTEL SUITE AND MISCELLANEOUS
$12,843.22

This medal does not honor our famous constitutional right of free speech! It is awarded to Politicians who will happily make a speech, free, anywhere and anytime . . . just as long as their expenses are paid, no matter how outrageously high they claim them to be.

### THE UNMITIGATED GALL AWARD

For bravely increasing Social Security taxes to guarantee everyone's old age benefits. Everyone's except Congressmen, that is too! They are not on Social Security, so their paychecks won't be cut! They have a much better pension system . . . paid for by the rest of us!

ARTIST & WRITER: AL JAFFEE

# A MAD LOOK AT...

# SKATING

ARTIST & WRITER: SERGIO ARAGONES

**Alfred E. Neuman
for President**

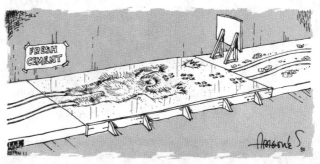

# MORE MAD CAN
# OF HISTORICA

**YOUNG EMPEROR NERO'S FIRST VIOLIN TEACHER, SHORTLY BEFORE HE QUITS**

**WM. SHAKESPEARE SHOWS HIS CONTEMPT FOR SOME BAD FIRST-NIGHT REVIEWS**

**DR. LIVINGSTON MEETS HIS FIRST TRIBE OF PYGMIES**

# DID SNAPSHOTS
# L CELEBRITIES

ARTIST & WRITER: PAUL PETER PORGES

**YOUNG KING DAVID TRAINS FOR HIS UPCOMING BOUT**

**QUEEN VICTORIA IS SLIGHTLY AMUSED**

**ADOLPH HITLER INVENTS THE GOOSESTEP**

CLEOPATRA CONTEMPLATES HAVING A NOSE JOB PERFORMED

KING MIDAS OVER-TIPS AS HE LEAVES PALACE BANQUET

CHRISTOPHER COLUMBUS WITH EARLIER MODELS OF THE EARTH

There's a new book on sale these days called "Life Spans" which lists the average length of life for people, animals, foods and other basic, standard things. Like for instance, the Life Span of an American man is 67.6 years, a walrus . . . 40 years, an ostrich . . . 25 years, and an octopus . . . 10 years. Now, all these facts may help you win money on a quiz show, but they're not much help in social situations, family life and other areas of day-to-day living. Therefore MAD now presents its own

# REALLY IMPORTANT AND RELEVANT LIFE SPANS

### THE LIFE SPAN OF AN EMBARRASSING PIMPLE IS
## 4 DAYS

. . . unless you've got several heavy dates and social functions planned, in which case it's always 13 days.

### THE LIFE SPAN OF A PRO FOOTBALL QUARTERBACK IS
## 84 GAMES

. . . depending on what shape his knees are in. (The Life Span of a Pro Football Quarterback's knees is 11 games).

### THE LIFE SPAN OF A NEW AIR CONDITIONER IS
## 3 DAYS

. . . after the 90-Day Warranty Period.

### THE LIFE SPAN OF A POLITICAL PROMISE BEFORE YOU REALIZE THE GUY WHO MADE IT HAS NO INTENTION OF CARRYING IT OUT IS
## 100 DAYS

### THE LIFE SPAN OF A MASS OF FRESH, CLEAN AIR OVER A LARGE AMERICAN CITY IS
## 3 SECONDS

ARTIST: PAUL COKER    WRITER: FRANK JACOBS

### THE LIFE SPAN OF A STEREO SET WITH NEW, BUILT-IN FEATURES BEFORE YOU COME ACROSS ONE WITH EVEN NEWER, BUILT-IN FEATURES IS
## 7 WEEKS

**THE LIFE SPAN OF A
MAFIA STOOL PIGEON
IS**

# OVER AS
# OF NOW

**THE LIFE SPAN OF AN HONEST, RELIABLE,
EFFICIENT, SMALL MANUFACTURER BEFORE
HE'S ABSORBED BY A DISHONEST, UNRELI-
ABLE, INEFFICIENT GIANT CONGLOMERATE
IS**

# 2 YEARS, 1 MONTH

**THE LIFE SPAN OF A SOUTH
AMERICAN DICTATORSHIP
IS**

# 54 DAYS

The Life Span of the Free Democratic Regime that replaces it is 54 days. And the Life Span of the Military Junta that replaces *it* is 54 days.

**THE LIFE SPAN
OF AN UMBRELLA
IS**

# 176 DAYS

However, the Life Span of its Possession by You is 9 hours, figured from the moment you purchase it until the time you stupidly leave it somewhere.

**THE LIFE SPAN OF $100 AT
A LAS VEGAS CRAP TABLE
IS**

# 9 MINUTES

**THE LIFE SPAN OF
A WEEKLY SALARY
IS**

# 4 HOURS

And the Life Span of a Weekly Salary supplemented with a "Cost Of Living Increase" is 4 hours and 5 minutes.

**THE LIFE SPAN OF AN
OBSCENE PHONE CALL
IS**

# 9 HEAVY
# BREATHS

**THE LIFE SPAN OF A MARRIAGE
OF TWO POPULAR FILM STARS
IS**

# 2 YEARS, 5 MONTHS

The Life Span of the Publicity about their Marriage Breaking Up is 2 years, 4 months.

**THE LIFE SPAN OF AN OPEN CAN
OF BEER BEFORE IT GOES FLAT
IS**

# 17 MINUTES

The Life Span of a Beer Drinker before he Falls Flat is 2 hours, 15 minutes.

**THE LIFE SPAN OF A NEW POPULAR CAUSE, SUCH AS "LEGALIZE WITCHCRAFT" OR "FREE THE ANAHEIM 7"**
**IS**

# 5 MONTHS

**THE LIFE SPAN OF A CHRISTMAS TOY**
**IS**

# 2 HOURS

. . . plus the time it takes you to put in the batteries.

**THE LIFE SPAN OF THE GOOD BEHAVIOR OF A MUGGER WHO'S PAROLED FROM PRISON WITH TIME OFF FOR GOOD BEHAVIOR**
**IS**

# 6 DAYS

**THE LIFE SPAN OF AN OUTDOOR SCULPTURE BEFORE IT IS SMEARED WITH GRAFITTI**
**IS**

# 27 MINUTES

**THE LIFE SPAN OF THE SPECIFIC BULGE YOU'RE TRYING TO ELIMINATE THROUGH EXERCISE OR DIET**
**IS**

# FOREVER

**THE LIFE SPAN OF A PAINFUL TOOTHACHE**
**IS**

# EXACTLY 41 HOURS

. . . beginning at 5 P.M., Saturday and lasting until 10 A.M., Monday, which is the earliest your Dentist can see you.

**THE LIFE SPAN OF YOUR LUST FOR A GIRL YOU'VE DECIDED YOU WANT TO MAKE OUT WITH**
**IS**

# 43 DAYS

The Life Span of your Interest in her after she Finally Agrees is 12 days.

**THE LIFE SPAN OF A PUBLIC PHONE BEFORE IT'S OUT OF ORDER**
**IS**

# 5 DAYS

**THE LIFE SPAN OF A TYPICAL ROCK BALLAD**
**IS**

# 1 WEEK

The Life Span of the Group that Recorded it is 3 weeks, or when the drummer gets busted for drug possession, whichever comes first.

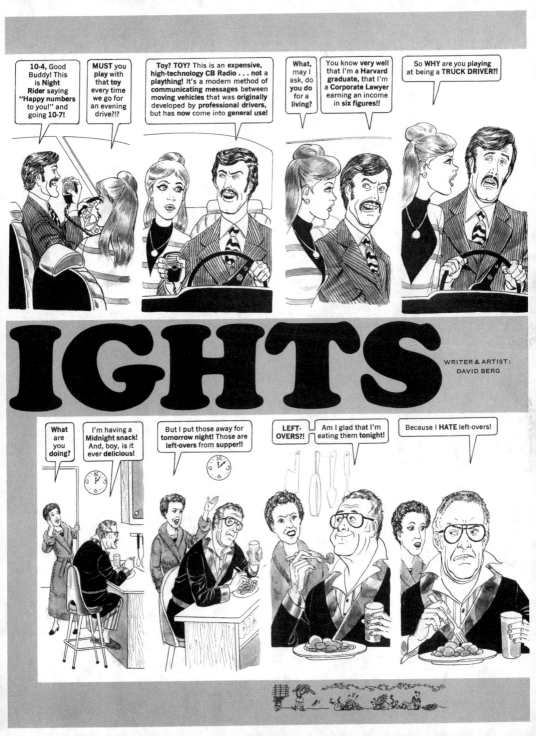

WRITER & ARTIST: DAVID BERG

# LOOK AT 'TS' TALK

WRITER AND ARTIST: PAUL PETER PORGES

When people want to burn calories to lose weight, they think about strenuous activities like swimming or jogging or tennis. Somehow, they never consider

# A MAD GUIDE TO... BURNING CALORI

### JUMPING TO CONCLUSIONS

225-350 Calories

### EATING CROW

**110-175 Calories**

### SWEATING OUT A DOCTOR BILL

**350-475 Calories**

### CROSSING A STREET AGAINST THE LIGHT

**250-325 Calories**

### WATCHING THE BOSS'S SECRETARY WALK BY

**450-575 Calories**

### CARRYING SUPERMARKET BAGS OUT TO THE CAR

**875-1025 Calories**

the simple everyday activities that are already burning up plenty of calories. We'll show you just what we mean as your slightly overweight Editors present:

# ES WITHOUT EXERCISE

ARTIST & WRITER: DON EDWING

## TAKING A FINAL EXAM

**800-1000 Calories**

## COMMUTING

**675-800 Calories**

## GETTING NAILED

**75-150 Calories**

## LEAVING FOR WORK FIVE MINUTES LATE

**350-425 Calories**

## GETTING AN ENVELOPE FROM THE I.R.S.

**375-450 Calories**

## WATCHING A PARKING LOT ATTENDANT DELIVER YOUR CAR

**525-675 Calories**

### BEATING AROUND THE BUSH

125-175 Calories

### GETTING STUCK FOR THE TAB

180-235 Calories

### ASKING FOR A RAISE

400-500 Calories

### LISTENING TO THE NEWS

50-85 Calories

### BEING CALLED ON THE CARPET

950-1400 Calories

### PUSHING YOUR LUCK

1100-1200 Calories

### DUCKING CONFERENCES

150-225 Calories

### MERGING ONTO A HIGHWAY

375-450 Calories

### GETTING UP IN THE MORNING

200-275 Calories

# AN AL JAFFEE SNAPPY ANSWERS TO STUPID QUESTIONS

## Gangland Episode

**Know what's fast becoming the most popular U.S. indoor pastime? The hottest pastime, as the following song will tell you, is...**

# PORN IN the U.S.A.

(Sung to the tune of Bruce Springsteen's *Born in the U.S.A.*)

Porn...now...real-ly gets a-round;
Yet we know a **place**...most **porn** is **found;**
No one's goin' out...to **down-town flicks**—
**Home** is where it's at...for **all your kicks.**

**Porn**...in the **U. S. A!**
Dig that **porn** in your **home today!**
Red-hot **porn** goin' **all the way!**
**Porn**...in the **U. S. A!**

**No sneakin' in** some **sleaz-y show**—
**Scared** you might be **seen** by **folks you know;**
**Watch** it in your **house**—a-void the **shame;**
**Chances** are that they...are **doin' the same.**

**Porn**...in the **U. S. A!**
**Far-out porn,** and it's **here to stay!**
They've got **porn** if you're **straight or gay!**
**Porn** was **born** in the **U.S.A.**

**Rent** from a **shop** where the **wild films** are;
**Watch** 'em on your **private V.C.R.;**
**Groove** the latest **tricks** of a **hot porn star!**

**Get** a load of **all** those **un-cut scenes**—
Now you really **know** what **"boob-tube" means;**

**Dem-o-crats fight** the **G. O. P;**
**Labor's** in a **battle** with **in-dust-ry;**
**Though** it's surely **true** they **dis-a-gree,**
**When** they all go **home,** guess **what**...they...**see?**

**Porn**...in the **U. S. A!**
Home-style **porn** goin' **night and day!**
**Porn**...in the **U. S. A!**
And it **sure** beats *Dallas* when you're **in**...the...**hay!**

**Porn**...off the **wall today!**
**Porn**...have a **ball today!**
**Porn**...get it **all today!**
Any-time that you **want** it in the **U. S. A!**

ARTIST: PAUL COKER    WRITER: FRANK JACOBS

# A MAD LOOK

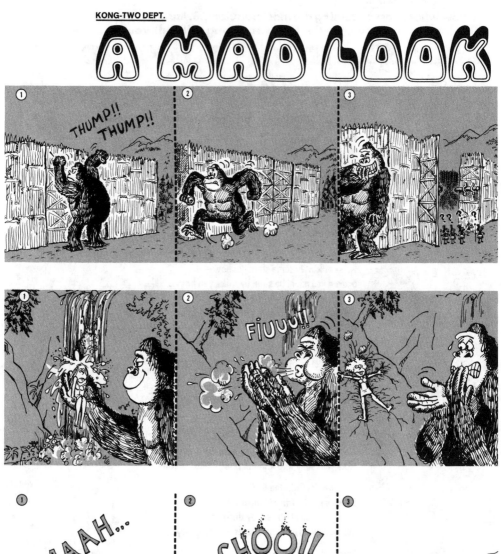

# AT KING KONG

ARTIST & WRITER: SERGIO ARAGONES

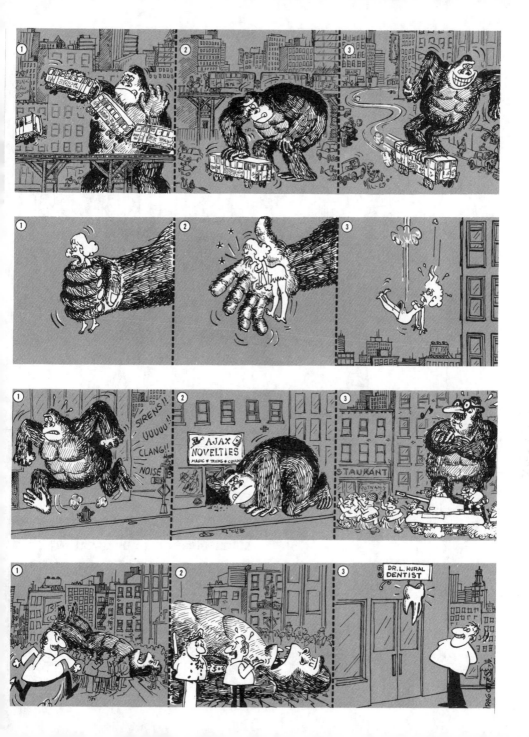

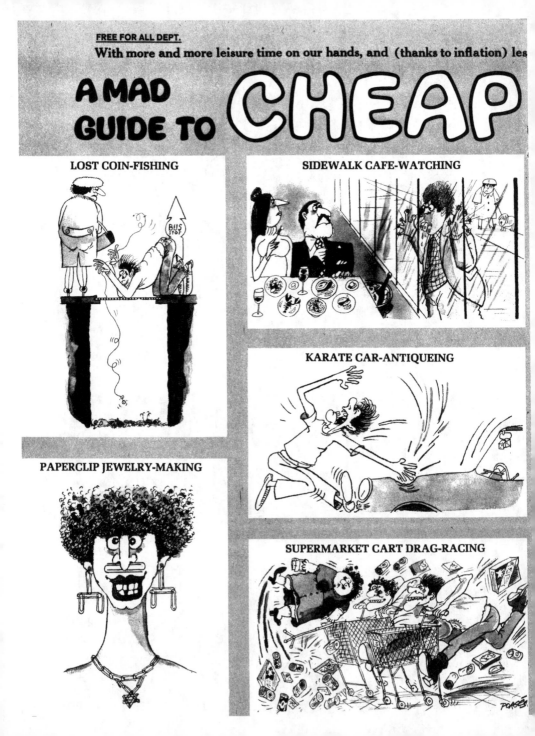

# A MAD GUIDE TO CHEAP

LOST COIN-FISHING

SIDEWALK CAFE-WATCHING

KARATE CAR-ANTIQUEING

PAPERCLIP JEWELRY-MAKING

SUPERMARKET CART DRAG-RACING

# EARLY ONE MORNING
# ON A DESERT ISLAND

## THE BRANDWRITING IS ON THE WALL DEPT.

Spray cans and magic markers are changing the face of America. Every day, new bits of irreverence are added to trains, buses, buildings and any other available public surface. Back in MAD #169, we shuddered to think of what might happen if those Graffiti Rascals ever started attacking that

# TRADEMAR

holy of holies, the Corporate Signature, with verbal comments. Now, we're back with the work of one special Graffiti Rascal . . . namely, Al Jaffee . . . and his attacks on some Corporate Signatures in his own inimitable style of *visual* comments. So here we go with a MAD Artist's contribution to

# K & GRAFFITI

ARTIST & WRITER: AL JAFFEE

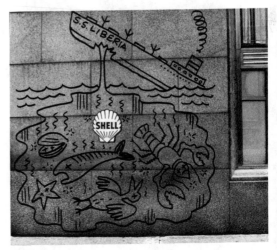

PHOTOS BY: JIM RUTH

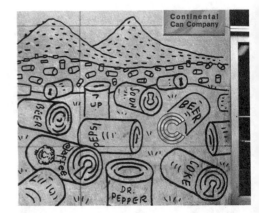

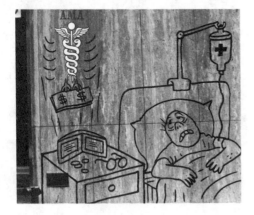

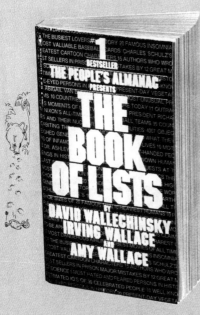

One of the most popular books in recent years is "The Book Of Lists." It's loaded with lists, such as "11 Prominent Coffee Drinkers," "10 Famous Snorers," "17 Animals With Pouches" and "The 12 Heaviest Humans." The only problem is: the book doesn't have much to do with everyday living! So MAD has done its usual thing, and now presents—

**WRITER: FRANK JACOBS**

## THE 8 EXPRESSIONS CAUSING THE GREATEST FEAR

1. "It's spreading."
2. "The I.R.S. is calling."
3. "Hold it right there, muthuh."
4. "I *am* trying to stop!"
5. "We're not alone."
6. "You're being traded to Cleveland."
7. "I can't kill it."
8. "There's no cause for alarm."

## THE 8 MOST EFFECTIVE MEDICAL COP-OUTS

1. "It's going around."
2. "It's all in your mind."
3. "It's probably inherited."
4. "It's too early to tell."
5. "It's too late to do anything."
6. "We'll run some tests."
7. "We'll run more tests."
8. "The tests are inconclusive."

## 9 VERY UNSUCCESSFUL PICK-UP LINES

1. "Would you like to see my boa constrictor?"
2. "Is that a false nose?"
3. "You look just like a hooker I knew in Fresno."
4. "I'm drunk."
5. "Hi, my friends call me Creepy."
6. "Would you like to come to a party in my toolshed?"
7. "I just threw up."
8. "You're ugly but you intrigue me."
9. "I had to find out what kind of woman would go out dressed like that."

## 9 LEAST INSPIRED MAD PREMISES

1. The Lighter Side of Terrorism
2. Terminal Diseases to Match Your Career
3. You Know You Should Change Your Sex When . . .
4. Hysterical Logarithms
5. Don Martin Looks At Tulsa
6. If Famous Celebrities Were Into Strip-Mining
7. The Degenerate's Mother Goose
8. Mad's Busboy of the Year
9. If Albanian Women Played Baseball

## 6 COMMENTS TO AVOID MAKING WITH A WOMEN'S LIBBER

1. "What's happening, baby?"
2. "Whaddya expect from a woman driver?"
3. "You're an elegant broad."
4. "She does it as well as a guy."
5. "What do you think of girl jocks?"
6. "So long, kid."

## 8 MEMORABLE MODERN DISASTERS

1. The Susan B. Anthony dollar
2. Billy Carter
3. "Star Trek—the Motion Picture"
4. The San Diego Padres
5. Ilie Nastase
6. "The Gong Show"
7. The U.S. Postal Service
8. "Super Train"

## 6 SUREFIRE LINES TO GET HIM TO BREAK OFF THE RELATIONSHIP

1. "I do karate chops in my sleep."
2. "I'm into not bathing."
3. "I collect dead spiders and keep them in jars in my closet."
4. "I start out the day with raw onions."
5. "I'm pregnant and I don't know who the father is."
6. "My Uncle Vito and his capo want to talk to you."

## 9 PIECES OF FLATTERY WE COULD DO WITHOUT

1. "You're a helluva good loser."
2. "You're really terrific to put up with my playing around."
3. "You're lucky—most men would have fractured *both* arms."
4. "You're brave—most men would have passed out from the pain."
5. "You take insults beautifully."
6. "You may not be good-looking, but you're sweet."
7. "You've been calm and cool all through this earthquake."
8. "You've taken your bankruptcy like a man."
9. "You never flinched when they mugged us."

## 7 POLITE COMMENTS YOU CAN MAKE TO A BORE WHICH SOUND LIKE YOU'RE LISTENING WHEN YOU'RE REALLY NOT

1. "Is that so?"
2. "Go on."
3. "Interesting."
4. "I didn't know that."
5. "Mmmm."
6. "Mmmm?"
7. "Mmmm!"

## 8 NAMES NOT TO NAME YOUR BABY BOY

1. Attila
2. Rasputin
3. Darth
4. Rover
5. Richard Milhous
6. Ayatollah
7. Satan
8. Betty Sue

## THE 7 LEAST BELIEVABLE COMMENTS

1. "Your check is in the mail."
2. "This won't hurt."
3. "I don't do this with every guy."
4. "He won't bite."
5. "I've got the perfect girl for you."
6. "No jury would ever convict you."
7. "Give us a call the next time you're in town."

## THE 8 LEAST COMFORTING PIECES OF GOOD NEWS

1. "Be glad it's only your transmission."
2. "We only have to pull the front ones."
3. "We know who fire-bombed your house."
4. "At least they didn't steal the silver."
5. "With good behavior, you'll be out in 10 years."
6. "He's alive—what's left of him."
7. "The blotches will disappear in time."
8. "Don't kill him—just work him over."

## 8 TOPICS TO STEER CLEAR OF AT A FORMAL DINNER

1. Descriptions of bread-mold.
2. Coping with the runs in Mexico.
3. Slaughter methods at the Chicago Stockyards.
4. Trunk murderers.
5. Raw sewage.
6. Leprosy.
7. Torture techniques in Turkish prisons.
8. Jungle rot.

## 7 UNSOLVED MYSTERIES OF MODERN MAN

1. Why is the shirt you want to buy available in every size but yours?
2. Why does your air-conditioner conk out during the worst heat-wave of the year?
3. Why does that celebrated "cold pill" bring relief to everyone but you?
4. Why does your plane leave from the most distant gate in the terminal?
5. No matter how many peanuts there are in a bowl, why do you eat all of them?
6. In a bar, why does the most obnoxious drunk strike up a conversation with you?
7. Why isn't this article listed in "The 9 Least Inspired Mad Premises?"

Scarcely a day goes by that we aren't exposed to some genius's new invention, concept or method of doing things. A few developments of recent years have been brilliant—like polio vaccine and long weekends for Columbus Day. But many others have been downright disgusting—like Grape-flavored ice cream and "The Osmond Family Christmas Show." Unfortunately, most of life's awfulness is still around, because we've accepted it with a resigned shrug...rather than joining forces to banish it forever with the one challenging question that no ridiculous innovation can withstand...mainly...

### WHO NEEDS...

...a car that costs $1,000 more because it has a recorded human voice rather than a buzzer to remind you that you left your key in the ignition.

### WHO NEEDS...

...a corner mailbox that has two mail pick-ups a day...at 10:00 A.M., and at 10:30 A.M.

### WHO NEEDS...

...skywriting that never produces a legible message, because the first part blows away before the last part is finally done.

### WHO NEEDS...

**STRICTLY LIMITED OFFER!** AN *HEIRLOOM* OF THE *FUTURE!*

GOLD-PLATED COLLECTOR'S ITEM

ONLY $69.95

...another enticing ad offering a "rare" collectible to the first ten million people who send money.

### WHO NEEDS...

...an ear-shattering motorized blower that clears leaves off the sidewalk less efficiently than the way it used to be done—quietly, with a broom.

### WHO NEEDS...

...one more golf tournament named after a Hollywood entertainer who now has ample time for golf because he can't get a job.

# NEEDS IT?

ARTIST: HARRY NORTH
WRITER: TOM KOCH

### WHO NEEDS...

...an English Lit assignment that requires 50 students to read the same book, when there's only one copy of it available at the local library.

### WHO NEEDS...

...still another calendar that illustrates each month with a different picture of a cat being loveable.

### WHO NEEDS...

...another TV SitCom that has nothing going for it except a kid who's considered cute because he's small for his age.

### WHO NEEDS...

...a new commemorative 14¢ stamp...when nothing we mail costs 14¢.

### WHO NEEDS...

...a new Arab Liberation Movement dedicated to blowing up everything in the world, including other Arab Liberation Movements.

### WHO NEEDS...

...that extra announcer brought in for World Series telecasts to give us a detailed explanation of everything the regular announcers just finished telling us.

## WHO NEEDS...

...another football Bowl Game...this one bringing together the teams that finished fifth in the Southeastern Conference and sixth in the Big Ten.

## WHO NEEDS...

...one more holiday contrived to make us feel guilty if we don't observe it by sending greeting cards.

## WHO NEEDS...

...your public TV station's appeal for funds so it can remain on the air long enough to make another appeal for funds.

## WHO NEEDS...

...a sale on the same designer jeans you spent your life's savings to buy at the regular price just last week.

## WHO NEEDS...

...an airline that offers "bargain fares" between Spokane and Dayton, when nobody in either city wants to go to the other one.

## WHO NEEDS...

...a guest on "Wall Street Week" who tells you how rich you'd be today if you'd bought the stocks that he'd recommended a year ago.

## WHO NEEDS...

...a reproduction of an antique that serves no purpose except to make people think that your valuable original is also a reproduction.

## WHO NEEDS...

...a form letter from a magazine urging you to renew your subscription, which is due to expire in just eleven more months.

## WHO NEEDS...

...a new brand of pet food...when half of every supermarket is already filled to the ceiling with pet food.

# A BASKET CASE HIGH UP ON THE 37ᵀᴴ FLOOR

ARTIST & WRITER: DON EDWING

JEST DESSERTS DEPT.

MAD hates to criticize a great old American tradition (or even a great old Canton-ese tradition), but it's a fact that the "wisdom" found in Fortune Cookies is down-right blah. Because Fortune Cookies are usually served in Chinese Restaurants, where the patrons come in all ages, genders and areas of interest. Hence, each "fortune"

# RELEVANT FOR
# FOR OTHER D

ARTIST: GEORGE WOODBRIDGE

must be worded vaguely enough to fit anyone who happens to receive it. On the other hand, Fortune Cookies are never served in such eateries as school cafeterias and prison mess halls, where those who gather have a lot more in common. Just imagine how meaningful and thought-provoking these messages could be if they introduced...

# TUNE COOKIES INING SPOTS

### BENEDICT ARNOLD HIGH SCHOOL
*"Go...Turquoise Traitors...Go!"*

3X = 15... THEREFORE, X = 5. REMEMBER THAT, OR YOU WILL SPEND MANY UNHAPPY YEARS IN ALGEBRA I.

POOR HIGH SCHOOL GRADES MAY NOT INDICATE LOW INTELLIGENCE, BUT YOU WILL FIND THAT ALL COLLEGE OFFICIALS THINK THEY DO.

HE WHO PURPOSELY FLUNKS "SEX EDUCATION" JUST SO HE CAN TAKE IT AGAIN IS EVEN WEIRDER THAN HE THINKS.

YOU TEND TO BE SCHOLARLY, SERIOUS AND INTROVERTED. THIS IS WHY TEACHERS LOVE YOU, AND SEXY CHEERLEADERS DON'T.

GIVING APPLES TO TEACHERS MAY HELP WIN PASSING GRADES ...BUT IF YOU ARE GOING FOR A SURE THING, GIVE CASH.

REFUSING TO EAT TODAY'S SLIME WILL GAIN YOU NOTHING. IT WILL MERELY BE REHEATED AND SERVED AGAIN TOMORROW.

WRITER: TOM KOCH

### GIGANTIC CONGLOMORATE CORPORATION
EMPLOYEES DINING MODULE "TIME IS MONEY! EAT FAST!"

TO SEEK RECREATION BY DIVING INTO THE TYPING POOL IS TO RISK BEING UP TO ONE'S NECK IN HOT WATER.

YOU HAVE AN OVERLY VIVID IMAGINATION. WHY ELSE WOULD YOU THINK YOU'RE WORTH MORE MONEY?

THOSE WHO ENRICH THEMSELVES IN SWIPED OFFICE SUPPLIES MAY SUDDENLY GROW POOR LACKING A WEEKLY PAYCHECK.

ENJOY THE FOOD HERE WHILE YOU CAN. IT'S BETTER THAN THE LUNCHROOM AT THE UNEMPLOYMENT OFFICE.

AN OPPORTUNITY FOR ADVANCEMENT MAY COME YOUR WAY TOMORROW. SO DON'T PHONE IN SICK AND RISK MISSING IT.

THOSE WHO ARE LUCKY IN LOVE BECOME UNLUCKY AT EMPLOYMENT WHEN THEY TELEPHONE LOVED ONES LONG DISTANCE ON COMPANY TIME.

# ONE AFTERNOON IN DOWNTOWN LOURDES

There are thousands of programs on the market that are supposed to be a boon to the home computer user. But come on! How many times do you need a merge mail program? Or a 48 column worksheet? If companies really want everyone to buy a home computer, then how about some...

# PRACTICAL FOR NORN

## THE "WHAT I WORE" PROGRAM

OUTFIT: blue blouse and grey skirt

WORN: 3/1 Bernie's party, 3/3 school, 3/8 school, 3/11 date with Nick

OUTFIT NEVER SEEN BY: Terry's parents, the bowling team, the Nickersons

## THE "NEVER REPEAT A JOKE" PROGRAM

JOKE: the one about the elephant and the ant

TOLD: the family, Bruce, Benny, Geri, no one at camp

CAN NEVER TELL: anyone of Armenian heritage

## THE "DATE TRACKING" PROGRAM

DATE'S NAME: Carol

WHERE WE WENT: The Big Taco restaurant

WHAT WE DID: went back to her house, watched tv, was asked to leave at 11 pm by her old man

WHAT I TOLD OTHERS WE DID: went back to her house, her parents were in Switzerland, stayed the night.

# COMPUTER PROGRAMS
## ...MAL EVERYDAY USE

ARTIST: PAUL COKER  WRITER: DICK DE BARTOLO

### THE "USELESS GIFT TRACKING" PROGRAM

GIFT: handmade scarf with cucumbers embroidered on it

FROM/WHEN: grandma/Xmas '82

WHERE IT'S HIDDEN: trunk in attic

CAN BE RE-GIVEN TO: anyone at the office

CAN'T BE RE-GIVEN TO: any family members or the mailman

### THE "GOOD PARTY" PROGRAM

FOOD NO ONE TOUCHED: the liver dip

FOOD THEY DEVOURED: Marilyn's crumb cake

NO MORE THAN TWO DRINKS FOR: Dennis, Sylvia

PEOPLE NOT TO SIT NEXT TO EACH OTHER: Lenny/Claire Bernie/Kate, David and anyone.

### THE "EXCUSE" PROGRAM

OCCASION: late for work

EXCUSES USED: dead battery (twice) train derailment, sick Aunt Betsy, dead grandmother

AVAILABLE: flat tire, dental emergency, mugging victim

A favorite Grown-Up complaint is that kids today don't know or care what's going on in the world. Well, what do they expect? A whole generation is being raised on the confusing double-talk of TV News. And maybe Parents can con themselves into thinking they understand all those mysterious new

# A LITTLE KID
# UNDERSTANDI

### Detente

. . . is like when the Class Bully agrees to stop threatening to beat you up after you promise to do all his Math homework on your new calculator.

### Classified Information

. . . is like the kind your Teacher writes in a note to your Parents, and then seals the envelope so you can't find out what it is, even though you're the one she's written about.

### The Domino Theory

. . . is a Grown-Up term for what happens when your Dad's Boss is forced by his Wife to sleep on the sofa, which makes him yell at your Dad all the next day, which makes your Dad get bombed on his way home from work, which makes your Mom send you upstairs to your room so you won't hear what happens next.

### Granting Diplomatic Recognition

. . . is like when you invite a kid to your Birthday Party—even though you don't like him very much—because you know he'll bring an expensive present.

words and bewildering new phrases of the TV Newscaster . . . but their kids are too honest to do that
They're the first ones to admit that they need help in deciphering the indecipherable. And so . .
MAD rushes to the aid of the younger generation with this vital Public Service Feature entitled

# 'S GUIDE TO
# NG THE NEWS

ARTIST: JACK DAVIS
WRITER: TOM KOCH

## Deficit Spending

. . . is like when you borrow so far ahead on your allowance that you can't ever get out of debt, unless you grow up to be the only 44-year-old person still getting an allowance.

## A Conflict of Interest

. . . is like when you're assigned as the Honorary Hall Monitor to see that nobody snitches stuff out of the lockers, and you're the main one who's snitching stuff.

## School Desegregation and Forced Busing

. . . are really the same thing. Adults have merely given it two different names so that those who are for it and those who are against it can both make it sound as if the other side is wrong.

## A Consumer Boycott

. . . is when all the Mothers get together and agree not to buy stuff their kids love to eat until the prices come down. (Oddly enough, Consumer Boycotts are never called to protest the rising costs of Grown-Up things like whiskey, beer and cigarettes.)

## A Covert Operation

. . . is what Grown-Ups call it when they get caught doing something they shouldn't do. By calling it that, they make sure of getting a medal instead of going to jail.

## Fringe Benefits

. . . are like when you agree to clean out your neighbor's garage for a lousy 50¢ cash because you know there's a whole stack of *Penthouse Magazines* under all that junk.

## Women's Liberation

. . . is a movement designed to convince everybody that girls with I.Q.s of 160 are as good as boys who can chin themselves 28 times without stopping.

## Declaring Bankruptcy

. . . is like when you owe money to all of your friends, and you announce that you're not going to pay it back, but they can't hit you right then because your Father is with you.

## A U.N. Cease-Fire

. . . is like when your Mom says it's okay to hit another kid if he hits you first, but not if he just looks like he might.

## Senior Citizens

. . . are what Middle-Aged People call Old People when they want to get rid of them without hurting their feelings.

## Bipartisanship

. . . is like when your Mom and Dad are both so completely against letting you take up "Hang Gliding" that there's no point in trying to play one of them off against the other.

## An Unannounced Candidate

. . . is like what you are when you see a girl you want to date real bad but you're scared to ask her until her brother can almost guarantee that she won't say "NO!"

## A Nuclear Deterrent

. . . is like when your folks buy a dog just so they can put a "Beware Of The Dog" sign on the front gate to scare away strangers . . . they hope.

## Strategic Arms Limitations

. . . is like when two guys agree to throw away so many weapons, they barely have enough left to kill each other more than once.

## A Recession

. . . is when your allowance stays the same for a long time because your Father asked for a raise and got turned down.

## A Depression

. . . is when you don't get any allowance at all for a long time because your Father asked for a raise and got fired.

# THE MAD S

### 8.3 SECONDS

. . . is the amount of time between when you first step into the shower till your phone starts to ring.

### 37.1 MINUTES

. . . is the amount of time you watch *The Tonight Show* before you doze off.

### 5 YEARS, 9 MONTHS, 2 DAYS

. . . is the amount of time you spend in your life looking for your keys.

### 3 DAYS, 2 HOURS, 1 MINUTE

. . . is the amount of time between when someone dies, and his heirs start laying claim to his worldly possessions.

### 3 WEEKS AND 2 DAYS

. . . is how long you're already back from vacation when the post card you sent your neighbor finally arrives.

### 9 MONTHS AND 3 DAYS

. . . is the time it takes for the foreign car part you need to be shipped.

### 14 MONTHS, 2 DAYS

. . . is how long you'll be dead when relatives stop coming to your grave.

### 4 MINUTES, 46 SECONDS

. . . is how much longer it takes your dog to find a suitable spot to do his thing whenever it is pouring outside.

### 4 DAYS

. . . is the amount of time between when the warranty on your TV runs out . . . and something goes wrong with the set.

ARTIST: BOB CLARKE

### 4 MINUTES, 10 SECONDS

. . . is the amount of time the average couple in a "Drive-In Movie" spends watching the action upon the screen.

# TOP WATCH

### 7 MONTHS AND 20 DAYS

. . . is how long after the Orthodontist promises to take off your braces that he finally does take the things off.

### 3 YEARS, 8 MONTHS, 9 DAYS

. . . is the amount of time it takes a worker to make up the money he lost when he went on strike for more pay.

### 1 MINUTE, 38 SECONDS

. . . is the time between when the winning horse crosses the finish line . . . and the horse that you bet on comes in.

### 13 DAYS

. . . is the time it takes the Post Office to deliver a letter cross town.

### 2 MINUTES, 12 SECONDS

. . . is the average time it takes a gal to find something in her purse.

WRITER: JOHN FICARRA

### 16 MINUTES, 8 SECONDS

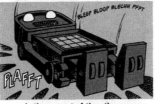

. . . is the amount of time the average battery in a new electronic toy lasts.

### 29 SECONDS

. . . is how long a guest is on a "Talk Show" before he plugs his latest film.

### 27 MINUTES

. . . is the time it takes you to wrap a child's birthday present that the little brat will rip off in 2 seconds.

### 12 SECONDS

. . . is the amount of time that passes between when a man picks up a copy of *Playboy* and he flips to the centerfold.

### 3 MINUTES, 22 SECONDS

. . . is the amount of time the average American spends listening to a Presidential address before shutting it off.

# <u>MORE</u> WAIT TILL YOU GET

...the rent strike you organized has failed.

...your smoke alarm has been set off by your neighbor's barbecue.

...during your vacation, all your homemade apple cider fermented.

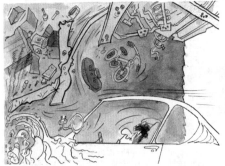

...your automatic garage door suddenly went on the blink.

...your neighbor has sold his house to the "Hell's Angels."

# HOME AND FIND THAT...

ARTIST & WRITER: PAUL PETER PORGES

...while you were at the laundromat, your old boyfriend who made good in Hollywood, has dropped by as a surprise.

...a swarm of Brazilian killer bees has followed their Queen and settled in the overhang over your front door.

...your upstairs neighbor has had a heart attack while he was lying in a running tub.

...your tomcat, Rodney, has returned with a love offering for you.

...your Mother's thrown out your complete mint collection of MAD.

# A MAD TREASURY OF
## *Shakespeare's Lesser Known Quotations*

ARTIST: HARRY NORTH, ESQ.
WRITER: DENNIS SNEE

Could Richard stop death? Could Henry? If they were here, you could ask them.

\* \* \*

Of valor, discretion is the better part; of dinner, dessert.

\* \* \*

O! The dawn! Would it only come back in half an hour!

Women, Mercutio, are the itch we gladly scratch.

\* \* \*

In such a night did Orestes take flight, and tripping on a pail, did break his ass.

\* \* \*

Trust not the woman, Horatio, who kisses her husband, then wipes her lips.

\* \* \*

Doth yonder fat man think himself thin? Bring him, then, thy mirror, and none of my mutton.

If your boots are heavy, take them off. But pray, not here.

\* \* \*

You speak of that adultress as if she were a rose, and you but a pound of fertilizer.

\* \* \*

Yea, his evil may live after him, but his best suit he takes to the grave.

\* \* \*

Her tears, Polonius, are as false as thy teeth.

\* \* \*

Youth, in froth and frolic, play. But when age doth come, no elder catches the speedy young tart.

\* \* \*

If something is rotten in Denmark, then haste; get thee to Sweden.

\* \* \*

Talk and talk and talk. Were it not for ears, who would know?

\* \* \*

Judge not Leonard by the length of his beard, nor its color, but by the number of crumbs therein.

\* \* \*

Lo, in Heaven there sits a judge no king can corrupt. Nor will he lend money, save to certain close friends.

\* \* \*

Better a solitary man than relatives in the bathroom.

\* \* \*

A tragic tale is best for winter. In summer, 'tis off to the beach.

Sad, sad, and sad again. His love is gone, but his wife remains.

\* \* \*

In the sight of men, take only your due. But when alone, grabbeth what you can.

\* \* \*

Gladly I would drink the hemlock, my son, but then who would wash the cup? Not you, for sure. The state of thy room announces your talents.

# THE MAD SI

ARTIST: BOB CLARKE

# CONNORS UPSETS McENROE
## Jimmy Leads In Product Endorsements

NEW YORK, A jubilant Jimmy Connors had reason to celebrate yesterday as he surpassed John McEnroe to again become the number one ranked player on the Professional Tennis Product Endorsement Circuit.

Connors, long time commercial spokesman for cameras, designer jeans, shaving cream and liquid bleach, was the undisputed champion until McEnroe gained notoriety and was asked to appear in ads for disposable razors, credit cards and sandwich bags. Fighting back from the unexpected losses of his breakfast cereal and antacid tablet accounts, the determined Connors struck three times yesterday, landing product endorsements for athlete's foot powder, life insurance and decaffeinated cola. The cola endorsement was particularly disturbing to McEnroe, who for years held a virtual lock in the soft drink category.

An incensed McEnroe says he will contest the ruling which scores his separate endorsements of Dorman's Swiss, Kraft Cheddar and Mafioso Romano as a single endorsement under the heading of "Cheese." Speaking with reporters, McEnroe said, "It's rulings like this that make a mockery of professional tennis."

# Hockey Player Sets Record
## PUCK HITS FACE FOR 1,000TH TIME

HALIFAX, CANADA Halifax Eels defenseman, Gordy Thwack, made history last night when his nose got in the way of a blistering slapshot off the stick of New Brunswick's Wayne Bugchuck, making Gordy the first player ever to get hit in the face by a puck 1,000 times. Gordy, whose nose was broken for the 218th time (26th time this year), has also been hit 186 times in the jaw, 307 times in the mouth, and 289 times in the eyes (169 left, 120 right).

A short ceremony followed the injury, during which Gordy was awarded the puck. "This is the happiest day of my life," said a toothless Gordy, who was immediately rushed to Halifax Hospital for the 95th time this season. He received eight stitches, moving him into third place on Hockey's All-Time Stitch List.

# LAST NIGHT'S MOVIE TITLE LEAGUE RESULTS

| | | | | |
|---|---|---|---|---|
| Jaws | 2 | | Nineteen | 41 |
| The Magnificent | 7 | | Oceans | 11 |
| North Dallas | 40 | | Summer Of | 42 |
| Catch | 22 | | How The West Was | 1 |
| Rocky | 3 | (1st) | Chapter | 2 |
| Superman | 2 | | Star Trek | 3 |
| Rocky | 2 | (2nd) | 9 To | 5 |
| Superman | 3 | | Halloween | 2 |
| Godfather Part | 2 | | Airport | 77 |
| History Of The World Part | 1 | | Death Race | 2,000 |

# PORTS PAGE

WRITERS: CHARLIE KADAU & JOE RAIOLA

## NBA TEAMS REALIGNED
### Hoopsters Don't Know Who To Play

SEATTLE, Players in the National Basketball Association are now considered the most bewildered athletes in the nation due to the realignment of teams as announced yesterday by Basketball Commissioner Nelson Chinski.

"We're all confused," said Los Angeles Center Kareem Abdul Giraffe, whose team showed up last night at the Kingdome to play Seattle, only to find a rodeo in progress. The Seattle team thought they were scheduled to play against Dallas in Chicago, as did nine other teams.

Commissioner Chinski's realignment, which many believe is the cause of the recent trouble, is as follows:

- Milwaukee and Chicago were moved from the Western Conference's Midwestern Division to the Eastern Conference's Central Division.
- Houston and San Antonio were moved from the Eastern Conference's Southern Division to the Northeast Conference's West Central Division.
- The entire East Central Division was moved from the Southwest's Northern Conference to the North South's Eastwestern Conference.
- Atlanta is now the only team in the Southern Conference's South Southern Division, and as a result, isn't scheduled to play anyone.

Commissioner Chinski told reporters, "Basketball is much more exciting now. Fans can never be sure if the teams will show up or where they'll be playing if they do. It's the best thing for the game."

## YOU BE THE UMP
### by Otto Skunk

In April of 1983, the Royals were playing the Angels in Anaheim, California. In the third inning, Kansas City third baseman, George Brett, hit a towering foul pop-up off pitcher Tommy John. First baseman Rod Carew attempted to make the catch while standing in foul territory. The ball hit his glove and landed in fair territory. Is the ball fair or foul? If you were the umpire, how would *you* call it?

### Answer

*If you were an umpire in April of 1983, you would have been on strike and walking a picket line outside of the play, and the only calls you'd be making would be for higher salaries and better benefits!*

## NEW FOOTBALL LEAGUE FORMED
### WILL PLAY ALL GAMES DURING HALFTIMES

LOS ANGELES, At a press conference this morning, sports promoter Kelly Lemon announced the formation of the Halftime Football League (HTFL). Lemon said HTFL games will be played during the fifteen minute halftimes at all NFL and USFL games.

After appointing himself Commissioner, Lemon explained what he called the 'outstanding features' of the new league. "From opening kickoff to the final gun we'll have four action packed three minute quarters. We'll be able to charge fans for seeing two games instead of one and best of all, no one will have to sit through those incredibly boring halftimes shows anymore."

Each HTFL game will have a three minute halftime, during which the games of the soon-to-be-formed Three Minute Football League (TMFL) will be played.

# A MAD EXPOSÉ OF SOME... PHON

ARTIST: JACK DAVIS

When Americans travel through the world, there are Tourist Guide Books that describe each country's natives, their interests and how they live. Unfortunately, there are no such Tourist Guide Books for Americans traveling through their own country that describe each region's natives, their interests and how they live. So we present...

# AN INSTANT GUIDE TO AMERICAN REGIONAL TYPES

ARTIST: PAUL COKER    WRITER: FRANK JACOBS

## NEW ENGLANDERS

| | |
|---|---|
| Resharpen their disposable razors. | Call their parents "Mr.—" and "Mrs.—" |
| Consider credit cards "tools of the devil." | Regard second generation Americans as "immigrants." |
| Refuse to buy paper clips without a 90-day warranty. | Believe the decline in morality began with the phasing out of suspenders. |

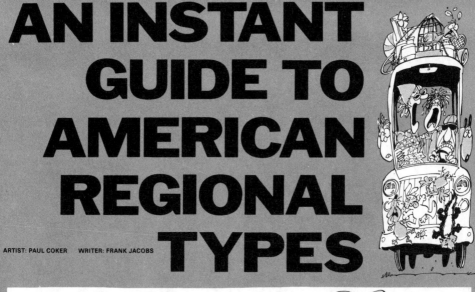

## NEW YORKERS

| | |
|---|---|
| Organize vigilante groups to patrol inside their apartments. | Yell "Hurry up!" during funeral eulogies. |
| Greet their party guests only after they've passed through a metal detector. | Check to see if their wallets are still there while attending religious services. |
| Freebase soot. | Frisk their children. |

## SOUTHERNERS

| | |
|---|---|
| Would like to vaccinate visiting Northerners. | Bury their hound-dogs in Confederate Flag shrouds. |
| Learn "Possum Cuisine" in High School Home Economics classes. | Soak their dentures overnight in glasses of Jack Daniels. |
| Share the chewing tobacco on their honeymoons. | Carry on feuds over swamp rights. |

## MIDWESTERNERS

| | |
|---|---|
| Polka in discos. | Hang out the American Flag on William McKinley's birthday. |
| Entertain visitors with home movies of their garage sales. | Snore with a twang. |
| Own "His-and-Hers" manure spreaders. | Regard "K-Mart" as a designer label. |

## SOUTHWESTERNERS

| | |
|---|---|
| Close schools for Apache holidays. | Name their children after obscure igneous rocks. |
| Train lizards to handle minor household chores. | Include token Navajos at Rotary Club meetings. |
| Hold Tupperware parties in abandoned cliff dwellings. | Rate a man by the horse-power of his pickup truck. |

## NEVADANS

| | |
|---|---|
| Propose double-or-nothing bets during I.R.S. audits. | Take odds on total highway deaths on major holidays. |
| Get rid of children they feel are unlucky. | Take out Medical Insurance to cover "Slot Machine Elbow." |
| Offer "Blackjack Card-Counting" as a High School elective. | Fast on Jimmy The Greek's birthday. |

## CALIFORNIANS

| | |
|---|---|
| Apply "Grecian Formula" to their aging poodles. | Lamé their Frisbees. |
| Freeze-dry cocaine. | Cast horoscopes for their cars. |
| Consider it trendy to jog during earthquakes. | Honor their dead with designer tombstones. |

## HAWAIIANS

| | |
|---|---|
| Rarely hula on the first date. | Enjoy hearing "The 1812 Overture" arranged for the ukulele. |
| Are buried with their surfboards. | Spend Saturdays watching slow-moving molten lava. |
| Take little interest in ice hockey. | Wear black leis to funerals. |

## TEXANS

| | |
|---|---|
| Believe that owning more than two 747's is pretentious. | Have unlisted area codes. |
| Refer to anyone less than six feet four as "Shorty." | Rent Oklahoma for picnics and family gatherings. |
| Protect their ranches with MX missiles. | Refuse to recognize the existence of Alaska. |

## ALASKANS

| | |
|---|---|
| Only say "Goodnight" once a winter. | Prepare delicious whale blubber quiches. |
| Organize "Sled Pools" during transit strikes. | Say "Hot enough for you?" when the mercury hits 40. |
| Play football on artificial tundra. | Feel very uncomfortable in crowded places like Wyoming. |

# YOUR MAD HOROSCOPE

## AIRES
### March 21—April 19

Your moon is now in the House of Pancakes and is expected to remain there for some time—what with two waitresses calling in sick and a third vacationing in Aruba. The A.M. is a very good time to take advantage of fools. However, seek the advice of an expert before attempting surgery on yourself or someone you love.

## TAURUS
### April 20—May 20

Due to a slight imbalance in the tides, there is some confusion among the stars as to whether or not you really exist. This question will be quickly resolved just as soon as someone makes an attempt to pick up your laundry. Rash decisions could prove very harmful today, so exercise great caution when selecting a salve.

## GEMINI TWINS
### May 21—June 21

New movement in the stars suggest that you are not twins at all but rather clones! This may be why your mother's face is always razored out of the family portrait. The evening is an excellent time for you to get together with persons whose ideas are similar to your own unless, of course, you are a real moron.

## MOON CHILDREN
### June 22—July 22

Make detailed plans for social activities you may wish to engage in later in the day. Then, later in the day, make detailed plans for social activities you may wish to engage in tomorrow. Repeat this routine faithfully throughout the remainder of the calendar year and you can easily avoid any kind of real work.

## LEO
### July 23—August 22

What was believed to have been the main star guiding your life now appears to be nothing more than an enormous chunk of Skylab still floating around the atmosphere. This means that any advice you've ever read in this or any other horoscope has been way off base. We sincerely apologize for any inconveniences suffered.

## VIRGO
### August 23—September 22

Some foreign intrigue. A short man in France is now plotting to overthrow your mother and move in with your father. Making matters worse, the short man is a bureaucrat. Meanwhile, your impatience with the legal process continues to wear thin. Your new plan to set fire to the judge's robes, however, remains unsound.

## LIBRA
### September 23—October 23

The main star influencing your fate has moved—leaving behind a flock of unpaid utility bills, and no forwarding galaxy. Until such time as we at Horoscope Central can locate the missing star, you're on your own. Best of luck with what you can only be described as a very bleak and altogether loathsome situation.

## SCORPIO
### October 24—November 21

You can make many of your loved ones much brighter today by giving them a quick coat of semigloss, outdoor paint. Puttying-up the holes, however, would be ill-advised. A lifelong loyalty has not been misplaced — it has been stolen — along with all of your traveler's checks. Remain healthy, but take your sick days.

## SAGITTARIUS
### November 22–December 21

A disturbing day. The moon cries out to you: "Haste makes waste!" while the Big Dipper cries out: "If you listen to the moon, you are crazy! He who hesitates is lost!" This is terribly confusing, while at the same time terribly boring — not unlike Presidential election debates. Your best bet is to hoard raw meats.

## CAPRICORN
### December 22—January 19

Your cusp has broken into the House of Leo while Leo was on a gas line, and has made off with a portable T.V., an electric can opener and a still-undetermined amount of cash. It would be improper for you to contact the proper authorities and vice versa. Avoid legal clinics, firing squads and well-lit alleyways.

## AQUARIUS
### January 20—February 18

A long and trusted friend may be in a bit of a testy mood today, so make allowances for a punch in the mouth, a bowl of exceptionally well-seasoned chile in your lap, or just some scathing verbal abuse. No new problems will develop during this month. Your old problems are more than sufficient to finish you off.

## PISCES
### February 19—March 20

You are the last of the Zodiac signs and this is certainly not by accident. You have relatively few, if any, friends; you are widely distrusted; and your bad taste in clothes appeals only to people's prurient interest while lacking any socially redeeming values. Start drinking heavily.

WRITER: JOHN FICARRA

Until recently, it was pretty easy to catagorize most comic strip heroes. They were either: (1) Noble and courageous; or (2) Funny, lovable clods. The bottom line was: They were generally decent people. Today, of course, we still have our share of positive personalities on the funny pages. But have you noticed there's a subtle, insidious element gradually taking over? Well, it's true! We call this

# THE TREND TOWARD ROTTENNESS IN THE COMIC STRIPS

For example, take a look at some of the more popular funny page heroes of today:

**First of all, there's "ANDY CAPP"…**

A rotten, amoral insect, who never did an honest day's work, or a worthwhile thing, in his whole entire life.

**And then, there's "ARNOLD"…**

An insensitive, insulting character who constantly nauseates people with his foul stories and vicious comments.

**And then, there's "CROCK"…**

A sadistic taskmaster who relishes causing his men pain.

**And finally, there's the king in "THE WIZARD OF ID"…**

A selfish, unenlightened ruler who overtaxes his subjects and punishes them for minor, or even non-existent crimes.

Well if this is the trend of the future, it's only a matter of time before the few remaining decent comic strip characters will have to shape up or ship out. Which brings us to this article … containing examples of what could happen …

# WHEN ALL COMIC STRIP C...

## BLONDIE

ARTIST: BOB CLARKE    WRITER: LARRY SIEGEL

DAGWOOD, AFTER ALL THESE YEARS, I FINALLY PUT A COUPLE OF **LOCKS** ON THE **BATHROOM DOOR**!

HEY... THAT'S GREAT, BLONDIE!

AT LAST! NOW I WON'T BE BOTHERED IN THE TUB ANY MORE BY NEIGHBORHOOD KIDS AND DOOR-TO-DOOR SALESMEN!

GEE, I NEVER DREAMED THAT YOU **CHEATED** ON DAGWOOD, BLONDIE! AREN'T YOU AFRAID HE'LL **WALK IN** ON US?

WHY DO YOU THINK I PUT ONE LOCK **OUTSIDE** THE BATHROOM DOOR?

PSST! BLONDIE! AM I TOO EARLY?

## ANNIE

ANNIE! WHAT'S **HAPPENED** TO YOU?! YOU FORGED MY NAME ON A **CHECK**! YOU BLEW MY **ENTIRE FORTUNE**! YOU HAD ME PUT IN **PRISON**! YOU HAD PUNJAB **DEPORTED** AS AN **ILLEGAL ALIEN**! AND NOW WE'RE **STARVING**!

**NOT** ANY **MORE**! SIT DOWN AND **EAT**!

IS THERE **ANY** NAUSEATING, VILE THING YOU **HAVEN'T** COMMITED LATELY...?

OH BY THE WAY, HOW'S **SANDY**?

DELICIOUS...!!

**ULP!**

## FAMILY CIRCUS

I'VE HAD IT UP TO **HERE** WITH KIDS! I WANT AN **ABORTION**!

YOU WANT **WHAT**? AN ABORTION?

WHY NOT? **LOTS** OF PEOPLE HAVE THEM!

BUT **NOT** WHEN THE KIDS ARE **ALREADY BORN**! THAT WOULD BE "**MURDER ONE**"! GO AHEAD **KILL** THEM! THEY'LL LOCK YOU UP AND THROW AWAY THE KEY!

OKAY... **FORGET IT**! I'M LEAVING AND **YOU** CAN HAVE **CUSTODY** OF THE **KIDS**!

WAIT A SEC! IF THEY BUY "**MANSLAUGHTER**," YOU COULD BE OUT IN **FIVE YEARS**! YOU'D **STILL** BE A RELATIVELY YOUNG WOMAN, AND...

# HARACTERS TURN ROTTEN

## CATHY

## PEANUTS

## BEETLE BAILEY

# SOME IMAGINATIVE MAD SUGGES

# RECYCLING YOU

ARTIST: AL JAFFEE

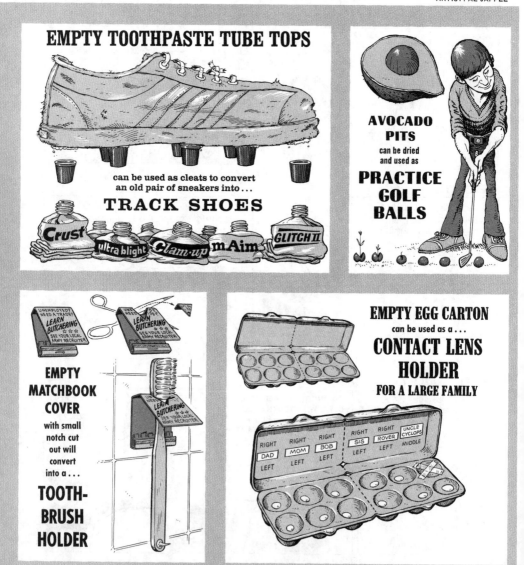

## EMPTY TOOTHPASTE TUBE TOPS

can be used as cleats to convert
an old pair of sneakers into...

### TRACK SHOES

Crust ultra blight Clam-up mAim GLITCH II

**AVOCADO PITS**

can be dried
and used as

### PRACTICE GOLF BALLS

**EMPTY MATCHBOOK COVER**

with small
notch cut
out will
convert
into a...

### TOOTH-BRUSH HOLDER

LEARN BUTCHERING ☆☆☆ SEE YOUR LOCAL ARMY RECRUITER

## EMPTY EGG CARTON

can be used as a...

### CONTACT LENS HOLDER

#### FOR A LARGE FAMILY

| RIGHT DAD LEFT | RIGHT MOM LEFT | RIGHT BOB LEFT | RIGHT SIS LEFT | RIGHT ROVER LEFT | UNCLE CYCLOPS MIDDLE |

WRITER: PAUL PETER PORGES

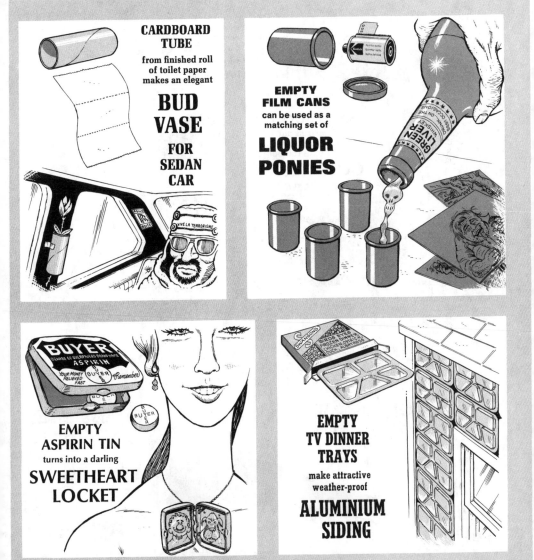

**CARDBOARD TUBE**

from finished roll of toilet paper makes an elegant

**BUD VASE**

FOR SEDAN CAR

**EMPTY FILM CANS**

can be used as a matching set of

**LIQUOR PONIES**

**EMPTY ASPIRIN TIN**

turns into a darling

**SWEETHEART LOCKET**

**EMPTY TV DINNER TRAYS**

make attractive weather-proof

**ALUMINIUM SIDING**

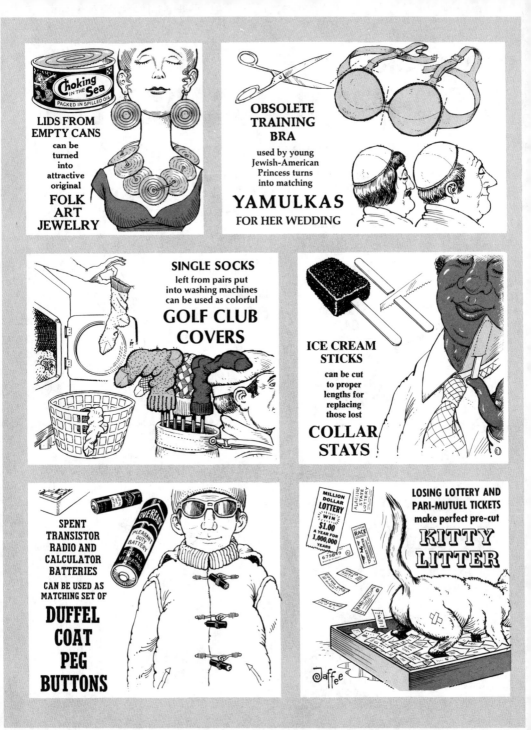

# ONE FINE DAY AT THE CORNER OF SOUTH FINSTER BOULEVARD AND FONEBONE STREET

# HOW CAN YOU PO

ARTIST: PAUL COKER

. . . a Politician who preaches energy conservation . . . and drives a big gas guzzler!

. . . a Health Food Store clerk . . . who looks like death warmed over!

. . . a Doctor who advises you to stop smoking . . . with a full ash tray on his desk!

. . . a commercial by a top star . . . when you read he got paid $150,000 to make it!

. . . the advice of a Dentist . . . who has (yecch) Denture Breath!

# SSIBLY BELIEVE...

WRITER: GEORGE HART

AB UNO DISCE OMNES

... that mastery of a school subject will help you to rise to the top of your chosen field ... when it's told to you by a teacher who's been in the same dead-end job for 30 years!

A.Y.E. W.T.K. A.B.B W.A.T.A.

... a guy who spends all his time selling a $10 course on "How To Get Rich Playing Blackjack"... instead of going to Las Vegas and getting rich that way himself!

...TV ads that tell you how wonderful milk is ... when they're paid for by the American Dairy Council!

... that white bread can "build strong bodies ten ways"... when it's so filled with chemicals, even bugs won't eat it!

... the United States Government, when it tells you smoking cigarettes is deadly ... and then subsidizes tobacco growers!

... a Senator who's been wealthy all his life ... and claims that he understands the problems of the poor!

For every woman there comes a day when she must write a letter ending the relationship with the guy who no longer is the man of her dreams. Such a missive is called a "Dear John" letter,

# MAD'S ALL INCLUSI

## "Dear John Letter"

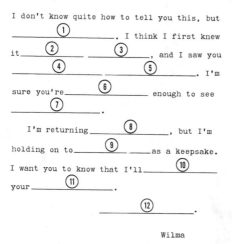

Dear John:

I don't know quite how to tell you this, but
_____(1)_____. I think I first knew
it ___(2)___ ___(3)___, and I saw you
_____(4)_____ ___(5)___. I'm
sure you're ___(6)___ enough to see
___(7)___.

I'm returning ___(8)___, but I'm
holding on to ___(9)___ as a keepsake.
I want you to know that I'll ___(10)___
your ___(11)___.

___(12)___.

Wilma

**1**
our romance is over
our affair is dead
I'm entering a convent
I loathe you
our horoscopes clash
you're a sickie
you need to bathe more
I'm a streetwalker
your nostrils offend me
there's a contract out for you
you're a schmuck
I'm in love with your sister

**5**
my best friend
my father
E.F. Hutton
my whoopee cushion
my spinach soufflé
Bert and Ernie
my avocado plant
my penpal in Ghana
my Franklin Mint Collection
the Oakland front four
my Billy Carter statue
that crazed monk

**9**
your photo
those oil stocks
my virginity
your neighbor Ralph
the results of the blood-test
your left ear
your suicide note
your mother
my sanity
your ant colony
your police record
Murray's leotards

and MAD would like to assist all women who have the unpleasant job of writing one. Here it is:
Simply fill in the numbered blanks from the corresponding numbered lists . . . and you'll have . . .

# VE DO-IT-YOURSELF

WRITER: FRANK JACOBS

**2**
that night
last year
skinny-dipping
tripping on tangerine seeds
last Arbor day
when you shackled me
when I threw up
when I saw that shrunken head
when your dwarf bit me
reciting "Gunga Din"
swapping tennis shoes
when your sheepdog went berserk

**3**
in your pad
in your camper
outside Poughkeepsie
under the bus
in your closet
while eating enchilladas
with Reverend Moon
in drag
at the Hare Krishna prom
on the funny farm
in a trance
with the Mondales

**4**
make a pass at
insult
ignore
punch out
pour syrup over
carve your initials on
tear the clothes off
apply leeches to
render impotent
yank the toupee off
sit on
exorcise

**6**
man
sensitive
open-minded
ashamed
stoned
gutless
scarred
Mongol
masochistic
senile
Republican
frostbitten

**7**
how miserable I've been
what a bore you are
your Datsun sucks
your acne is terminal
I've had a sex change
there is no Mid-East solution
we're first cousins
there is no Santa Claus
I'm allergic to your hamster
I dig sanitation men
that I'm bionic
that "The Gong Show" stinks

**8**
your ring
your love-letters
your Darth Vader poster
your pet rock
to the commune
those slides of Altoona
your dentures
to sleeping around
our matching Snoopy bibs
your Bicentennial truss
to Saturn
your bag of immies

**10**
always treasure
never forget
try to blot out
inform the I.R.S. about
always feel unclean about
never scoff openly at
make a movie based on
tell the "Enquirer" about
inform the asylum about
get nauseous thinking of
tell my priest about
be a lot better off without

**11**
friendship
senility
new life as a clone
Eskimo incarnation
capo Angelo
cocaine habit
passion for fieldmice
Jackie Mason imitations
embarrassing rash
eggplant fetish
screwing up World War II
hatred of Tampa

**12**
Fondly
Sincerely
Painfully
Eat your heart out
With disgust
With great relief
Up yours
Your undying enemy
Best to your frog Leonard
Now bug off
Good luck on your parole
Regards to your creepy family

# IF THEY CAN PUT A MAN ON THE

ARTIST: JACK DAVIS

∴ invent a parking meter that can make change of a dollar bill!?

...market a roll of Scotch tape that's easy to start every time!?

...devise a "child proof" medicine bottle that isn't also adult-proof!?

...design a raffle ticket that has enough space for you to write your name, address and telephone number!?

...invent a "Smoke Detector" that knows the difference between a real fire and a hamburger that's cooking!?

...make a better-grade golf shirt that doesn't have a tacky little animal insignia over the pocket!?

...make a "permanent press" garment that doesn't need touching up with a cool iron!?

...develop an effective way to keep fast-food French fries hot!?

...knit a better-looking toupee for Howard Cosell!?

# MOON, THEN WHY CAN'T THEY...

WRITER: JOHN FICARRA

... make a toaster that actually toasts the way the dial is set!?

... invent an electric can opener whose blade is easy to keep clean!?

... manufacture ice cube trays that allow for easy removal of the cubes!?

... manufacture a ballpoint pen that doesn't leave a little blob of ink on the page whenever you start to write!?

... construct a picture frame that doesn't slide crooked every time someone walks by it!?

... develop a clear plastic wrap that doesn't bunch up and cling together the second you pull it off the roll!?

... print a newspaper that doesn't make your hands black as you read!?

... judge ahead of time that a motion picture or a Broadway play is a bomb!?

... manufacture a helicopter that can actually reach Iran!?

... manufacture a box of cookies that can be opened at either end!?

... list the correct "Tonight Show" guests in the paper's TV listings!?

... construct a check and window envelope that line up correctly!?

# IF THEY CAN PUT A MAN ON THE

... make a tiny screw for eyeglasses that doesn't come loose regularly!?

... invent a popcorn machine that pops all of the kernals!?

... design a shirt collar that doesn't keep popping out of a man's suit jacket!?

# MOON, THEN WHY CAN'T THEY...

... train parking attendants to drive at a normal speed!?

... construct a really sound-proof wall between twin movie theaters!?

... develop a spray deodorant whose fumes don't choke you to death every morning!?

# ONE AFTERNOON IN ACAPULCO

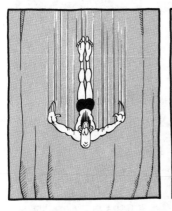

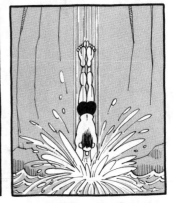

# THE MAD

ARTIST: PAUL COKER, JR.

### Don't You LIKE...

. . . your playful
new purebred dog?

### Don't You LOVE...

. . . how she frolics
with the other dogs?

### Don't You HATE...

. . . trying to dispose of
nine mixed-breed puppies?

### Don't You LIKE...

. . . the surprise of stumbling
onto an exotic new restaurant?

### Don't You LOVE...

. . . the surprise of tasting an
exotic new Mid-Eastern dish?

### Don't You HATE...

. . . the surprise of waking up at
3 AM with an exotic new heartburn?

### Don't You LIKE...

. . . discovering a new
exciting board game?

### Don't You LOVE...

. . . inviting your friends
over to play your new game?

### Don't You HATE...

. . . spending the first three
hours figuring out the rules?

WRITERS: FRANK JACOBS AND MARYLYN IPPOLITO

# ...HATE BOOK

### Don't You LIKE...

...renting a beach house for the summer?

### Don't You LOVE...

...the sand...the surf...the sea air...the sun...the sports?

### Don't You HATE...

...the uninvited relatives and friends who freeload all summer?

### Don't You LIKE...

...sleeping late on your birthday?

### Don't You LOVE...

...being served breakfast in bed by your husband and kids?

### Don't You HATE...

...having to clean up the mess they made in the kitchen?

### Don't You LIKE...

...the liberated age we live in?

### Don't You LOVE...

...feeling unhibited and free of the restrictions of society?

### Don't You HATE...

...being an unwed mother?

## Don't You LIKE...

... having a father who is very interested in your schoolwork?

## Don't You LOVE...

... conning him into doing your Math homework for you?

## Don't You HATE...

... getting a failing mark on the Math homework he did?

## Don't You LIKE...

... settling down to watch Monday Night Football on TV?

## Don't You LOVE...

... watching your favorite football team in action?

## Don't You HATE...

... Cosell telling you you're watching the poorest-played game in five years?

## Don't You LIKE...

... meeting someone from a foreign country?

## Don't You LOVE...

... learning his language so you can really communicate?

## Don't You HATE...

... discovering that boredom is world-wide?

## Don't You LIKE...

... finding the willpower to stick to your diet?

## Don't You LOVE...

... finally losing twenty-five pounds?

## Don't You HATE...

... hearing overweight friends tell you how scrawny and sickly you look?

### Don't You LIKE...

...going to
Tag Sales?

### Don't You LOVE...

...picking up a fabulous
floor lamp for only $15.00?

### Don't You HATE...

...spotting a store unloading
the same lamp for only $9.95?

### Don't You LIKE...

...sitting next to
the school grind?

### Don't You LOVE...

...copying his answers
during a Chemistry exam?

### Don't You HATE...

...being so stupid you
can't even *copy* correctly?

### Don't You LIKE...

...being a worker
protected by a Union?

### Don't You LOVE...

...your Union leaders demanding and
getting you a $10-a-week increase?

### Don't You HATE...

...hearing that Management was
prepared to go as high as $15?

### Don't You LIKE...

...having an Uncle
who owns a toy store?

### Don't You LOVE...

...when he visits
you on your birthday?

### Don't You HATE...

...getting a Savings Bond
from him as your present?

# A COLLECTION OF VITAL TEMP
# THE MAD THI

ARTIST: BOB CLARKE

**12°**

...is the temperature of the average toilet seat on the average Winter morning.

**95°**

...is the minimum the temperature always is when your air conditioner konks out.

**52°**

...is how much warmer the Kiddie Wading Pool always is compared to the Adult pool.

**23.7°**

...is the difference in the temperature between your first and second slices of Pizza.

**98°**

...and sunny is always the temperature the day you have to leave a vacation resort.

**27.3°**

...is how much cooler the wind against your ears feels right after a short haircut.

**110°**

...is the temperature of your dog's breath whenever he pants over you while you're sleeping.

**38°**

...is how much colder it always is at the cemetery when you attend a funeral.

**315°**

...is the temperature inside the sneakers of the winner of the annual Boston Marathon.

**9°**

...is the average temperature of your Doctor's stethoscope when he tries to examine you.

**57°**

...is how much the water temperature in your shower changes in the three seconds between when you adjust it perfectly until you step into the tub under it.

C

130
120
110
100
90
80
70
60
50
40
30
20
10
0
-10
-20
-30
-40

WRITER: JOHN FICARRA

**F**

260
240
220
200
180
160
140
120
100
80
60
40
20
0
-10

### 103.7°

...is your temperature when your Mother finally announces to the world, "I think it's time we called the Doctor!"

### 75.5°

...is the temperature when the chewing gum stuck to the bottom of your school desk starts to get yecchy again.

### 104.5°

...is the minimum the temperature must be for your Mother not to say as you go out... "Take a sweater for later on!"

### 25°

...is how much the temperature of the food ordered in a restaurant drops from the time it leaves the kitchen until the time the waiter serves it to you.

### 35°

...is how much your temperature rises when a girl you want to impress tells you your fly is open.

### 34.4°

...is the hottest those artificial heating lamps will ever keep fast-food French fries.

### 768°

...is the temperature of the average tenement in the South Bronx on an average evening.

### 91°

...is how hot it has to be before Johnny Carson can do a joke about how hot it is.

### 4000°

...is the temperature inside your car's overheated radiator when you take the cap off.

### 92.3°

...and humid is the temperature when the tape holding up your posters gives out.

### 212°

...was the temperature in your fish tank the night the electric heater went haywire.

Don't you just love it when you run to your mail box in hopes of finding that somebody's sent you five bucks for some old debt because you haven't paid your rent and you don't have a dime for food . . . but the only letter there is a piece

# MIXED-UP JUNK M

ARTIST: HARRY NORTH, ESQ.

Dear Swinging Single:

How many nights have you sat around alone, wondering where all the good-looking guys are hanging out?

Well, here's your chance to join "The After Midnight Swinging Singles Club" at our special introductory price, and banish loneliness forever! Just fill out the applica-

Dear Potential Homeowner:

"White Oaks" is no ordinary housing development, and that's why this pre-opening offer is not going to everyone! Located almost entirely within Wasp Woods, "White Oaks" will be an exclusive residential community made up of the most desirable families. So if you're the type of person we're looking for, why not come out to "White Oaks" today, and let us show you our planned private community of Luxury

Dear Lover of Fine Foods:

Your reputation as a knowledgeable gourmet is on record. But how much do you really know about the proper wines to serve with such gourmet dishes as Quenelles De Brochet or Tournedos Rossini or Poulet A La Creme?

The "World Book Of Wines" will put at your fingertips

Dear Home Handyperson:

What's your next home improvement? A finished basement? A swimming pool? A guest room?

Whatever your plans, "Home Handyperson Magazine" can help you with any of these projects, and of junk mail that starts out: *"We know you are the kind of man who appreciates the value of a well-made $300 suit, which is why this offer is being sent to men like you!"* Well, we wonder what other goofs are being made because of . . .

# AIL MAILING LISTS

WRITER: DICK DE BARTOLO

**Dear Discerning Homemaker:**

You probably haven't had your rugs and or furniture cleaned lately because you just can't find someone you can trust with your valuable and cherished furnishings and floor coverings.

Well, with "Luxury Cleaners," your worries are over!

Dear Business Executive:

Isn't it time that a busy man like yourself stopped missing those important after-hour dinner engagements and business meetings because your secretary can't be at your side 24 hours a day?

"Pocket Gal Friday," can end all that! This new

Dear Householder:

It's an unpleasant thought, but what if a fire were to wipe you out tonight? Just take a look around you. What if everything you owed were reduced to ashes? Could you survive such a catastrophe? "Mutual Fire Insurance"

Dear Fellow American:

Tired of being screwed by your government—the people who you helped elect? Well, now you can join thousands of your fellow citizens in an attempt to clean up the mess in Washington and bring honesty and integrity back to gov-

Whenever there's a strike, it's usually called by a group that we depend on for vital goods and services, like dairy workers, garbagemen or teachers. (That is, if you consider teachers vital?!?) Unfortunately, the clods and bimbos who continually mess up our lives or irritate us seem to never walk off the job! It is with these annoying folks in mind that we now present the picket lines of some...

# STRIKES WE
## ...and nev

# T.V. EVANGELISTS

TV EVANGELISTS UNION LOCAL 22:5 ON STRIKE

NO PAY—NO PRAY

WE WANT MORE HAIR SPRAY!

WE WANT FREE TOOTH CAPPING

# INTERNAL REVENUE WORKERS

BOO!

INTERNAL REVENUE SERVICE
ON STRIKE FOR
( SEE LINE 27 OF THIS SIGN)
NO TAX COLLECTIONS!
NO NIT-PICKING AUDITS!
NO HOUNDING OF CITIZENS!
NO HARRASSMENT OF ANYONE!
WE WILL ALLOW EVERY DEDUCTION TAKEN, NO MATTER HOW OUTLANDISH!
WE WILL NOT AUDIT ANYONE

1040 OR FIGHT!

# TOBACCO GROWERS

TOBACCO GROWERS OF AMERICA ON STRIKE FOR BETTER HEALTH BENEFITS!

WE ARE FUMING!

WE DON'T NEED NO

SMOKE 'EM OUT!

NO MORE STR

WE'LL USE OUR LAND TO GROW HEALTHFUL FOOD INSTEAD OF TOBACCO BEFORE WE GIVE IN!

# D LIKE TO SEE OCCUR
## er see settled!

ARTIST: GEORGE WOODBRIDGE     WRITERS: CHARLIE KADAU & JOE RAIOLA

## SLASHER FILM PRODUCERS

## KU KLUX KLAN MEMBERS

Have you ever wondered *why* it rains every time you wash your car? Are you puzzled *why* the warranty on your TV runs out the day before your picture tube blows? The answer is obvious! We are all at the mercy of mysterious, unstated laws that have the power to make the young feel old, the wise look foolish and the strong turn into mush! In other words, we're all subject to

### THE "ON SALE" PRINCIPLE

Over 80% of all "Storewide Sales" take place the week after you've bought something at "Full Price."

### THE CRAMMER'S MAXIM

If you study nine out of ten areas of American History, it's the tenth area that will appear on that final exam.

### CRAMMER'S MAXIM COROLLARY

No matter how long the exam, you will come up with the answers you omitted five minutes after the exam is over.

### THE SERVICE CALL AXIOM

A malfunctioning TV set or appliance needing a service call will work perfectly when the service man arrives.

### THE CORPORATE TRUISM

The job security of a new corporate executive increases at the same rate as his urge to make waves decreases.

### CORPORATE TRUISM COROLLARY

The delegation of job responsibility increases at the same rate as the realization that you're screwing up.

# D LAWS

## SECOND EDITION

**ARTIST: PAUL COKER**
**WRITER: FRANK JACOBS**

### THE GASTRONOMIC LAW

The enjoyment of any food is always in inverse proportion to its "nutritional value."

### THE GIVE-AND-TAKE PRINCIPLE

If a bill and a check are mailed to you from the same city on the same day, the bill will arrive 4 days before the check.

### THE SPORT'S-FAN'S THEOREM

A phone call you have to take always coincides in time and length with the greatest moment of the televised game.

### THE SHOPPER'S LAW

The more you desire a shirt in a store window, the less likely it is they'll have it in your size.

### THE VACATION PRINCIPLE

The more anticipated the trip, the greater the chance you'll get sick the day before you're due to leave.

### THE RESTROOM MAXIM

The more urgent your call to nature, the greater the chance that every stall will either be occupied . . . or out-of-order.

For every inflight meal that you eat without barfing, you get a bonus of 10,000 miles.

For having to use a restroom in disgusting condition, you collect 15,000 bonus miles.

Almost every airline flying today has a "Frequent Traveler Bonus Plan"—a system whereby regular passengers are given points for the miles they fly. Well, the folks here at MAD fly a lot, and often use airplanes to do it. But we don't think passengers should be given bonus points for the miles they fly, we think passengers should be given points for the hassles and aggravations they're forced to put up with! So, while we doubt this will ever get off the ground, here's

# A FREQUENT FLYER BONUS PROGRAM WE'D LIKE TO SEE

**ARTIST: JACK DAVIS**          **WRITER: DICK DE BARTOLO**

For every 10 minutes your flight is d

"Ladies and Gentlemen, this is the Captain. Just wanted to report that everything is fine up here."

For every boring announcement the Captain makes when you're trying to sleep, earn 500 bonus miles.

If "Utah Backroads" (or a similar publication) is the only magazine available, earn 5,000 bonus miles.

For every boring story told to you by the passenger sitting next to you, you are awarded 1,000 bonus miles.

For every one of your bags damaged, you collect 15,000 bonus miles.

is delayed, you collect 1,000 bonus miles.

For the movie being so bad that you walk out on it, earn 50,000 bonus miles.

For being assigned a seat in the smoking section, when you are a non-smoker, earn 25,000 bonus miles.

For being assigned a seat next to a crying baby, earn 5,000 miles. (If you are a non-smoker and get assigned a seat next to a crying baby that smokes, earn 25,000.)

# A MAD LOOK AT SOME NOT-SO-FAMOUS FIRS

## "THE K-MART THANKSGIVING DAY PARADE"

## "SMOKEY THE SNAKE"

## "WYOMING FRIED CHICKEN"

## "THE SAN FRANCISCO MARATHON"

# T ATTEMPTS

ARTIST: AL JAFFEE   WRITER: MIKE SNIDER

## "ABC'S 'WIDE WORLD OF WEATHER'"

## "MINIATURE POLO"

## "PREPARATIONS 'A THROUGH 'G'"

## "OYSTER McNUGGETS"

# JUST ONCE, w

... find a Cop when you need one!

... spill coffee on a Waitress!

... yell at the Boss for being late!

... have a blind date turn out to be the girl of your dreams!

... and have her feel the same way about you!

... think of the perfect put-down the minute you need it, not two days later.

... charge your Doctor for all the time you spent in his waiting room!

... hear some Medical news that's right up your alley!

... make a Repairman lose almost a whole day's work waiting for you!

WRITER: DICK DE BARTOLO    ARTIST: HARRY NORTH, ESQ.

# OULDN'T YOU LIKE TO

... hear some encouraging news from the Government!

... get on the line that moves the fastest!

... cut off a Telephone Operator while she's talking to a friend!

... pass up a cab driver, leaving him standing outside in the rain!

... see a famous Designer wearing something with your name on it!!

... see a Cigar Smoker get deathly ill from the odor of your cologne.

... ignore a Waiter who's in a big hurry. .

... be the person they call to ask what you think of the show that's on the TV!

# IF LIBRARIES SOLD A

# ADVERTISING SPACE

ARTIST: BOB CLARKE    WRITER: WILLIAM GARVIN

# BEAT THE RECESSION WITH THESE HELPFUL MAD PENNY

Buy your perishables before week-end closing time . . . when you can bargain.

Have your kids bring home their Free School Lunch leftovers in Doggie Bags.

If necessary, use alternate means of long-distance communications.

ARTIST: PAUL COKER, JR.

Have your kids design and execute . . . and then hand deliver . . . your family's Christmas Cards.

Eliminate unnecessary Doctor bills. Brush up on "Home Remedies" and take care of your family's minor medical problems by yourself.

Give your family homemade haircuts.

Spray on socks with washable paint.

Grow or produce your own Gourmet food.

# PINCHING HINTS

Encourage your kids to build appropriate Birthday, Wedding or Bar Mitzvah gifts in your home (or their school) workshop.

corks float – keep half of teabag dry – for later use.

Tea

PIN CORKS

Invent clever money-saving methods like this "Teabag-Saver" which keeps half the teabag dry for later use.

WRITER: PAUL PETER PORGES

When in need of professional advice, try consulting experts casually at parties.

For entertainment, return to the simple (and cheap) ways of yore.

Give your kids interest-bearing notes instead of their usual cash allowance.

Save fuel by saving hot water. Bathe "Japanese Family Style."

Drop in on your rich relatives during their mealtimes.

Use any available free transportation.

Keep your food budget low. Tell disgusting stories at the table.

Scan local newspapers and clip those special "Sale" and "Money-off" coupons.

Eliminate expensive reading material! Send for interesting free Government pamphlets.

Start wearing old, patched clothes . . . and pretend you're "with it."

Get together with your neighbors and friends and form "Magazine Pools."

Make your own toilet paper.

# THE MAD BATHROOM COMPANION

## TURD IN A SERIES

By "The Usual Gang of Idiots"

Edited by Nick Meglin & John Ficarra

Introduction by Gilbert Gottfried

# Introduction

**GEE,** *The MAD Bathroom Companion.* Thinking about it leaves me totally flushed (sorry, I couldn't resist). This is a perfect idea because every time I go to the bathroom, I usually take an issue of *MAD* with me. I find the pages come in handy when I run out of toilet paper. Sometimes I'll use two pages at once, for that extra double-quilt comfort. Although, one time, the ink rubbed off, and I walked around all day with a picture of Alfred E. Neuman on my ass.

But enough about my regularity. I want to tell you about when I was a kid. Like many *MAD* readers, I guess my fascination with the magazine started when my mother bought me an issue (now you know why I still read at a first-grade level).

Reading *MAD*, I had many favorites. I was a big fan of Don Martin's work. His cartoons always had strange, made-up noises written in them, like "POIT!" and "FARRAPPGHT!" Then, of course, he would end them with a character being flattened by a piano, a boulder, etc. *MAD* published a few Don Martin books that I had to have, and I soon realized that 75% of the books were POIT! and FARRAPPGHT!

There was "The Lighter Side of…" cartoons by Dave Berg. I always liked Dave Berg's work, not because he was funny or hip. But because he was like that unhip uncle who would put a mop on his head and say, "Hey, look at me. Look at your Uncle Mel! I'm a Beatle, 'yeah, yeah!' I'm a Beatle." Unfortunately, now that I've gown up, I've become the guy with the mop on his head. "Hey, kids, look at me! Look at your Uncle Gilbert! I'm a parrot!" Of course, at that point parents frantically rush over, scoop up their children, and call the cops as I make a hasty retreat.

There were also those tiny cartoons on the margins of the pages. Those amazed me when I thought the artist drew them that tiny. When I found out he drew then normal size and they were shrunk down to tiny, I never got over it.

I always enjoyed "Spy vs. Spy." After a while, though, I did wonder why—in this day and age and with all our advanced technology—the Spies would have to resort to a giant punching glove on a spring for assassination purposes. Since then I have discovered inside information that the glove with a spring is something the CIA has had in development for several years now. They're also working on painting a large bomb like a pretty girl Spy so when you run over and kiss it, she explodes. Once again, *MAD* was ahead of its time.

Then there was the inside back cover of the magazine that you had to fold in to get the joke. Even as a kid I would look at the unfolded picture and think, "Why does that guy's shoulder look like a face and his cigarette look like a car? Still, what Al Jaffee did was always fun, like his "Snappy Answers to Stupid Questions." I always wondered why his characters couldn't just ignore the person or just hit the guy like I do to people when they ask me stupid questions. Or, for that matter, even when they *don't* ask me stupid questions, I still hit them. I just like hitting people. Hey, we all need a hobby.

I have a vague childhood recollection—it may have been in *MAD*, but I'm not positive—that there was a cartoon with a girl in her underwear and a guy saying "Gesundheit!" The gist of it, I guess, was that evidently the man had sneezed so hard he blew the girl's clothes off. (Okay, I know it was just a drawing, but it still got me excited.) To this day, whenever I sneeze, I get turned on.

"Yecch!" was a popular word with *MAD* Magazine as well. The film parodies drawn by artist Mort Drucker would always make use of it, doing things like "Titan-yecch" or "The Yecch of Living Dangerously." Although I will say it was a real thrill when Drucker did a takeoff of *Beverly Hills Cop 2* (I don't remember what the title was, probably "Beverly Hills Cop Yecch") and he drew a picture of me as the accountant. My life had come full circle—I could finally wipe my ass with my own face. It's a neat trick, you should try it some time.

But enough about me, enjoy the book. With this new volume of the *MAD Bathroom Companion*, everyone can take *MAD* where it really belongs—in the toilet.

**—Gilbert Gottfried**

Gilbert Gottfried appears in three articles in this book. Find them!

Why did the former child
TV star cross the road?
*To escape police chasing him for either
shoplifting, drug trafficking, or
soliciting a transsexual prostitute!*

Why did the euthanasia
advocate cross the road?
*To pull the plug on a terminally
comatose patient so he could
get to "the other side."*

What's the difference
between euthanasia and
watching the Buffalo
Bills in the Super Bowl?
*Euthanasia is painless!*

How many former child TV stars
does it take to change a lightbulb?
*Former child TV stars can't afford a
lightbulb because their parents and
managers have squandered their money!*

What's the difference between
euthanasia advocates
and David Duke supporters?
*Euthanasia advocates have
no use for the braindead!*

How many euthanasia advocates does
it take to change a lightbulb?
*One. But he changes it before
it burns out, so the lightbulb
can "go with dignity."*

# STS ON OLD JOKES

ARTIST: MORT DRUCKER          WRITER: DENNIS SNEE

There seems to be a new "Religion" currently attracting great masses of followers across our land. Many sheep are straying from the folds of Protestantism, Catholicism and Judaism to become devotees of this movement called "Dufferism" At least,

# A Psalm For A S

ARTIST: PAUL COKER, JR.

*The Pro is my Shepherd;*
*I shall not Slice.*

*He maketh me to Drive Straight*
*down Green Fairways;*

*He leadeth me Safely*
*across Still Water-Hazards;*

*He restoreth my Approach Shots.*

*He leadeth me in the Paths of*
*Accuracy for my Game's Sake.*

*Yea, though I chip through the Roughs*
*in the shadows of Sand Traps,*
*I will fear no Bogies.*

that is how it must appear to all the discouraged Ministers, Priests and Rabbis who look out over their congregations on Sabbath mornings and see so many of the men missing. And so, until these Prodigal Sons return, MAD snidely offers them:

# abbath Morning

WRITER: WILLIAM GARVIN

*For his Advice is with me;*

*His Putter and Irons, they comfort me.*

*He prepareth a Strategy for me in the presence of mine Opponents;*

*He anointeth my head with Confidence: The Cup will not be runneth over!*

*Surely Birdies and Eagles shall follow me all the Rounds of my Life,*

*And I will score in the Low Eighties—*

*Forever!*

Just as there are two sides to every war, so are there two sides to every Comic Strip. Ever since Snoopy (of "Peanuts") started telling us about his run-ins with The Red Baron, we've wondered about The Red Baron's version of this historic struggle. Well, now the story can be told! Recently,

# Adventures Of

## OR "Happiness Ist Ein

ARTIST: JACK RICKARD

MAD's Research Staff returned from Europe with several installments of a German Comic Strip he uncovered while perusing early 1918 copies of the Hamburg Post-Dispatch. And so, for the first time in the United States, here is the other side of the story . . . mainly the hitherto unpublished . . .

# The Red Baron

## Kleine Kaput Beagle"

WRITERS: FRANK JACOBS & BOB MUCCIO

# ONE DAY ON THE BRIDGE

# A PORTFOLIO OF

HOOT OWL

rabbit

KAN**G**a**ROO**

ORM

B**A**T

**S**ion

M**●**USE

C**O**W

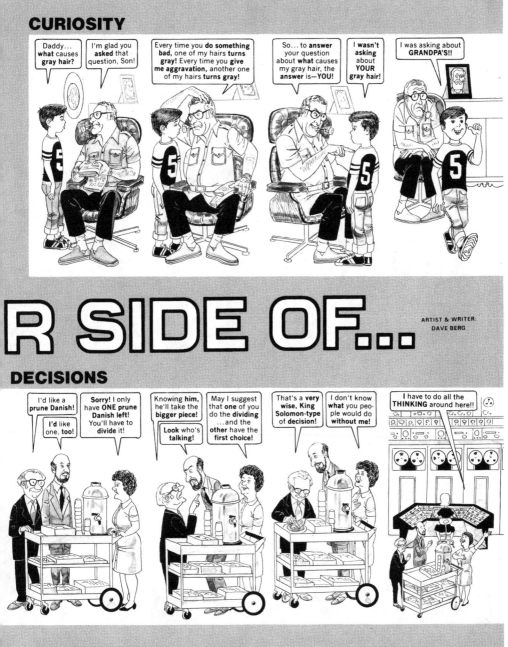

# A MAD LOOK AT

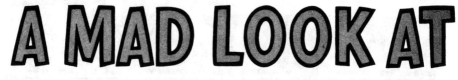

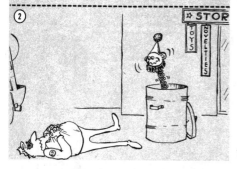

# GARBAGEMEN

ARTIST & WRITER: SERGIO ARAGONES

## WISE GUIDE DEPT.

**MAD has come up with a device to shake up those indifferent and incompetent people you too often find yourselves at the mercy of. It's called a "Rattler". A Rattler is not something you use on the Innocent, but rather as a Defensive Weapon on people who intimidate you: the surly cab driver, the wise-guy waiter, the nasty sales clerk . . . anyone who has developed an inverted snobbery about his work and views anyone less expert as an inferior. If you run into such a person, why not try out some of these . . .**

# MAD R

## ...FOR SHAKING UP **WAITERS AND WAITRESSES**

No . . . I'd only like **HALF** a table! I'm not very **hungry!**

I'd like an **empty plate!** I'm on a **very strict diet!**

How about sitting down and **joining** me? Then we can **split the check,** and I won't leave a **tip!**

Can you bring me some **extra silverware!** I have the **same set** at home, and I'm **missing** a few pieces!

I'll have the **same** thing that I ordered yesterday! I **didn't TOUCH** it yesterday!

I'll have the **steak dinner** . . . with no potatoes . . . no vegetables . . . and no **meat!**

The menu looks good! I'll eat **THAT!**

I'm very **intimidated** by **Waiters!** So may I **start tipping** you **NOW?**

Miss, would you be **offended** if I **sent out** for some **food?**

My compliments to the **Chef** . . . for having the **nerve** to pass **this** stuff off as **food!**

Hey, this food isn't **half bad** . . . it's **ALL bad!**

Waiter, give me a **very small check!** I'm in a **hurry!**

## ...FOR SHAKING UP **BARBERS**

I **know** it's my turn, but I just can't stop reading these **three-year-old magazines!**

Before you touch my hair, can you show me **proof** that you're **Italian?**

I'd like it **longer** in the **back,** . . . and **thicker** on **top,** please!

**Never mind** the haircut! Just tell me your idictic **opinions!**

Tell me, do you **shave legs?**

## ...FOR SHAKING UP **TELEPHONE OPERATORS**

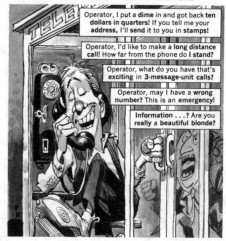

Operator, I put a **dime** in and got back **ten dollars in quarters!** If you tell me your **address,** I'll send it to you in **stamps!**

Operator, I'd like to make a **long distance call!** How far from the phone do **I stand?**

Operator, what do you have that's **exciting** in **3-message-unit calls?**

Operator, may I have a **wrong number!** This is an **emergency!**

**Information** . . .? Are you **really a beautiful blonde?**

# ATTLER S

ARTIST: JACK DAVIS    WRITER: LARRY GORE

### ...FOR SHAKING UP **SALES HELP**

Does this come with **two pair of pants?** The **TIE**, I mean!

Do you have anything that's marked down to "**FREE**"?

I'd like to see something **terribly overpriced!**

I'd like to get this **exact same suit** . . . but in a **completely different style!**

I need a **complete new wardrobe!** Can you recommend a **good store?**

Do you have something **much too large** for me! **I love alterations!**

How soon can I **return** this?

May I **charge** this . . . to **YOU?**

### ...FOR SHAKING UP **ELEVATOR OPERATORS**

To the **Penthouse**, driver . . . and **don't stop** for any lights!

Do you get **extra pay** for flying **dangerous missions?**

How could they send a **kid** up in a crate like **this?**

**Twice** around the **building**, driver! We're in **love!**

Would the **4th floor** take you out of your way?

Here's a **buck!** Take me to **another building!**

Uh . . . where's the **Men's Room** in this car? I think I'm going to be **sick** . . .

### ...FOR SHAKING UP **CAB DRIVERS**

I'm from **out of town!** How about a **tour** of your **famous slums?**

Driver, drop me off at the **nearest cab!** I'm in a **hurry!**

Is it true that in this State, **tipping** is illegal?

That's the **second** pedestrian you **MISSED!** Are you **sure** you haven't been **DRINKING?**

Stop the cab! That's **not your picture!**

**Drive slowly!** I'm looking for a **date!**

Would you mind turning off the meter? The **ticking** gives me a **headache!**

Where's the **Men's Room** in this cab? I think I'm going to be **sick** . . .

# You Know You're REA

### You Know You're REALLY A BORE When ...

... you're at the beach, and your date
buries himself in the sand ... completely.

### You Know You're REALLY A BORE When ...

... a letter you wrote home to your Mother is returned
unopened with the notation: "Nobody here by that name!"
... and the notation is in your Mother's handwriting.

### You Know You're REALLY A BORE When ...

... obscene phone-callers hang up on *you*.

### You Know You're REALLY A BORE When ...

... you're in Confession, and your
Priest interrupts you to ask: "What's a
3-letter word for a European Blackbird?"

### You Know You're REALLY A BORE When ...

... people at parties always seem
to mistake you for a hypnotist.

### You Know You're REALLY A BORE When ...

... even the Avon Lady won't call on you.

### You Know You're REALLY A BORE When ...

... your psychiatrist has "Let's Make A
Deal" on his TV set during your sessions.

### You Know You're REALLY A BORE When ...

... you overhear the F.B.I. man who's
tapping your phone humming to himself.

# LLY A BORE When...

ARTIST:
PAUL COKER, JR.

WRITER:
STAN HART

### You Know You're REALLY A BORE When ...

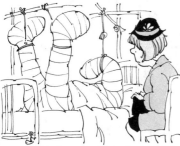

... your friend cuts your visit short by saying, "I've got a million things to do!" ... and he's in traction.

### You Know You're REALLY A BORE When ...

... your dentist makes you keep the cotton swabs in your mouth until you're out of his office.

### You Know You're REALLY A BORE When ...

... your guests *ask* to see your home movies.

### You Know You're REALLY A BORE When ...

... your teacher thanks you for answering a question before you finish answering it.

### You Know You're REALLY A BORE When ...

... the barber puts a hot towel over your face, and you're only getting a haircut.

### You Know You're REALLY A BORE When ...

... a girl breaks a date with you in order to go to a Montreal Expos-San Diego Padres double-header.

### You Know You're REALLY A BORE When ...

... the little old lady you've helped half-way across the street runs the rest of the way herself.

### You Know You're REALLY A BORE When ...

... your whole life suddenly flashes before your eyes, and it doesn't even hold your interest.

# A QUICK STROLL

It doesn't take a genius to see that our cities are in big trouble these days. Mass Transit is in a shambles, streets are caving in around us, and employee productivity is down. Take a look at this typical city to see what we.mean...

Now for the really bad news. When you turn this page, you're going to see some of the dumbest ideas, proposals and solutions ever conceived in an article called

# MAD'S SUGGESTIONS FOR HOW OUR CITIES CAN SOLVE THEIR PROBLEMS
## (While Clearing A Little Extra Cash On The Side!)

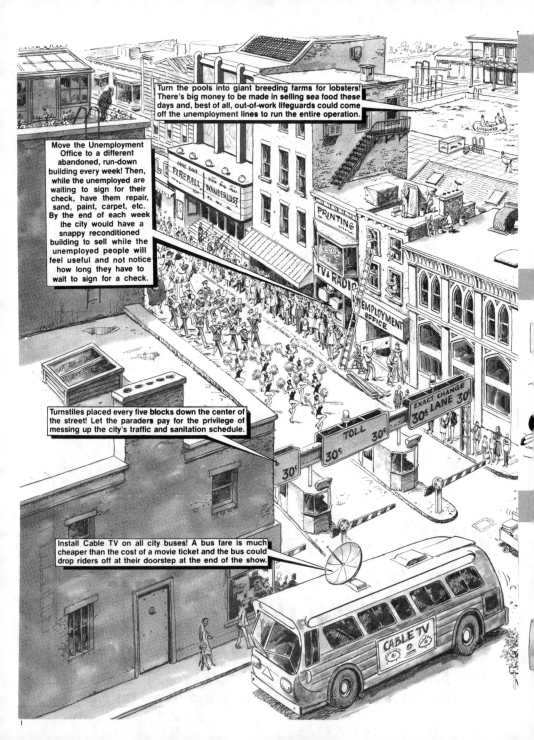

# A MAD LOOK AT...
# OBEDIENCE TRA

Since an unruly dog can be a pest, and a well-trained dog can be a wonderful companion, the "Obedience School For Dogs" has become very popular lately. However, the same can be said for kids! Since an unruly child can be a pest, and a well-trained child can be a joy...

# WHY NOT "OBEDIENCE SCHO

## AND WHY NOT "OBEDIENCE SCHOOLS FOR HUSBANDS"?

# INING

ARTIST & WRITER: DEAN NORMAN

# OLS FOR KIDS"?

Wouldn't it be great if we could train kids to obey a few simple commands, such as ...

## AND WHY NOT "OBEDIENCE SCHOOLS FOR WIVES"?!?

DEAN

How do you advertise a re-release of something like . . . say . . . "Snow White and the Seven Dwarfs" or "Born Free" to modern movie audiences? The answer, my friends, is written in these ads . . . the answer is written in these ads. So follow their example, and stretch the truth, like we've done with these

# VIE REVIVALS

WRITER: FRANK JACOBS

**He was A MAN DRIVEN MAD by a DESPERATE LONGING**

*To touch—*
*To fondle —*
*To possess*

**THE FORBIDDEN FLESH THAT TORMENTED HIS DESIRE!**

**AHAB—**

A Man of the World Consumed by Waves of Passion! He had All He Desired—EXCEPT The One He Desired Most of All!

**MOBY—**

A Shimmering Creature of Abnormal Appetites Whose Soft, Curved, White, Tantalizing Body was TOO WILD Ever to be Possessed!

## A RAW, NAKED STORY— PULSATING WITH PASSION!

# MOBY DICK

"Goes to great depths . . . a whale of a climax!"—De Generate, STAR

# YOUR MAD HOROSCOPE

TODAY'S BIRTHDAY:

Your birthday was last month, schmuck! Ask your mother for the *full* story!

## ARIES
### March 21—April 19

Dramatic developments! Some strong astrological forces clash—leaving your Moon Over Miami. Don't worry! This is not a Blue Moon, so you will bask in a magnificent Moonglow as Moonlight Becomes You. If any part of this horoscope confuses you, consult one of your parents or a friendly cocktail-hour piano player.

## TAURUS
### April 20—May 20

Romantic entanglements can pose some problems so lay off the S&M for awhile. Focus on career matters, making sure your finger is not in front of the lens. The PM is an excellent time for love, so make sure you have an extra $50 tucked in your wallet should the opportunity arise. (Put the rest of your cash in your shoe.)

## GEMINI
### May 21—June 21

The Big Dipper and the Little Dipper are jointly sending you messages. They're doing this to cut down on postage and handling charges which, as you know, are astronomical. The stars warn you that things at home are not what they appear. Beware especially of a Colonial-style sofa, a five speed blender or a bearded child.

## MOON CHILDREN
### June 22—July 22

A funny day. A washed-up comic in the Catskills is planning a big comeback at your expense. His words carry great weight, as does your blind date this evening. A small change in personnel where you work greatly improves conditions for everyone involved. In other words, you're getting the ax sometime this morning.

## LEO
### July 23—August 22

Your stars point to a new cycle and it's a beauty!—a bright red 10-speeder! Unfortunately, one of the foot pedals is missing, as are the screws for the hand brakes. Until these parts are ordered, it's back to riding the bus. Take heart! Make the most of your current success. Incredible as it may seem, you've peaked.

## VIRGO
### August 23—September 22

A troubling day. A piece of poultry is not as dead as you think, and is just waiting for you to open that refrigerator door. A business deal may take you out of town, but only a blind idiot would take you out to dinner! You refuse to think about anything but "the present". Buy him a shirt, and get it over with!

## LIBRA
### September 23—October 23

Financial strains preoccupy you, but it's the neglected physical strain that could leave you with a hideous limp. Thoroughly test a new love before falling for him or her head-over-heels. (Use either a True-or-False or Multiple Choice format. Essay questions never work right and will take you much longer to grade.)

## SCORPIO
### October 24—November 21

As you enter a new cycle, the stars are promising you an intense romance with a Leo. Normally, you would be compatable. In this case, however, the stars are referring to Leo Flogs—the town drunk and a suspected carrier of malaria and mail. Your idea spells profit. What is unknown is how do you spell relief?

## SAGITTARIUS
### November 22—December 21

Your moon is in the House of Representatives, where undercover FBI men are secretly filming its acceptance of a bribe. You have private wishes and opinions that are best left unvoiced as they are disgusting and depraved. A surprise promotion comes when a co-worker takes a leave of absence to give birth to your child.

## CAPRICORN
### December 22—January 19

Personal sacrifices for a child will bring you instant fame and financial gains. Then again, so probably would your sacrificing *of* a child! Appealing offers are not what they seem, so be prepared for a letdown when a current love finally lets you put your hand in her blouse. A horrible disease arises at school.

## AQUARIUS
### January 20—February 18

Some astral forces are playing tug-of-war with you now, so next time you buy a shirt, be sure to get a longer sleeve length. Work while others play, and you will grab the brass ring. You can either wear it on your pinky, or sell it for scrap. Cut through red tape. However, please do not fold, spindle or mutilate it.

## PISCES
### February 19—March 20

An indecisive attitude on the part of someone you rely on for advice could get you into real trouble. Then again, it may not. Work keeps you from family affairs and family affairs keep you from work. Just what exactly you do all day remains one of life's great unsolved mysteries.

WRITER: JOHN FICARRA

It always happens! You plot and you plan and you work to carve out a perfect little life for yourself. But no matter how carefully you look before you leap, and save

# Don't You Feel Li

**DON'T YOU FEEL LIKE A SCHMUCK...**
...preparing for winter with the best snow tires money can buy...     ...and winding up stuck behind a guy who didn't!

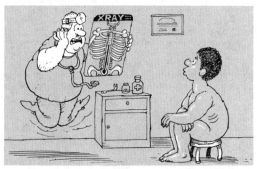

**DON'T YOU FEEL LIKE A SCHMUCK...**
...eating fish to cut down on cholesterol...     ...and accumulating enough mercury in your system to kill a whale!

**DON'T YOU FEEL LIKE A SCHMUCK...**
...putting on an expensive exotic perfume...     ...and the person you're spending the evening with smells like a goat!

for a rainy day, some event—completely beyond your control—brings the whole scheme tumbling down. And as you sit there in the rubble and ruin of your best-laid plans—

# ke A Schmuck?!

ARTIST & WRITER: AL JAFFEE

**DON'T YOU FEEL LIKE A SCHMUCK...**
... obeying your County's anti-pollution laws ...

... when your water comes from another County with no such laws!

**DON'T YOU FEEL LIKE A SCHMUCK...**
... getting to the theater early to get a good seat ...

... and at the last minute, an eight-foot giant picks the only empty seat left ... the one directly in front of you!

**DON'T YOU FEEL LIKE A SCHMUCK...**
... doing all you can do to avoid catching a cold ...

... and some careless, sick slob coughs right in your face!

**DON'T YOU FEEL LIKE A SCHMUCK...**
... paying a fortune to fly in order to save time ...   ... and spending the time you save in an airport traffic jam!

**DON'T YOU FEEL LIKE A SCHMUCK...**
... spending months, training your dog to
"go" in one special out-of-the-way spot ...   ... while your neighbor lets his dog loose to "go" wherever it pleases!

**DON'T YOU FEEL LIKE A SCHMUCK...**
... taking perfect care of your teeth for thirty-three years ...   ... and blowing it all on one stupid barroom argument!

**DON'T YOU FEEL LIKE A SCHMUCK...**
... compressing your garbage into neat little packs ...   ... and the neighbors' loose stuff ends up all over your lawn!

**DON'T YOU FEEL LIKE A SCHMUCK...**
...making sure you're insured to the hilt...

...and your *un*insured Mother-in-Law's 14-month illness wipes you out!

**DON'T YOU FEEL LIKE A SCHMUCK...**
...coaching, advising and helping your fellow worker for years, because he's sending his son through college...

...and the kid finally graduates...right into your job!

**DON'T YOU FEEL LIKE A SCHMUCK...**
...moving to the country to escape the sounds of the city...

...without first checking out the sounds of the country!

**DON'T YOU FEEL LIKE A SCHMUCK...**
...buying a new garment with a special washing instruction label sewn right into the lining...

...and the first moron who launders it completely ignores the label!

# LOOK SLIM AND T
# DIET OR STRENUC

MINGLE WITH PEOPLE THAT ARE FATTER THAN YOU ARE

WEAR CLOTHES THAT ARE TWO SIZES TOO BIG

CAREFULLY CHOOSE EMPLOYMENT THAT WILL HIDE YOUR GIRTH

USE CORNERS AND ENTRANCES TO REDUCE YOUR APPEARANCE

PROPER HAIR AND BEARD STYLE CAN GIVE YOUR FACE THAT LEAN AND HUNGRY LOOK

# RIM WITHOUT

# US EXERCISE

ARTIST AND WRITER: PAUL PETER PORGES

TRY TO EMPHASIZE YOUR OUTSTANDING FEATURES

ALWAYS SELECT OVERSTUFFED FURNITURE TO SIT IN

MAKE CLEVER USE OF HOUSE PLANTS TO YOUR ADVANTAGE

WEAR DARK CLOTHING...AND THEN TRY TO STAND AGAINST DARK SHADOWY BACKGROUNDS

ALWAYS DATE PEOPLE THAT ARE EVEN FATTER THAN YOU

One of the most popular fashion phenomena among young people these days is the T-shirt with a message. You've seen them (and probably wear them). They've got messages like "Property of Alcatraz," "Kiss Me, I'm Italian," "My Folks Visited

# T-SHIRTS WITH MESSA

Las Vegas And All I Got Was This Lousy T-Shirt," and so on. Well, we think that instead of sporting clever but rather impersonal machine-made comments, people should reveal their true thoughts about themselves and their shirts with these

# AGES WE'D LIKE TO SEE

ARTIST: GEORGE WOODBRIDGE          WRITER: LARRY SIEGEL

# THINKING

**MESSY EATERS**

WRITER: PAUL PETER PORGES

**SLOBBERING AUNTS**

**PARK MASHERS**

# ONE EVENING AT HOME

The Mobile Home craze is sweeping the world. But the trouble is, Mobile Homes

# CUSTOMIZED M

## ...THAT REFLECT WHERE

ARTIST & WRITER:

GREECE

ANY CITY IN THE U.S.A.

ALASKA

GEORGIA

SAUDI ARABIA

all look pretty much alike. They lack ethnic character. So why not design...

# MOBILE HOMES
## THEIR OWNERS ARE FROM

PAUL COKER, JR.

WESTERN U.S.A.

WESTERN OZ

THE VATICAN

JAPAN

INDIA

NEVADA

Recently, someone published a book called "Children's Letters To God."
It was so popular, another book was published called "More Children's
Letters To God." Now, that one is so popular, by the time you read this

# Answers To Children'

WRITERS: DICK DeBARTOLO & DONALD K. EPSTEIN

Dear Bruce,
I am sorry it rained last Sunday
when you were supposed to have
your Boy Scout Hike, but I
cannot send you a copy of my
"Guaranteed Long-Range Forecast"
to avoid disappointments like
that in the future.
Faithfully yours,

Dear Lisa,
Your forthcoming trip to California
sounds very exciting. I would love
to see you, too, but TWA does not
stop here on the way to Los Angeles.
Fondly,

Dear Tommy,
The reason you cannot find me
in the telephone book is that
my number is unlisted.
Best wishes,

Dear Mary,
My notes about your
behavior are written
in the Big Book in
indelible ink. But
thank you anyway for
the nice eraser.
Love,

Dear Beth,
I am sorry, but it is
not up to me to make
bacon "kosher."
Sincerely,

Dear Laurie,
Yes, I am watching you all
the time. But that is no
excuse for not taking a bath.
Love,

Dear Jerry,
I do spend a lot of time in
Brooklyn, but that was not
Me you saw on the IND subway
last Saturday afternoon.
Love,

Dear Sharon,
I was very pleased to learn
that you think of your good
deeds as "deposits in the
Bank of Life." However, I
do not have the facilities
for sending you a regular
monthly statement.
Best regards,

article, they'll probably publish one called "Still More Children's Letters To God." Well, it seems to us that there's an awful lot of one-way letter-writing going on, so MAD remedies the situation with

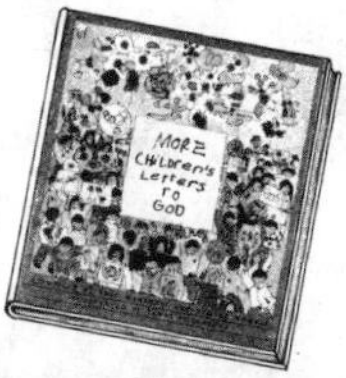
MORE Children's Letters To GOD

# s Letters–From GOD

PHOTO BY D.P.I.

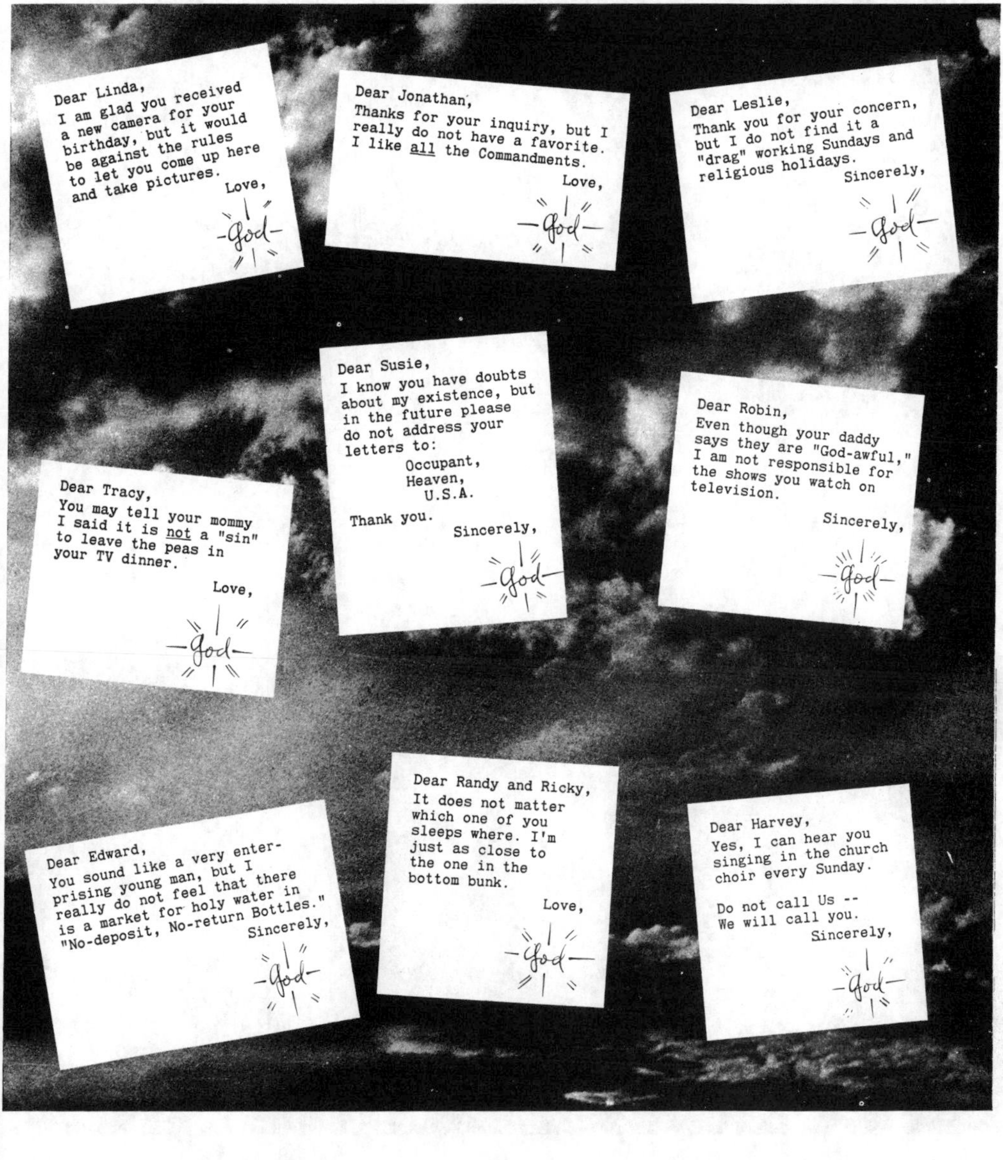
Dear Linda,
I am glad you received a new camera for your birthday, but it would be against the rules to let you come up here and take pictures.
Love,
God
Dear Jonathan,
Thanks for your inquiry, but I really do not have a favorite. I like all the Commandments.
Love,
God
Dear Leslie,
Thank you for your concern, but I do not find it a "drag" working Sundays and religious holidays.
Sincerely,
God
Dear Susie,
I know you have doubts about my existence, but in the future please do not address your letters to:
Occupant,
Heaven,
U.S.A.
Thank you.
Sincerely,
God
Dear Robin,
Even though your daddy says they are "God-awful," I am not responsible for the shows you watch on television.
Sincerely,
God
Dear Tracy,
You may tell your mommy I said it is not a "sin" to leave the peas in your TV dinner.
Love,
God
Dear Edward,
You sound like a very enterprising young man, but I really do not feel that there is a market for holy water in "No-deposit, No-return Bottles."
Sincerely,
God
Dear Randy and Ricky,
It does not matter which one of you sleeps where. I'm just as close to the one in the bottom bunk.
Love,
God
Dear Harvey,
Yes, I can hear you singing in the church choir every Sunday.
Do not call Us --
We will call you.
Sincerely,
God

# MAD SALUTES
## THE OUTPUT OF
# AMERICAN INDUSTRY

CONCEIVED BY MAX BRANDEL

Pro Football is slipping in popularity because the guys in charge have decided to cut down on the violence. They've even made it illegal to dance after creaming an opponent. And our other violent sport, Hockey, is also cleaning up its act. It's cutting down on fighting, and a player can be suspended just for conking somebody with his stick. So fans have been looking elsewhere for their sports entertainment, and they are turning in increasing numbers to that old standby, Wrestling...which is our excuse for presenting another of our ridiculous Primers.

# THE MAD WRESTLING PRIMER

ARTIST: JACK DAVIS    WRITER: LOU SILVERSTONE

## Chapter One

See the people standing on line.
It is a long, long, long line.
There are Doctors and Lawyers on line.
There are Artists and Writers on line.
There are Teachers and Brokers on line.
They are waiting to buy tickets to a Wrestling Match.
Do they enjoy Wrestling because they like violence and bloodshed?
No...they claim they like to watch Wrestling for the laughs.
They also claim they like to read "Playboy" for the interviews.

## Chapter Two

See the man.
He weighs over three hundred pounds.
He looks like he escaped from the zoo.
When he enters the ring, he hits the Referee,
He curses the Announcer,
He spits at the Crowd.
Is this ugly slob a Wrestler?
No, he is only a Manager...
If he is only a Manager...
Can you imagine what his Wrestler is like?

## Chapter Three

## Chapter Four

## Chapter Five

See the man in the striped shirt.
He is the Referee.
His job is to control the Wrestlers,
And to see that they obey the rules.
The Referee weighs 97 pounds.
Each Wrestler weighs over 250 pounds.
How do they expect a 97 pound man
To control over 500 pounds of angry Wrestlers?
They don't.
It wouldn't be any fun if he could.
Which is why Wrestling is such a popular sport.

See the terrifying man.
He is a Wrestler.
He is "The Wild Man From Borneo."
He bites the ropes.
He bites the microphone.
He bites the Referee.
What does he do to his opponent?
Don't ask.
His Manager claims he found him in the jungles of Borneo.
He really found him working in a "7-11 Store" on Staten Island.
Why do they call him "The Wild Man From Borneo"?
Would you pay $12 to see "The Grocery Bagger From Staten Island"?

See the Wrestlers.
The one on the left is an American Indian.
His name is "Chief Bloody Scalp."
His favorite hold is "The Tomahawk Decapitator."
Next to him is "Captain U.S."
His favorite hold is "The Red, White & Blue Eyeball-Gouger."
Next to him is "The Polish Assassin."
His favorite hold is "The Warsaw Light Bulb Twister."

Now see the last Wrestler on the right.
He doesn't have a fancy name.
He doesn't have a flashy costume.
He doesn't even have a gimmicky hold.
He's just an expert in Scientific Wrestling.
This guy is never going to make it
As a Professional Wrestler.
Even if he was the National Amateur Champion.

## Chapter Six

See the Beauty Parlor.
This is where Ladies go to have their hair done.
They have it bleached and styled and set.
What is that huge man doing in the Beauty Parlor?
He is a Wrestler.
He is having his hair bleached and styled and set.
Isn't that a sissy thing to do…
Having his hair bleached and styled and set
In a Beauty Parlor?
Sure…!
But YOU tell him!

## Chapter Seven

See the Wrestlers holding up their belts.
Those are Championship Belts.
Does that mean they are all Champions.
Absolutely.
One is the AWA Champ; one is the SWA Champ;
One is the SWT Champ; one is the WC Champ;
One is the WWT Champ and one is the WWA Champ.
Wrestling is the only sport
Where there are more Champions than Challengers.

## Chapter Eight

See the Wrestlers on TV
They look like two fat slobs.
But the Announcer says they're in great shape.
They aren't doing anything but falling on top of each other.
But the Announcer makes their match sound like World War III.
Is there something wrong with the Announcer's eyes?
No…he can see very well.
He can see himself on the Unemployment Line
If he tells it like it is.

## Chapter Nine

See the angry Wrestling Fans.
They take their Wrestling very seriously.
They believe that everything that happens
In the Wrestling Ring is for real.
See them beating up on a Spectator.
Punch, punch, kick, kick.
Why are they beating up on this poor man?
Because he said that Wrestling is a phony.
And this makes Wrestling Fans very angry.
P.T. Barnum would have loved Wrestling.
Because he said "There's a sucker born every minute."
Too bad the angry Wrestling Fans can't see
That the Spectator they're beating up on
Is the only one who's really getting hurt in the Arena tonight.

Okay, gang, here we go again with another visit behind the scenes of an American institution

# A MAD PEEK BEHIND

# THE SCENES AT A SHOPPING CENTER

ARTIST: BOB CLARKE    WRITER: STAN HART

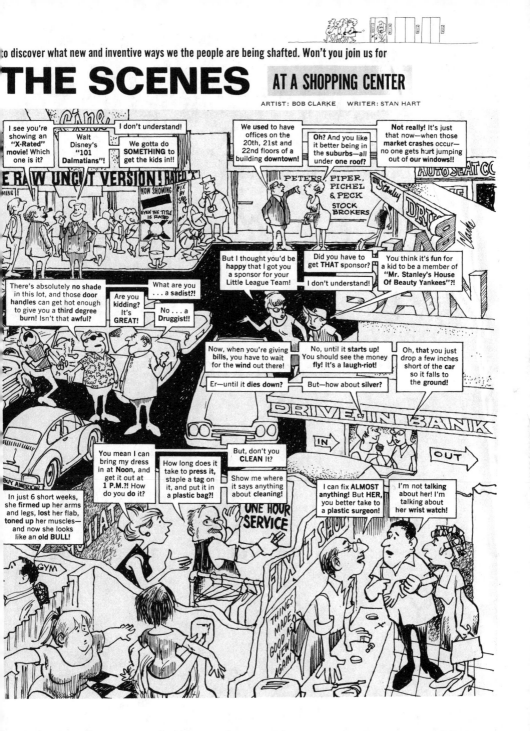

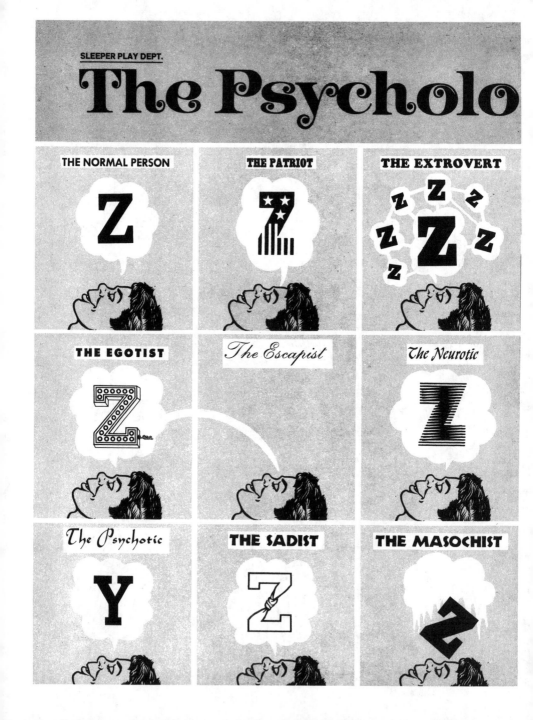

# gy Of Snoring

WRITER: FRANK JACOBS

## THE INTROVERT

## The Non-Conformist

## THE INHIBITED

## the mystic

## The Amnesiac

## THE ALCOHOLIC

## The Inferiority Complex

## The Persecution Complex

## The Insomniac

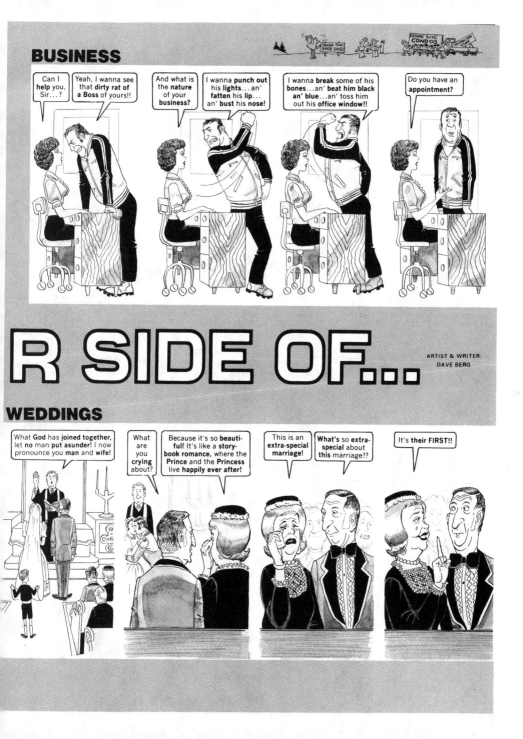

# At The Academy Of Electric Fan Repair

# INSTANT TV REPL

KARPOV'S MOVE OF KNIGHT'S PAWN FROM Q-6 TO Q-7

DOUBLE FOUL COMMITTED DURING N.I.T. TOURNAMENT

UMPIRE'S CHECK OF WEATHER DURING RAIN DELAY

EXCITED CONTESTANT'S LEAP ON "THE PRICE IS RIGHT"

# AYS We Would Rather Not Have to See

ARTIST AND WRITER: PAUL PETER PORGES

FOURTH FALSE START MADE AT THE WANAMAKER MILE

MATING DANCE PERFORMED BY OSTRICHES ON "NOVA"

SPEARING PENALTY INCURRED AT STANLEY CUP PLAYOFF

DESIGNATED HITTER WAITING IN ON-DECK CIRCLE

"Catch 22" was a best-selling book that later was made into a successful movie. In case you didn't read the book or see the movie, it was about an Air Force bombardier who doesn't want to fly any more dangerous missions. Since there's an Air Force regulation which states that if you're insane, you can't fly, our

# MAD'S REAL LIF

You've had season tickets to an NFL team for years, and they always lose, but you're afraid of giving up those season tickets because the team might start to win, so you keep on going to the crummy games year after year . . .

*. . . but since the stadium is sold out year after year, the owner doesn't have to do anything to improve the team!*

You cannot date unless the guy comes to the house so your Father can meet him...

*. . . but if he ever meets your date he'll never let you go out with him!*

The only way a dentist can find hidden cavities is if he X-rays your teeth . . .

The Law says that when you reach the age of 16, you can get your driver's license . . .

*. . . but if you drive the family car, his insurance rates will triple, so your Old Man says, "Forget it—until you're 25!" .*

Your parents, the government and nutrition experts tell you that you're ruining your health by eating junk food . . .

hero tells his shrink that he's crazy and therefore, according to regulations, he doesn't have to fly. But there's a catch — Catch-22 — which states that if you don't want to fly dangerous missions, it proves you're sane — and therefore you have to keep flying! Ridiculous, huh? Well, how about this second collection of

# E "CATCH 22'S"

ARTIST: PAUL COKER
WRITER: LOU SILVERSTONE

If you can only get your very own pad, you'll finally be free to do whatever you want without having to ask your parents' permission . . .

. . . but you'll be so busy doing the things your parents did for you, like cooking and cleaning and laundry, etc., that you won't have time to do whatever it was you wanted to do!

. . . but what you can get from X-rays is a helluva lot worse than a cavity!

If you don't give the school bully your lunch money, he'll kill you . . .

. . . but if you do give him your lunch money, you're gonna starve to death!

. . . but if you give up junk food, your health will be totalled by starvation, because that's the only food you like!

If you don't study for exams, you'll flunk and have to spend another year in school—which is unthinkable . . .

. . . but if you do study and graduate, then you'll have to go out and find a job—which is even more unthinkable!

STRIP TEASE DEPT.

In past issues, MAD has presented All-Inclusive, Do-It-Yourself versions of Newspaper Stories, Songs, Comedy Routines, etc. Now, for all you "Peanuts" fans who have fun reading the strip, here is your chance to have fun writing it. (Hey, Charlie Schulz! If you want to take a vacation, feel free to take advantage of this clever article!) Simply fill in the numbered balloons from the corresponding numbered lists, and you'll be creating...

# MAD'S ALL-INCLUSIVE DO-IT-YOURSELF PEANUTS COMIC STRIP

ARTIST: JACK RICKARD    WRITER: FRANK JACOBS

### 1

YOU'RE A **BORN LOSER** !

YOUR **HEAD** COULD DOUBLE AS A **SOFTBALL!**

EVERYONE **ABUSES** YOU!

YOU GIVE **LIVING** A **BAD NAME!**

YOU'VE GOT A **PIN-CUSHION** FOR A **BRAIN!**

YOU'RE THE **JOKE** OF THE **NEIGHBORHOOD!**

### 5

IN **YOUR** HONOR !

TO PAY **TRIBUTE** TO YOUR **LEADERSHIP!**

ON **YOUR** BIRTHDAY!

SO THE **GANG** CAN SHOW YOU HOW WE **FEEL!**

TO KICK OFF "**CELEBRATE CHARLIE BROWN WEEK**"!

YOU'LL **REMEMBER** THE **REST** OF YOUR **LIFE!**

Recently, we asked one of our idiot artists to do a drawing of a School Prom. Unfortunately, he didn't do a very good

# HOW MANY MISTAKES CAN

job. In fact, he made a lot of mistakes...:20 in all. And now, it's up to you to find them. So c'mon! Let's see...

# YOU FIND IN THIS PICTURE?

## ANSWERS

1. The teachers are not making asses of themselves on the dance floor.

2. Collectively, there is less than $20,000 worth of orthodontia in this room.

3. The Varsity Football jock is carrying on an intelligent conversation.

4. This guy married his high-school sweetheart *before* she got pregnant.

5. The guy bragging about the number of girls he's gone to bed with is telling the truth.

6. The teenager is having a tough time finding a drug connection.

7. The two girls who discovered that they're wearing the same dress are still having a good time.

8. The Drama Major is not talking only about herself.

9. The guy's mustache took him less then nine months to grow.

10. This guy respects this girl for her mind.

11. The guy patting his friend on the back did not stick a "Kick Me!" sign there.

12. The guy who invited the girl home to hear his stereo really wants her to hear his stereo.

13. Students are refusing to buy the answers to the upcoming finals.

14. This guy realizes that he's too drunk to drive.

15. The Photographer is not taking a picture while the couple blinks.

16. The student wearing sneakers with his tuxedo feels out of place.

17. The girl wearing the "D" cup bra actually *needs* a "D" cup bra.

18. The students have tied their ties without help from their fathers.

19. The teenager pretending to be drunk is actually drunk.

20. There are no food-fights going on at the buffet table.

ARTIST: ANGELO TORRES

WRITER: CHRIS HART

# AT BIRDS

ARTIST & WRITER: SERGIO ARAGONES

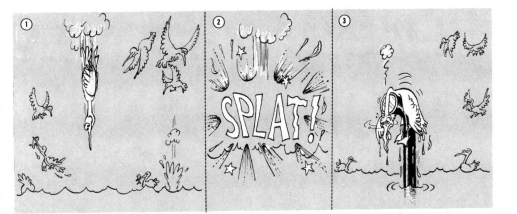

# HAS ANYBODY EV[

A DUNCE CAP  OR A BURGLAR WEARING A "LONE RANGER" MASK

OR A NEWSBOY YELLING "EXTRA! READ ALL ABOUT IT!"  OR A MAGICIAN 1

TIED TO THE END OF A STICK  OR AN INDIAN THAT EVER SAID "HOW!" OR "

OR A LADY FLIRTING WITH A MAN BY DROPPING HER HANDKERCHIEF  OR A

IN A DOOR  OR TWO DRUNKS STAGGERING UP THE STREET SINGING "SWE

OR A BILLY GOAT EATING A TIN CAN  OR THE "LIFE OF THE PARTY" WEA

ED OUT WITH SOAP  OR A MAN DRINK CHAMPAGNE FROM A LADY'S SHOE

WAITING FOR HER HUSBAND WITH A ROLLING PIN  OR A REPORTER WITH A

# ER REALLY SEEN...

ARTIST: GEORGE WOODBRIDGE    WRITER: LARRY SHARP

OR SOMEONE THROWING AN OLD SHOE AT A CAT ON A FENCE

THAT EVER SAID "ABRA CADABRA"        OR A HOBO WITH HIS BELONGINGS

"UGH!"        OR A JUG OF WHISKEY WITH "XXX" MARKED ON IT

A SAFE FALLING FROM A HIGH WINDOW        OR A SALESMAN PUT HIS FOOT

ET ADELINE"        OR A ST. BERNARD WITH A KEG OF BRANDY

ING A LAMPSHADE ON HIS HEAD        OR A KID GETTING HIS MOUTH WASH-

OR "STARS" WHEN YOU'RE HIT ON THE HEAD        OR A WIFE

"PRESS" CARD STUCK IN HIS HAT BAND        OR A FUNNY ARTICLE IN MAD?

We've read that people who live in big cities are becoming soft and flabby because of limited opportunities for sports and exercise. Well, we at MAD say that's ridiculous. People who

# UNAVOIDABLE EXERCISES

ARTIST: AL JAFFEE

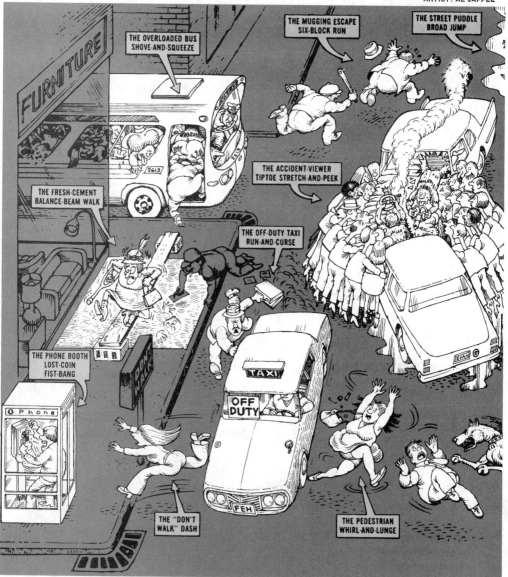

live in cities get all sorts of exercise without even realizing it. As a matter of fact, they can't avoid getting exercise, as you'll see in this panorama, depicting many and varied . . .

# FOR THE URBAN DWELLER

WRITER: FRANK JACOBS

One of the keys to the success of the Rocky series is the thrilling, charismatic villains Sly Stallone invents: Apollo Creed! Clubber Lang! Drago! But who's left? Where are Rocky's next opponents going to come from? We think Sly plans to pilfer old movies for Bad Guys to fight. Here are the scenerios for...

# ROCKY V, VI, VII, VIII, IX, X, XI OR,

## THE ITALIAN SCALLION VS THE GREAT HOLLYWOOD VILLAINS

ARTIST AND WRITER: TOM HACHTMAN

## THE ROCKY OF OZ

In his first musical, Rocky, the lovable boxer without a brain, battles Margaret Hamilton, The Wicked Witch of The West! In the closing seconds of the fight, Rocky is saved from being counted out when a giant tornado picks up the Champ, carries him over the rainbow, and dumps him back in South Philly!

## ROCKY BATTLES THE EMPIRE

It's Rocky vs the heavy breather of the universe, Darth Vader! On the night of the fight, Rock learns that Darth (aka "Lazer Fists") is really Don King! Can Rocky call on "The Force" in time to save the Boxing Federation? Is Don King Rock's long lost father? May the fists be with you in this battle of slow wit vs evil!

## ROCKYDEUS

In this lavish costume drama, Rocky mocks his rival Salieri by donning boxing gloves and pounding out one of the poor man's bland melodies on the clavier. Salieri beseeches God, "Why did you choose this moronic brute for such gifts and not me?!" This is the cultural Rocky film the critics have been asking for!

## ROCKY THE THIRTEENTH

## JOHN CARPENTER'S THE THING IN THE RING

Rocky suffers his most brutal beating when he meets the summer camp champ, Jason, "The Mutilator"! Will this battle of the sequels really be "The Final Chapter"?? A blood lover's delight!

All of Rocky's former foes merge into one big, mutating lump and return for a rematch. If Rock isn't careful this slithering "Thing" will mimic his cellular structure and Rocky movies will never be the same—or just possibly more alike than ever!

## ROCKY FLEW OVER THE CUCKOO'S NEST

## ROCKY DEAREST

Rocky fakes being punch-drunk to get into psychiatric hospital for a rest. But once in, he faces his meanest opponent yet—Nurse Cratchett! In round one, Big Nurse gives Rock a dose of medication! In round four, she zaps him with electro-shock! In round 10, she hits him with a frontal lobotomy! Will any of this punishment have a noticeable effect on the Champ??

Faye Dunaway is charming as Joan Crawford—until the blood starts to spill! The minute one itsy bitsy drop soils the spotless canvas, Rocky finds himself down for the count—scrubbing the mat! As the referee cries, "NO WIRE HANGERS!" a dazed Rocky wonders if this could be his last tangle!

Who would have ever thought that one day you'd be able to walk into a grocery store and find Paul Newman's face on a bottle of salad dressing or spaghetti sauce? We won-der, can it be long before other famous personalities follow Paul's lead and intro-duce products of their own? In the future, ...ccess in show business no longer be

# MAD'S CELEBRIT

BRONSON
**T.V. DINNER**

The frozen meals for those with a Death Wish

BILLY GRAHAM CRACKERS

Now in six saintly new shapes!

John
**CANDY BAR**

MAKES A *Splash* IN YOUR STOMACH!
1,000 CALORIES IN EVERY BITE!

Burt **Reynolds Wrap**

the only aluminum foil that's wrapped up in itself!

measured by the number of hit movies, TV shows or records someone has, but rather by the number of products featuring their face and name on the labels? If your answer to our last question is yes (or even maybe) then grab your cents-off coupons and look for a shopping cart with four wheels that work! You're ready to join us on a tour of

# y SUPERMARKET

ARTIST: BOB CLARKE    WRITERS: JOE RAIOLA & CHARLIE KADAU

MARK *Virginia* HAMILL
MAY THE PORK BE WITH YOU!

ALPHABETTE MIDLER SOUP MIX
50 OFF-COLOR WORDS IN EVERY BOWL!
CENSORED! CENSORED! CENSORED! CENSORED! CENSORED! CENSORED! CENSORED! CENSORED!

ARNOLD SCHWARZEN EGG ROLLS
STRONG FLAVOR    FAT FREE
ADDS MUSCLE TO EVERY MEAL! STRONG FLAVOR! FAT FREE!

BRYANT GUMBALLS
TRY ONE TODAY—SHOW YOUR FRIENDS

# On A Saturday Afternoon

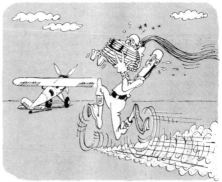

In issue No. 180 (Jan. '76), we ran an article we didn't think very much of! But, we were wrong. People wrote in and told us how much they loved it. And so, since

# TIME FLIES...TIN

### TIME FLIES...

...when you're playing a video game.

### TIME DRAGS...

...when your friend is playing it.

### TIME FLIES...

...during your summer vacation.

**ARTIST: PAUL COKER**

### TIME FLIES...

...when a beautiful nurse
is giving you a rub-down.

### TIME DRAGS...

...when a male nurse
is giving you a rub-down.

### TIME DRAGS...

...when you're waiting
for the phone to ring.

### TIME FLIES...

...when you're trying to answer
it before the caller hangs up.

### TIME FLIES...

...between the times you
have to take your dog out.

### TIME DRAGS...

...while you're waiting for him to
finish what you took him out to do.

### TIME FLIES...

...when you're in a deep sleep.

we're very sensitive to our readers' likes and dislikes, we're running this new version of the article, a mere seven years later! And you thought we didn't care!

# ᴧE DRAGS.... (AND VICE VERSA)

### TIME DRAGS...

...until the next one starts.

### TIME FLIES...

...when you take a final exam.

### TIME DRAGS...

...when you wait for the results.

WRITER: STAN HART

### TIME DRAGS...   TIME FLIES...

...when you're waiting for the girl to get undressed.

...when she is undressed.

### TIME DRAGS...   TIME FLIES...

...between bank deposits.

...between bank withdrawals.

### TIME DRAGS...

...when you have insomnia.

### TIME DRAGS...

...when you wait for the pizza to go from "boiling" to just "red hot."

### TIME FLIES...

...when the same pizza goes from "red hot" to "ice cold."

**YOU KNOW YOU'RE IN A SECOND MARRIAGE WHEN...**

... she insists that her diamond engagement ring be a lot larger than the one you gave your first wife.

**YOU KNOW YOU'RE IN A SECOND MARRIAGE WHEN...**

... you suddenly see trouble and heartache ahead as your kids and his kids start a huge fight ... at your wedding.

**YOU KNOW YOU'RE IN A SECOND MARRIAGE WHEN...**

... he comes home with a bouquet of "Happy Anniversary" flowers ... and it's the date of his *former* anniversary.

RE-WEDDED BLITZ DEPT.

# YOU KNOW

## SEC

## MARI

### WH

ARTIST & WRITER

**YOU KNOW YOU'RE IN A SECOND MARRIAGE WHEN...**

... you have to go to work in order to make ends meet because of your Husband's incredible alimony payments.

**YOU KNOW YOU'RE IN A SECOND MARRIAGE WHEN...**

... you find yourself stuck with amusing his kids when they visit him on Sunday ... while he watches football.

## YOU KNOW YOU'RE IN A SECOND MARRIAGE WHEN...

. . . your Wife told you everything before you were married
. . . except that her Son is the drummer in a Punk Rock Band.

## YOU KNOW YOU'RE IN A SECOND MARRIAGE WHEN...

. . . your Husband told you everything before you were married
. . . except that his Daughter runs with the "Hell's Angels".

## YOU KNOW YOU'RE IN A SECOND MARRIAGE WHEN...

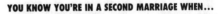

. . . your new Mother-In-Law keeps calling
you "Nancy". . . and your name is Mary Lou!

LLOYD GOLA

## YOU KNOW YOU'RE IN A SECOND MARRIAGE WHEN...

. . . he raves about the fun you had the last time you were
in Las Vegas . . . and you've never been to Las Vegas before.

## YOU KNOW YOU'RE IN A SECOND MARRIAGE WHEN...

. . . you are horrified to discover that your second Husband
is actually starting to make your first Husband look good.

Here we go with another vital MAD Public Service Feature
... this one designed to instruct you in the tricky art of

# INTERPRETING THE NEWS

WRITER: GARY ALEXANDER

## WHAT THEY SAY...  WHAT IT MEANS...

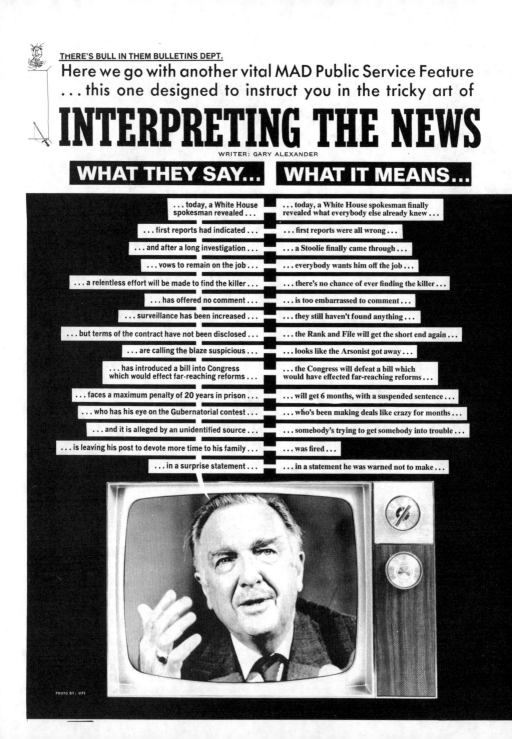

| WHAT THEY SAY... | WHAT IT MEANS... |
|---|---|
| ... today, a White House spokesman revealed ... | ... today, a White House spokesman finally revealed what everybody else already knew ... |
| ... first reports had indicated ... | ... first reports were all wrong ... |
| ... and after a long investigation ... | ... a Stoolie finally came through ... |
| ... vows to remain on the job ... | ... everybody wants him off the job ... |
| ... a relentless effort will be made to find the killer ... | ... there's no chance of ever finding the killer ... |
| ... has offered no comment ... | ... is too embarrassed to comment ... |
| ... surveillance has been increased ... | ... they still haven't found anything ... |
| ... but terms of the contract have not been disclosed ... | ... the Rank and File will get the short end again ... |
| ... are calling the blaze suspicious ... | ... looks like the Arsonist got away ... |
| ... has introduced a bill into Congress which would effect far-reaching reforms ... | ... the Congress will defeat a bill which would have effected far-reaching reforms ... |
| ... faces a maximum penalty of 20 years in prison ... | ... will get 6 months, with a suspended sentence ... |
| ... who has his eye on the Gubernatorial contest ... | ... who's been making deals like crazy for months ... |
| ... and it is alleged by an unidentified source ... | ... somebody's trying to get somebody into trouble ... |
| ... is leaving his post to devote more time to his family ... | ... was fired ... |
| ... in a surprise statement ... | ... in a statement he was warned not to make ... |

In major league baseball it doesn't matter how lousy a player you are—even the most anemic scrub is qualified to be immortalized in a baseball card, while some of the game's most integral characters will never know 3X5 cardboard fame! It's time this gross injustice was corrected by adopting MAD's suggestions for...

## LUCKY THE LEECH
**TEAM MASCOT**

### LUCKY THE LEECH
*TEAM MASCOT*

**Fun Facts:** The amount of garbage and junk food thrown at Lucky by the fans during a typical homestand would feed the Republic of Tunisia for one year.

Everyone who has ever donned the Lucky mascot suit has died of heat prostration within 36 hours of taking the job.

**Quote:** *"Okay, fans! Give me a 'J'! Hey, c'mon, give me a 'J'! Let's go—ow! Stop kicking me! Help!"*

# MAKING BASEBALL CARD
# COLLECTIONS COMPLETE

## A Tribute To Our National Pastime's Unsung Heroes

ARTIST: JOHN POUND

WRITER: DESMOND DEVLIN

## PHIL RONZONI
**TEAM ANNOUNCER**

### PHIL RONZONI
*TEAM ANNOUNCER*

**Fun Facts:** Was behind the mike for a record 17 consecutive games without once announcing the score.

His campy singing of "Take Me Out to the Ballgame" during the seventh inning stretch never fails to inspire any true fan to cast a teary eye toward the broadcast booth and say, "Now I know what death is like."

**Quote:** *"Mmmm-mm, these crumb buns from Sal's bakery are great. I believe they've been heated up...Hey, what's that man doing on third? Did a run score? Bernie, what happened?"*

## MARGO ADDLED

### ROAD TRIP BIMBO

**Fun Facts:** As part of her 50–50 settlement, demanded that she be credited in the official league stat book with 108 of Suede Bugs' 216 hits in 1989.

Margo was "appalled" at the sensational media circus that publicized only the cheap, smutty aspects of her story, and said so in an interview in *Panthouse Magazine*, where she appeared naked.

**Quote:** *"I'll be able to correct that hitch in your stroke as soon as we check the films."*

---

### RICHARD MILHOUS SPINEGRABBER

**TEAM OWNER**

BANK

RMS

---

## RICHARD MILHOUS SPINEGRABBER XIII

### TEAM OWNER, NEW YORK—NEW JERSEY—DENVER—PHOENIX—OKEEFENOKEE YANKOVICHS

**Fun Facts:** Last September, he canceled Fan Appreciation Day, kept all the ticket money, and told the fans he really appreciated it.

He's moved his team so often that there are skidmarks on home plate; pioneered the first Port-A-Stadium.

**Quote:** *Complimented on his big fat money belt, he said, "But I'm not wearing any belt!"*

---

## "SQUINTY" LONGSTREET

### UMPIRE

**Fun Facts:** The somewhat plump "Squinty" was able to assist the Pittsburgh field crew last season during a rain delay by covering the pitcher's mound with a pair of his shorts.

He got such a thrill from bumping manager Pete Moss during a heated argument that the two bought a bungalow when the season ended.

**Quote:** *"Is it four strikes and three balls, or the other way around?"*

**?**

---

### ANDY ANABOLIC

**TEAM DOCTOR**

M D

---

## ANDY ANABOLIC

### TEAM DOCTOR

**Fun Facts:** Once called off an operation on account of rain and covered his patient with a tarp.

First doctor to offer free checkups for fans on "Groin Pull Night."

**Quote:** *"Get out there and play, you've got another lung!"*

---

## WALLY ALZHEIMER

### USHER

**Fun Facts:** Because he feels that baseball's past is its finest legacy, Wally hasn't cleaned his seat rag since 1978.

Alzheimer boasts the only toupee in the game that is actually made out of artificial turf.

**Quote:** *"Hey you! Yes, you with the semi-automatic rifle! Lemme check your stub!"*

---

### POINDEXTER SABERMETRIC

**STATISTICIAN**

---

## POINDEXTER SABERMETRIC

### STATISTICIAN

**Fun Facts:** Can compute any player's stolen bases/caught stealing ratio in seconds, yet doesn't know who won the World Series last year.

Poindexter sells stats to agents for contract negotiations that conclusively prove why most players are "uncrowned MVPs," and sells stats to the owners that prove those same players are uncoordinated schmucks!

**Quote:** *"Every time I watch Pride of the Yankees I cry, not so much because Lou Gehrig dies but because I might've paid sixty bucks for him in rotisserie!"*

# A MAD LOOK AT PAL

# M READING

ARTIST & WRITER: SERGIO ARAGONES

Let him throw his very own party!

Perform a trick for him!

Give him a full day of belly-scratching!

Play "Happy Birthday" on a
high-pitched dog whistle!

Give him the use of your lounger for the day!

Help him dig holes in your neighbor's lawn!

# CAN DO FOR HIS BIRTHDAY

WRITER AND ARTIST: PAUL PETER PORGES

Let him sleep where he wants to!

Share his hobby with him!

Have a drink with him at his private bar!

Dress up as a mailman and let him chase you!

Walk him the very moment he wants you to!

Collect several weeks of garbage for him to go through!

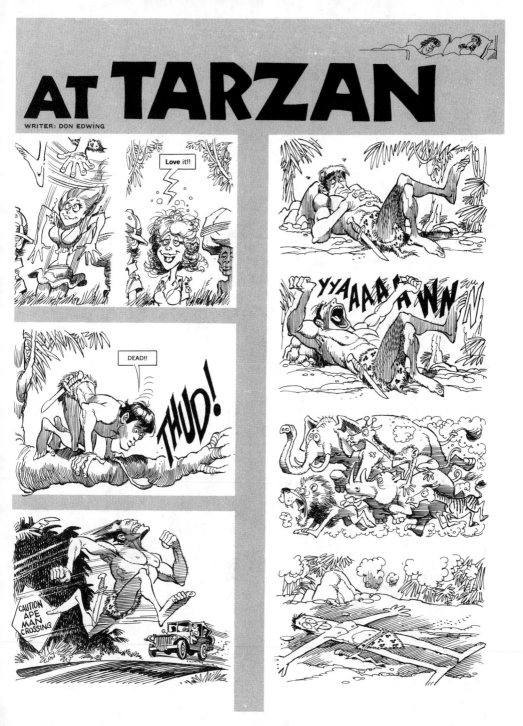

**For Outstanding Achievement In
Stretching A "Two-Hour Idea"
Into A Five-Part Mini-Series**

**Best Performance By An Actor
Or Actress In A Talk Show
"Plug" For A Failing Series**

STATUES OF LIMITATIONS DEPT.

# TV EMMY AWARDS

**Best Dramatic Series Kept On By A
Network As An Example of "Quality
Programming"...Despite The Fact
That No One Ever Watches It**

**For Outstanding Achievement In
Creating A Maudlin, Tear-Jerking
Scene In A SitCom When The Writers
Couldn't Think Of A Funny Ending**

**Outstanding Achievement In SitCom Writing For the Best-Disguised "Re-Working" Of An Old "I Love Lucy" Plot**

**Most Innovative Use Of A Car-Chase Wind-Up In An Action/Adventure Series To Cover Up Bad Writing**

# WE'D LIKE TO SEE

ARTIST: MICHAEL MONTGOMERY    WRITER: MIKE SNIDER

**Best Scene Or Line Of Dialogue Used Out-Of-Context In A Network Promo To Make A Show Look More Titillating Than It Actually Is**

**For Outstanding Achievement In Packing A Dramatic Show Episode With Over-The-Hill "Guest Stars" That Nobody's Heard Of For Over Ten Years**

Are you getting bored with those tiresome bumper sticker messages you see on just about every car these days? It's time to strike back! How?? For each idiotic message you cannot stand, write an

# SNAPPY ANSWERS TO ST

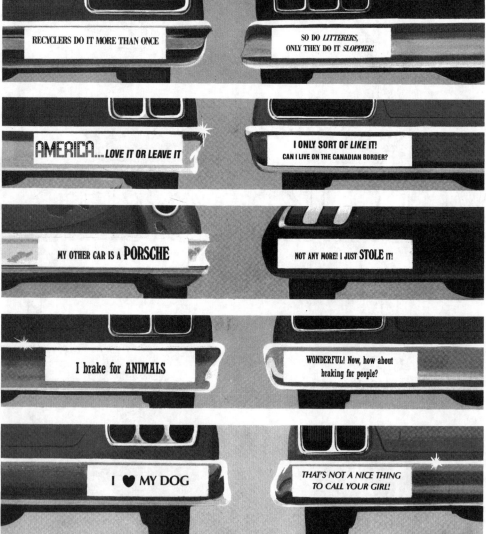

RECYCLERS DO IT MORE THAN ONCE

SO DO *LITTERERS,*
ONLY THEY DO IT *SLOPPIER!*

AMERICA....*LOVE IT OR LEAVE IT*

I ONLY SORT OF *LIKE* IT!
CAN I LIVE ON THE CANADIAN BORDER?

MY OTHER CAR IS A **PORSCHE**

NOT ANY MORE! I JUST **STOLE** IT!

I brake for **ANIMALS**

WONDERFUL! Now, how about
braking for people?

I ♥ MY DOG

*THAT'S NOT A NICE THING
TO CALL YOUR GIRL!*

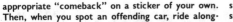

# UPID BUMPER STICKERS*

STUPID QUESTIONS" IS PURELY BECAUSE WE SWIPED IT!     ARTIST: BOB CLARKE     WRITER: LARRY SIEGEL

Some of you hot shots have probably taken a "Drivers Ed" course, and maybe even passed a written exam to get your state license. So now you think you're ready to climb be- hind the wheel and handle any situation that comes up, eh? Well, we've got news for you, Booby! All those rules you learned, about slowing down at deer crossings and avoiding

# THE MAD PRACTI

1. If you suddenly realize that you are driving the wrong way on a one-way street, you should...

A. start driving backwards a whole lot faster than the oncoming traffic is moving forward._____
B. prepare to tell the policeman that you're from England, where driving rules are all the opposite of ours._____
C. switch into the lane reserved for oncoming buses, and start to pray that you're on a route that has lousy, infrequent service._____

2. When you pass the scene of an accident and see law officers waiving the traffic through...

A. stop and thank the policemen for kindly pointing out the grisly sight to you._____
B. pass on by as directed, but then "rubberneck" by staring into your rearview mirror for the next half a mile._____
C. plow into the accident so you can collect from the insurance companies of the other drivers involved._____

3. When driving with a back seat full of restless children...

A. turn around and look each one in the eye while scolding them, so they will know you mean business._____
B. take your hands off the wheel long enough to grab the worst offender by the throat, and shake him until his teeth rattle._____
C. twist the steering wheel sharply back and forth, so the kids will be too busy picking themselves up off the floor to whine._____

7. Upon realizing that you've just slammed and locked your car door with the only car keys inside...

A. pay the thief who's breaking into a nearby car to break into yours._____
B. climb in through the sun roof. If your car doesn't have a sun roof, go buy a can opener at a nearby store so you can install one._____
C. do what everyone else does: stand there staring through the side window at your keys as if that's going to help somehow._____

8. If you accidentally drop a lighted cigarette while the car is in motion;

A. roll down your windows and immediately drive through a car wash._____
B. roll up your windows and proceed, knowing that the fire will go out as soon as it has used up all the oxygen inside the vehicle._____
C. immediately slip off your shoes, because it's a lot easier to locate something hot on the car floor when you're barefoot._____

9. If your contact lens should pop out while you're driving at high speed, you should immediately...

A. shut your eyes, because seeing only fuzzy images of oncoming traffic is dangerous._____
B. speed up, so you can reach your destination quickly and begin looking for your lost lens._____
C. dive to the floor and hunt for it, since you can no longer see anything through the windshield anyway._____

left turns into fire stations, will only be of use to you once or twice in your driving lifetime. You haven't really been tested or even informed about the practical driving decisions you'll be required to make every day. Lucky for you MAD has corrected this terrible oversight. Quiz yourself and discover the motoring skills you lack with

# CAL DRIVING TEST

ARTIST: PAUL COKER    WRITER: TOM KOCH

---

4. To avoid being delayed by meandering senior citizens in crosswalks...

A. blow your horn suddenly, and then drive under them when they all jump straight up into the air._____
B. open the passenger door and graciously offer to drive them to the nearest curb._____
C. Always carry a bullhorn so you'll be prepared to announce that Hugh Downs is autographing free copies of the Readers Digest for all who hurry over to the Community Center._____

---

5. If your car conks out in a strange town, and you're broke...

A. find a temporary job in the area to earn money for the repair bill. Anything that pays over $1000 a week should be adequate._____
B. try to map out a route home that's downhill all the way, so you won't need an engine that runs._____
C. push your car into the nearest vacant lot and prepare to live there until you hear that you've come into a large inheritance._____

---

6. When flagged down by a policeman for failing to come to a complete stop at a "full stop" sign...

A. tell him you have such a souped-up engine that your car goes 20 miles an hour in neutral._____
B. say something in any foreign language, so he'll assume you didn't know what the word on the sign meant._____
C. confuse him by citing Einstein's Theory to prove that nothing in the universe ever comes to a complete stop._____

---

10. If you see red lights flashing to warn you that a bridge is out...

A. suggest to the flagman that he tighten his light bulbs so they'll stop blinking._____
B. remember what Burt Reynolds always does and speed up, so you can hurtle across the river without needing a bridge._____
C. roll up the windows before proceeding, so your car will float longer after it hits the water._____

---

11. The best way to take revenge on a rude motorist is to...

A. point frantically at his rear tire until worry forces him to stop and check out the situation._____
B. take down his license number and then report his car to the police as a stolen vehicle._____
C. flash a phony badge, gesture to him to pull over, and then whiz on past him when he complies._____

---

12. If you decide to park in a space that's marked with this symbol...

A. prepare to tell the judge that you thought the sign meant "Absolutely No Unicycle Parking"._____
B. tell anybody who glares at you that your disability doesn't show because it's mental (and dangerous)._____
C. immediately put the hood up, so you can claim that your car is disabled, even if you're not._____

13. If you become involved in a "fender bender" accident that is clearly your fault...

A. announce that you have plenty of collision insurance, and then give the other driver the name of a fictitious insurance company._____
B. make light of the damage you've caused by insisting that his crushed grill can easily be snapped back into place._____
C. suggest that your victim take off before your armed bodyguard arrives to "handle things" for you._____

14. When required to drive the family cat to the veterinarian all alone...

A. wear a bird cage over your head for protection, in case Kitty panics and starts clawing everything in sight._____
B. be alert for special problems if you step on the brake pedal suddenly and feel your foot come down on something warm and soft and furry._____
C. stuff the cat into the glove compartment, and then drive at top speed to reach your destination before the air supply gives out._____

15. When you're late for work and try to finish dressing while driving...

A. at least put on your trousers before leaving the house, because that's impossible to do while operating a moving motor vehicle._____
B. be sure to stay off cobblestone streets while applying lipstick, unless you're satisfied to look like an Amazonian witch doctor._____
C. never apply false eyelashes on the freeway, because a thumb seen at that close range can easily be mistaken for a flesh-colored tanker truck._____

16. When leaving your car parked in a sunny spot makes your steering wheel to hot to touch, you should...

A. Press the mysterious button marked "Cruise Control" and hope that it's some kind of device that enables the car to steer itself._____
B. Obtain enough dimes from a nearby bank to feed the parking meter until evening, when the sun will probably go down._____
C. tell your pesky little brother who always wants to drive your car that you've finally decided to let him._____

17. When the driver behind you honks because you failed to notice that the red light just turned to green...

A. glance in the mirror to check the size and gender of the honker before deciding whether or not to make an issue of this._____
B. give the familiar obscene gesture to indicate that you still consider yourself to be superior to him, even though you tend to daydream._____
C. jump out and hand the other driver a dollar, explaining that it's your payment for wasting five seconds of his valuable time._____

18. In case of disabling car trouble on along a busy interstate highway...

A. stay in your parked car with the windows rolled up and the doors locked, because it's better to die of suffocation than be knifed by a passing maniac._____
B. choose the most annoying passenger in your group to walk to a gas station for help._____
C. leave your car in the highway lane where you stalled, so that the first car that comes along will push you into the next town at 60mph._____

# INSTRUCTIONS FOR GRADING YOURSELF

The correct answer to each odd-numbered question is "C". The correct answer to each even-numbered question is "A". Except for questions numbered 4, 10, 12, and 16, where this is not the case, as any fool can see. Credit yourself with 8 percentage points for each correct answer.

We realize, of course, that this would give you a total score of 144 percent if you got them all right. However, you couldn't have done that, because all of the multiple choices for at least seven of the questions have been scientifically programmed to be wrong anyway. So there!

# WHILE CLAMMING IN NEW JERSEY

SHKLIKSA!

DIG DIG DIG DIG DIG DIG

SHKLURK

PLUNK

SHKLIZICH!

DIG DIG DIG DIG DIG

**CHOW MEIN LINERS DEPT.**

The idea of Fortune Cookies dates back thousands of years. Unfortunately, so do most of the fortunes you find in them. They're usually filled with boring words of wisdom like "The seed of Knowledge that falls upon a barren mind will not flower!" or "The wise man will learn from his mistakes!" Well, it seems to us that people living in the "Now Generation" need

SAVE OUR FORESTS! PLEASE RETURN THIS FORTUNE TO YOUR WAITER FOR RE-CYCLING!

V.D. IS ONE SECRET YOU SHOULD NOT SPREAD AROUND.

*As you sit here eating, there is a 75% chance that your house is being robbed.*

TIRED OF CHINESE FOOD? NEXT TIME TRY "ROCKY'S PIZZA"!

**FORTUNE COOKIE ADS GET READ! FOR A SPACE IN A COOKIE LIKE THIS ONE, CALL:**
Business Biscuits Enterprises, Incorporated, 42 Main Street, City—555-9900

# LEGALIZE ACUPUNCTURE!

**Why bother to save for a rainy day? You only get soaked by inflation!**

An apple a day could give you more pesticides than your body can tolerate.

THE GRASS IS ALWAYS GREENER ... FOR THE PUSHER.

# FORTUNE COOKIES
## THAT ARE RELEVANT

WRITTEN BY: DICK DE BARTOLO & DON EPSTEIN

CRIME DOES NOT PAY... INCOME TAXES!

**BOYCOTT LETTUCE!**

Please open another cookie. The Fortune you have reached is not in service at this time!

**BE CAREFUL OF WHAT YOU TALK ABOUT! THE TEAPOT MAY BE BUGGED!**

EATING THIS COOKIE CAN BE HAZARDOUS TO YOUR HEALTH. IT CONTAINS EMULSIFIED GLYCOL, HYDROGENATED BENSOMENICAINE, PLUS BTA AND BHA.

Walk softly and carry a big stick. It's the only way you won't get mugged.

LIVE LONGER! BREATHE LESS OF TODAY'S AIR!

BYE, BYE BLACKBIRD... AND ALL THE OTHER ENDANGERED SPECIES!

A DOG IN THE BUSH IS WORTH TWO ON THE SIDEWALK!

Larry Bird's Bird and Michael J. Fox's Fox enjoying an afternoon in James Wood's Woods

"What's in a name?" is the old question sometimes asked. Well, it depends! As

# THE

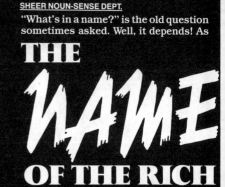

## OF THE RICH

ARTIST: MORT DRUCKER

Robert Plant's Plant, Pete Rose's Rose and George Bush's Bush in Sally Field's Field

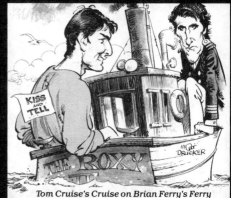

Tom Cruise's Cruise on Brian Ferry's Ferry

Gerald Ford's Ford meeting Harrison Ford's Ford

you'll see in the following stupid scenes we've managed to come up with!

# GAME
## AND FAMOUS

WRITER: J. PRETE

*Kirstie Alley's Alley directly behind Darryl Hall's Hall*

*Judas Priest's Priest condemning Billy Idol's Idol*

*Rev. Moon's Moon in Elton John's John*

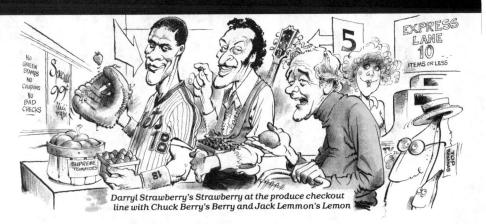

*Darryl Strawberry's Strawberry at the produce checkout line with Chuck Berry's Berry and Jack Lemmon's Lemon*

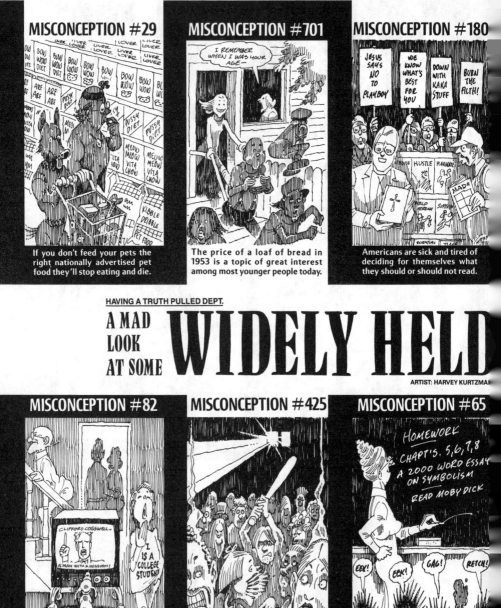

## MISCONCEPTION #29

If you don't feed your pets the right nationally advertised pet food they'll stop eating and die.

## MISCONCEPTION #701

The price of a loaf of bread in 1953 is a topic of great interest among most younger people today.

## MISCONCEPTION #180

Americans are sick and tired of deciding for themselves what they should or should not read.

**HAVING A TRUTH PULLED DEPT.**

# A MAD LOOK AT SOME WIDELY HELD

**ARTIST: HARVEY KURTZMAN**

## MISCONCEPTION #82

The best way for a candidate to "win over" voters is to pre-empt their favorite television show with a half-hour political spiel.

## MISCONCEPTION #425

People who wait in line and pay $5.00 for a theater seat would much rather listen to a neighbor's "running commentary" than watch the movie itself.

## MISCONCEPTION #65

Students have plenty of time for extra homework—especially since their other four or five teachers don't believe in assigning any.

## MISCONCEPTION #14

Attractive women can't resist obscene propositions from sweaty, overweight men in smelly T-shirts.

## MISCONCEPTION #213

Elevators are intelligent beings and sense impatience when someone bangs their buttons repeatedly.

## MISCONCEPTION #566

Nothing stimulates conversation like a mouthful of Novocain, dental instruments and fingers.

# MISCONCEPTIONS

WRITER: MIKE SNIDER

## MISCONCEPTION #31

Especially in high-speed traffic, using directional signals before making a lane change is unnecessary between experienced drivers.

## MISCONCEPTION #7

DRIVER ON BOARD

There is nothing that shows your cleverness and wit better than a store-bought "gag sign" which five million people already own.

## MISCONCEPTION #37

The proper greeting for a caller to a Customer Service line is 25 minutes of "The Hollywood Strings Play the Best of Barry Manilow."

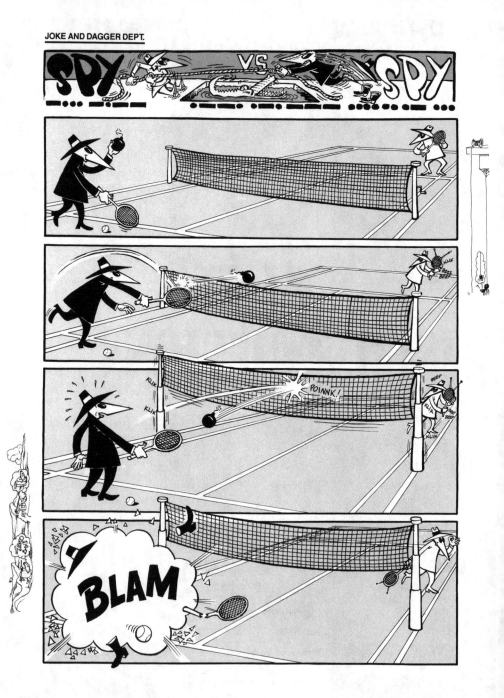

You've read poems that glorify trees and Paul Revere and stuff like that. Let's face it—they're out of date. We're in the 1980s, and what deserves glorifying are the items that assist us every day and enrich our lives. You know, things like the Walkman, the blender and the VCR. Which is why Mad now presents

# ODES TO
# APPLIANCES, GADGETS
## AND OTHER MODERN CONVENIENCES

ARTIST: GEORGE WOODBRIDGE     IDEA: MARILYN ATKINS     WRITER: FRANK JACOBS

## O WALKMAN!

*O Walkman! My Walkman!*
*I groove the tapes you play;*
*Your 'phones stay wrapped*
*        around my head*
*From dawn till end of day.*

*O Walkman! My Walkman!*
*You fill my life with sound;*
*Because of you, I now block out*
*All other sounds around.*

*O Walkman! My Walkman!*
*I hear you, there's no doubt;*
*I only wish I could have heard*
*The truck that wiped me out.*

## THE VCR

*The VCR's a loyal pal,*
*        A friend you truly care for,*
*Because it guarantees you'll see*
*        The shows that you weren't there for;*
*Two thousand shows I've taped so far;*
*        Each night I tape a new one;*
*Who knows, perhaps there'll come a day*
*        I'll find the time to view one.*

## THE MICROWAVE

Blessings on thee, Microwave;
Countless minutes I now save;
Like a flash, you work with ease,
Roasting meats and melting cheese;
Turning out a cherry pie
In the twinkling of an eye;
Baking apples double-quick—
What's your secret? What's the trick?
Some great magic you possess;
What it is, I cannot guess;
Once my cooking spelled disaster;
Now it's just as bad—but faster.

## THE NAUTILUS

The Nautilus keeps me in trim
Just like a workout at the gym;
For half an hour, twice a day,
I strain to melt the flab away;
I lift and pull and stretch and push
To flatten gut and tighten tush;
You'll find this well-designed machine
Will make your body trim and lean;
It helps, of course, the makers say,
To use it ev'ry waking day;
But best of all, I should explain,
You'll love it if you're into pain.

# BLENDER, BLENDER

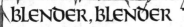

*Blender, blender, on my shelf,*
*Mixing foods all by yourself,*
*Pulverizing chicken chunks*
*Into spreads and dips and dunks.*

*Blender, blender, wondrous toy,*
*Source of gastronomic joy;*
*Chopping, churning while you work,*
*Like some wacko gone berserk.*

*Blender, blender, bladed friend,*
*Slicing carrots end to end;*
*Thanks to how you mush and mince,*
*I create a perfect blintz.*

*Blender, blender, fast and slick,*
*Making sauces rich and thick;*
*Faithfully, you'll serve me well*
*Till my diet's shot to hell.*

# phones

*I think that I shall never own*
*A tool more handy than the phone;*
*A phone with which I keep in touch*
*With inlaws, old-time pals and such;*
*A phone that also sometimes rings*
*With calls from schmucks and dingalings;*
*A phone that bill collectors use*
*For giving me unwelcome news;*
*A phone with calls that airheads make*
*Who've dialed my number by mistake;*
*A phone I pick up half asleep*
*To hear some heavy-breathing creep;*
*On second thought, I've come to fear*
*There's less to phones than meets the ear;*
*In fact, with one more nuisance call*
*I may not own a phone at all.*

There's a new book out called **Doublespeak,** which reveals how governments, advertisers and the media deceive us with twisted words and phrases. Like when hospitals refer to death as "terminal living." Or when a nuclear-plant explosion is called "energetic disassembly." Or when artificial leather is touted as "virgin vinyl." It's all part of a sneaky trend to make the bad seem good, the disgusting sound appealing, the deplorable seem acceptable! Yes, **Doublespeak** is on the rise, so we better prepare for the time...

# WHEN
# TAKES

ARTIST: SERGIO ARAGONES

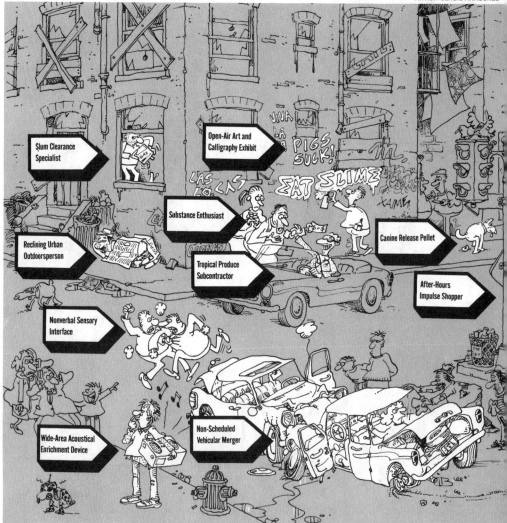

# "DOUBLESPEAK" OVER COMPLETELY

WRITER: FRANK JACOBS

# PATTERNS

# OF SPEECH

ARTIST: BOB CLARKE
IDEA BY MAX BRANDEL

GUIDED MUSCLES DEPT.

Today, thousands of health-conscious people are not only jogging, but submitting their bodies to all kinds of pun-ishment in Health Clubs across the country equipped with Nautilus exercise machines. Now, as we see it, the real

# SPECIALIZED NAU
# FOR PRACTICAL EVE

ARTIST: AL JAFFEE

## A Neck-Stretching Machine

*To develop your neck muscles, thereby enabling you to ex-tend your head great distances in different directions...*

*...for cheating on school exams, aptitude tests, etc.*

## A Shoulder-Building Machine

*To strengthen shoulder muscles so that you will be able to carry enormous weights over long periods of time...*

*...for all you music lovers who get your kicks out of forcing your preference in music on helpless passersby.*

problem with Nautilus machines is that outside of making you look like a poor man's Arnold Schwarzenegger, they've got very little practical value. Which is why we'd like to offer any interested entrepreneur our suggestions for

# TILUS MACHINES RYDAY ACTIVITIES

WRITER: LARRY SIEGEL

## A Wrist-Conditioning Machine

*To recondition and strengthen your weak, stiff wrists so they will be able to function with hair-trigger speed...*

*...in order to hang up a phone quickly when you run into one of those witless, moronic answering machine messages.*

## A Back-Strengthening Machine

*To harden your neck, buttocks and thigh muscles...*

*...so you'll survive being dragged away from demonstrations.*

# A Contortion-Training Machine

*To make your body supple and loose in order to enable it to twist into positions it has never been in before...*

*...for making out in a BMW with a 5-speed stick shift.*

# A Steel Punching Bag

*To develop tremendous strength in hands and knuckles...*

*...for punching out those broken pay telephones and video games and cigarette machines that never return your money.*

# An Over-All Body-Building Machine

*To build up your entire body for the vital "Decathlon of Life"...*

*...in order to run fast enough to escape nuclear plant leakages, to leap high enough to clear toxic waste dumps, to swim strongly enough to out-distance oil slicks and 7 other catastrophic events too horrible and disgusting to mention.*

# ONE DAY IN A GARAGE

What's the newest thing on the science front? White bread…?! Boy, are you out of touch! No, it's the "Voice Synthesizer," a miniature computer chip that "talks." So far, we already have clocks that "speak" the time,

# WHAT IT WILL BE LIKE WH

ARTIST: PAUL COKER

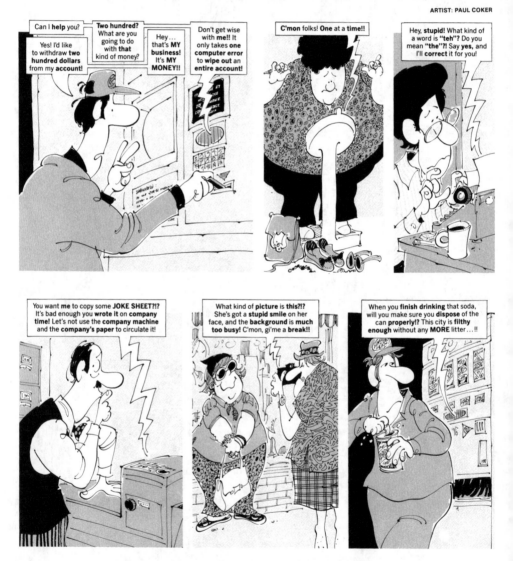

and autos that "tell" when something is about to go wrong mechanically. How long will it be before just about everything has a voice? Oh, just about the time it will take you to read this article which we've titled:

# EN EVERY DEVICE "TALKS"

WRITER: DICK DE BARTOLO

That's a **SLUG** you dropped in, Buddy! If you want to make a **free call,** how about the one the **cops'll** let you make after I **call them** and they **arrest you?!**

Hey! Someone get the guy who owns this **car** and tell him he's only got **five minutes left...!!**

Boy, you're gonna be **some sick kid** if you eat all this **junk food!** Ever hear of **vegetables? Salads? Cereals? Huh??**

CHIPS 95

I'm just about out of **milk,** and I'm really low on **eggs,** and I can use—

That's your **third cup!!** If I were **you,** I'd make sure I stopped in the **bathroom** before I started my hour trip to work!!

Hey, **Idiot...** why do it the **slow, painful way** with **cigarettes...?!** Why not just run in front of a **bus** and get it over with **quickly?!**

## A SERVING OF SPARE FIBS DEPT.

We all do idiotic, embarrassing things. Then we try to blab our way out with excuses that are even more idiotic. Why? Because when you wait till the last minute, you concoct lousy

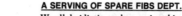

# MAD'S ALIBIS FO

## TO POLICE

ARTIST: JACK DAVIS    WRITER: TOM KOCH

I only carry burglar's tools so I won't have to wake my folks if I lose my house key.

I was at Yankee Stadium for the entire evening, and all 26,424 fans can verify that.

I said that it's my first offense because I didn't realize you're counting felonies, too.

## TO COACHES

When I mentioned those statistics, I meant that my lifetime **fielding** average is over .300.

I figured scoring for the wrong team would throw those guys off guard for the rest of the game.

I didn't play my best because my guidance counselor said I must stop being so competitive.

## TO EMPLOYERS

I didn't show up for work that day because I honestly thought Halloween was a legal holiday.

I'd have brought that to your attention but I didn't want to make trouble for You-Know-Who.

Obviously you and I interpret *Employees' Rights* Paragraph No. 78.9 in two different ways.

lies! So we say, "Be prepared!" Memorize some good alibis! But don't be caught reading this article—because we won't be able to help you! *That* kind of goof-up is not covered in...

# R ALL OCCASIONS

## TO PARENTS

There was no way I could have known it was after curfew because a mugger took my watch!

I purposely left my clothes on the floor to help insulate the room and cut your heating bill.

A prowler must have broken in and left all those copies of *Penthouse* on my closet floor.

## TO SWEETHEARTS

I know we made a commitment to each other, and all the rest of the people I date respect that.

Normally I wouldn't ask you to pay, but my credit's so good at most places I don't carry cash.

The lipstick stains are from a female paramedic who goes around **saving** lives with free demonstrations of artificial respiration.

## TO TEACHERS

I did not write that term paper for fear it would be so good I'd set a standard that I couldn't live up to.

I took yesterday off because I thought nobody cared. But now that I know you missed me, it was completely worth it.

That excuse note doesn't look like my mother's handwriting because she's sick in bed with exactly the same thing I had.

Back in 1968 (MAD #116), we published some "Ads We Never Got To See"...a collection of ill-fated advertising campaigns that sounded good when they were first created, but upon reflection certainly

# MORE ADS WE NI

# EVER GOT TO SEE

ARTIST: HARRY NORTH    WRITER: DICK DE BARTOLO

# ONE NIGHT IN THE ACME RITZ CENTRAL ARMS WALDORF PLAZA STATLER HILTON GRAND HOTEL

We're told that the most miraculous thing about computers is their ability to store and feed back millions of bits of information. But in MAD's opinion, that's not the most miraculous thing about computers. The real miracle is that not one of the millions of facts they have stored away is the correct spelling

# IF COMPUTERS AI

…why do they assume you want to receive 800 identical copies of the same mail order catalogue?

…why do they spread the word that you're responsible for all of the 1983 and 1984 parking tickets issued to a car that you sold in 1981?

…why does the increasing amount of information they spew out to TV weathermen only make the forecasts more inaccurate?

…how come they're always telling you that you're making an error, but they can never tell you what it is?

…what is their logic in letting 14,000 murders go unsolved while they devote full time to nailing you on some old traffic warrant?

…why do they blithely pass along a ridiculous meter reading that makes your monthly electric bill higher than the one for Yankee Stadium?

of our name, or our accurate address, or a single smidgeon of data about us that is completely right! As each of us wastes hours and hours trying to correct the garble spewed out by some crazed silicon chip, we are bound to wonder how that much stupidity can be produced with such unfailing regularity...

# RE SO BRILLIANT...

ARTIST: GEORGE WOODBRIDGE    WRITER: TOM KOCH

...why can't they report your correct wages to the I.R.S., especially when it's a known fact that the I.R.S. will always believe a computer and assume the taxpayer is lying?

...why can't they find someone to write a computer instruction manual who knows how to put together a simple sentence?

...why do they invariably select the phone numbers of the elderly, the unmarried and the childless to receive their annoying calls about diaper service?

...how do they figure that your bank balance could have dropped from $1,854 to $18.54 during a month you didn't make any withdrawals?

...why do they insist that "JOHNSMITH" is all one word, and must be alphabetized under "J" until its poor owner gets around to acquiring a first name?

...why do companies that install them immediately have to hire lots of extra employees just to correct computer errors?

# A MAD LOOK AT AMUSEM

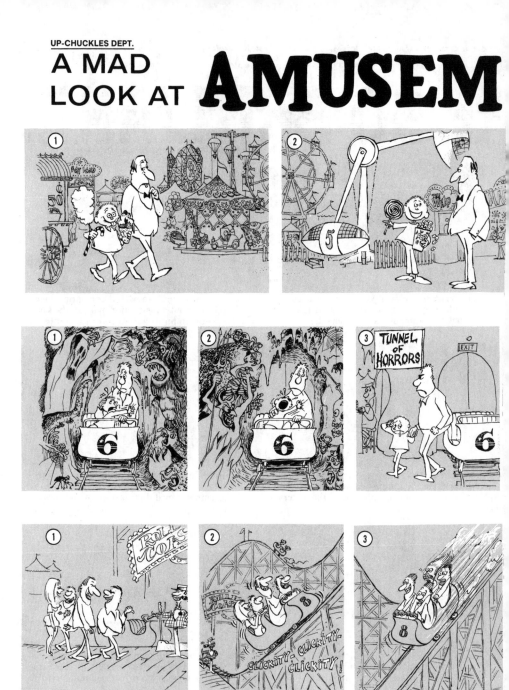

# ENT PARKS

ARTIST & WRITER: SERGIO ARAGONES

TUNNEL OF HORRORS

EXIT

FUN & PICTURES

FUN & PICTURES

Aragones

# PASTIMES

TREE TUG-OF-WAR

ARM WRESTLING WITH IRONING BOARD

DRIP-DRIP SING-A-LONG

TWISTER-DODGING

# for NERDS

WRITER AND ARTIST: PAUL PETER PORGES

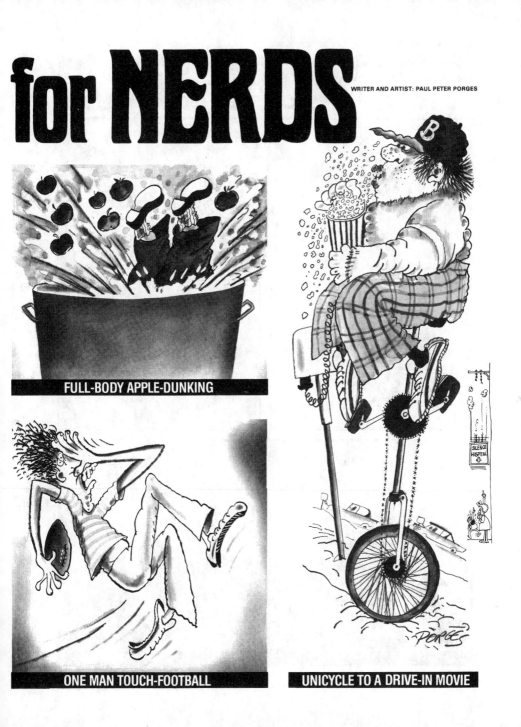

FULL-BODY APPLE-DUNKING

ONE MAN TOUCH-FOOTBALL

UNICYCLE TO A DRIVE-IN MOVIE

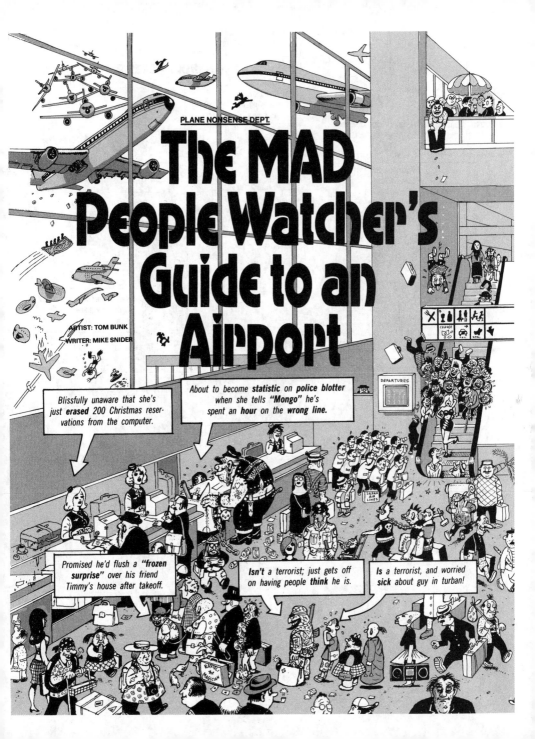

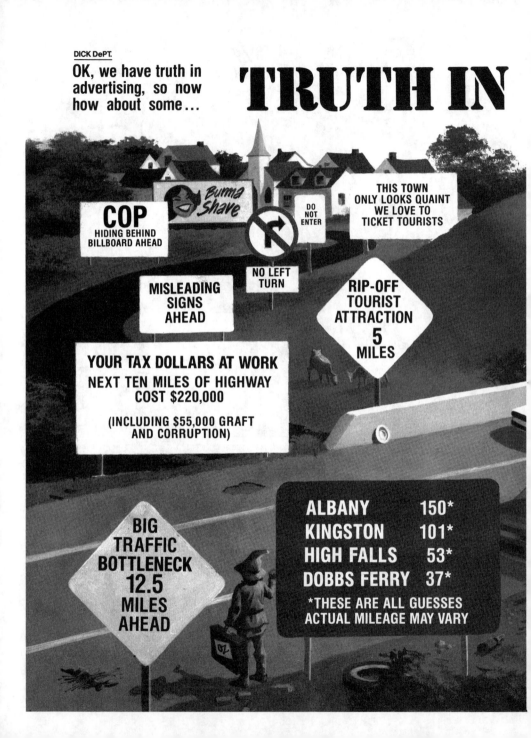

# ROAD SIGNS

ARTIST: BOB CLARKE
WRITER: DICK DE BARTOLO

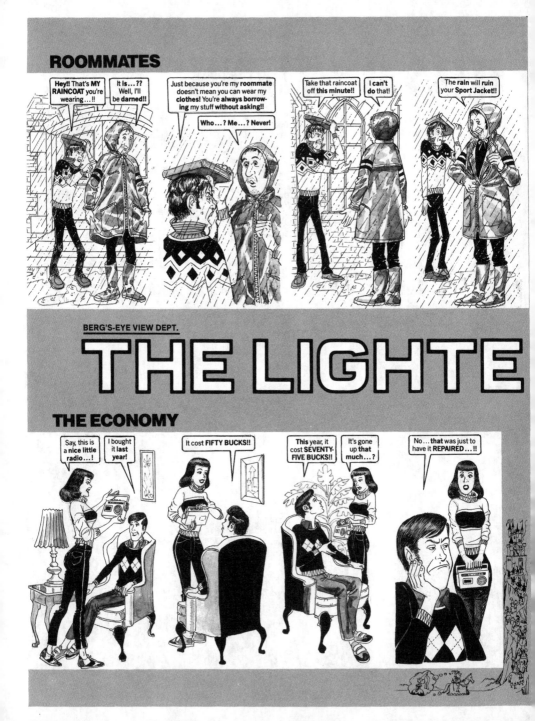

Thinking about what career to get into? Wondering whether or not you'll fit in? Well, here's the first in a series of tests designed to help you choose your future line of work. Mainly, discover your true abilities by taking...

# MAD'S APTITUDE TEST NUMBER ONE
# WILL YOU MAKE A
# GOOD DOCTOR?

1. You are a surgeon who is operating on another doctor's patient. Through a mix-up of X-rays, you remove the patient's kidneys instead of his appendix. Who should take responsibility?
   A. You, if you have good malpractice coverage.
   B. The other doctor, if you have a sharp lawyer.
   C. The hospital, if both of you have sharp lawyers.
   D. Any of the above.

2. You should be able to tell that the above is:
   A. A white blood cell.
   B. A streptococcus germ.
   C. The 4th green at Rolling Hills Golf Course.
   D. All of the above.

3. Complete this sentence: You should study to be a specialist, because _ .
   A. Unlike GPs, you don't have to mess with low income-producing ailments such as head colds and sore throats.
   B. A fancy title like cardiologist or dermatologist by itself jacks up your income 100%.
   C. Only another specialist in your exact same field can tell when you botch up a diagnosis.
   D. All of the above.

4. Complete this sentence. You should study to be a GP, because _____ .
   A. You can refer cases to a specialist and split his fee.
   B. You get to try out a lot more new and different fun drugs and see what happens.
   C. You can collect more of those little $20 and $30 office visits in pocketable tax-free cash.
   D. All of the above.

5. While being examined in his doctor's office, a patient goes into shock. The most probable cause is:
   A. The doctor kept him sitting only five minutes in the waiting room.
   B. The doctor is giving advice to another patient by phone, instead of making him come into the office.
   C. The doctor wrote out a prescription that was totally legible.
   D. All of the above.

6. Complete this sentence: A proper "Bedside Manner" is _____ .
   A. Seeming concerned about a patient's ailment while all the time trying to figure out if the I.R.S. will allow the business deduction you took for both your Cadillac and souped-up Alfa Romeo.
   B. Asking friendly questions about a patient's job in order to get a line on his income bracket so you can take him for the maximum fee he can stand.
   C. Making a hospital patient believe that the 30 seconds of chitchat you spend with him each day is evidence of your deep personal concern.
   D. Any of the above.

7. When a doctor runs a series of tests, he can be reasonably certain that they:
   A. Will be inconclusive.
   B. Are unnecessary.
   C. Will cost the patient a minimum of $100 in lab fees.
   D. All of the above.

8. As a doctor, it will be helpful for you to be connected with a top-rated hospital. Why?
   A. The comfy Doctor's Lounge is a great place to hide out in when you're ducking those pesky emergency calls.

ARTIST: GEORGE WOODBRIDGE
WRITER: FRANK JACOBS

B. Just the mention of the hospital's name can often net you a 50% increase in the size of your fee.
   C. Walking through the halls in a white coat and a stethoscope around your neck and hearing yourself being paged is a groovy ego trip.
   D. All of the above.

9.

As a doctor, you discover this auto crash victim on the highway. Your first concern is to:
   A. Do nothing until you have proof of his ability to pay.
   B. Do nothing until he signs a release stating you won't be sued for malpractice.
   C. Tell him to drink plenty of liquids and call your nurse for an appointment.
   D. Any of the above.

10. When a doctor is unable to pinpoint an ailment, which of these cop-outs is most effective?
   A. "I'd explain what you've got, but it's so technical you wouldn't understand it."
   B. "It's too early to tell."
   C. "It looks like nothing, but if it's still bothering you next week, call up for another appointment."
   D. Any of the above.

## SCORING

*If you answered "D." to all the questions, you have the ability to make a fine Doctor.*

Recently, a West Coast minister wrote a best-selling book entitled *All I Really Need to Know I Learned in Kindergarten.* At MAD our immediate response was, "What took you so long, Reverend?" We've always known that kindergarten teaches kids how to share, how to pick up their toys, and how to operate heavy machinery. But most kids learn other skills *long* before age five—how to brown nose, how avoid blame and how to play dumb! Just think back and surely you'll agree with us that...

# ALL YOU NEED TO KNOW YOU LEARNED IN NURSERY SCHOOL

ARTIST: PAUL COKER    WRITER: TOM KOCH

If you think you may mess things up, be sure there's someone else handy to blame it on.

Never volunteer for anything unless you're positive someone else will get picked.

Only guys with empty sand pails say they'll stop throwing sand in your face if you'll stop throwing it in theirs.

Don't waste time crying until there's somebody important around to hear you.

The only good time to start a fight is when the other person isn't ready.

If you never do anything, you can't get chewed out for doing part of it wrong.

Being offered a cookie by somebody who doesn't even like you usually means it's a lousy cookie.

After you break something, be sure you're not still there when someone finds out.

Never do your best, or they'll expect you to be that good every time.

We've had it! We're fed up! We're STEAMED at the way Hollywood keeps ripping off comic strips! Batman, Superman, Dick Tracy, Popeye and plenty of others have been turned into stinky movies by

# IF *Famous*

## WERE MA

# COMIC

### THE GODFATHER   By Charles Schulz

### PSYCHO   By Cathy Guisewite

producers who can't think up original ideas of their own. MAD thinks turnabout is fair play! It's about time the comic strip business did some ripping off of their own! Yeah!! Just imagine…

# Movies

## ADE INTO

# STRIPS

ARTIST AND WRITER: RUSS COOPER

**HONEY, I SHRUNK THE KIDS   By Bill Watterson**

**LEAN ON ME   By Garry Trudeau**

Do you stick your foot in your mouth so often that you know the shoe size of your face? Are

# A MAD GUIDE TO SOCIAL
## How Not to Go fr

ARTIST: BOB JONES

your manners so awful that even Morton Downey Jr. avoids you? Then this course is for you! It's

# BEHAVIOR

## m Bad to Worse!

WRITER: CHRIS HART

# ONE DAY DURING A CAVALRY ATTACK

**WASH BORED GAMES DEPT.**

*Do you remember when your family would go on those long boring car trips? And do you remember how your Mother would try to keep you kids entertained with "Auto Bingo"... that stupid little game with the cows and stop signs, etc.? Well, what we have here is a similar game for another boring activity kids have to do with their parents. Here's*

# LAUNDROMAT
# BINGO

ARTIST: BOB CLARKE          WRITER: RURIK TYLER

OVER-LOADED MACHINE

TANGLED CARTS

ADVICE-SEEKER

TV ADDICT

TANGLED CLOTHES

# MAD MINI-MOVIES
# Featuring The Fickle Finger Of Fate

ARTIST & WRITER: AL JAFFEE

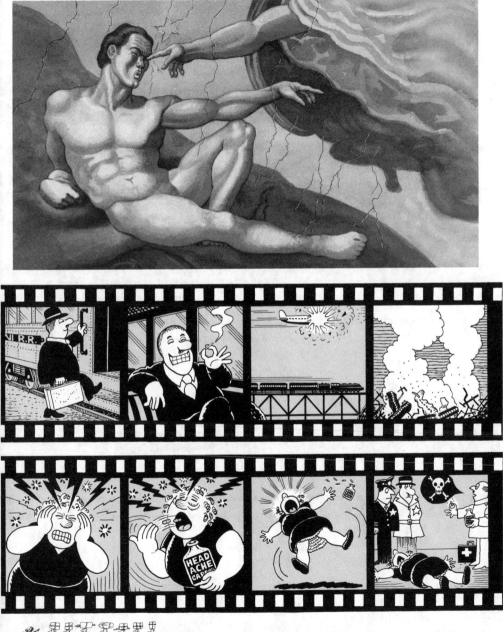

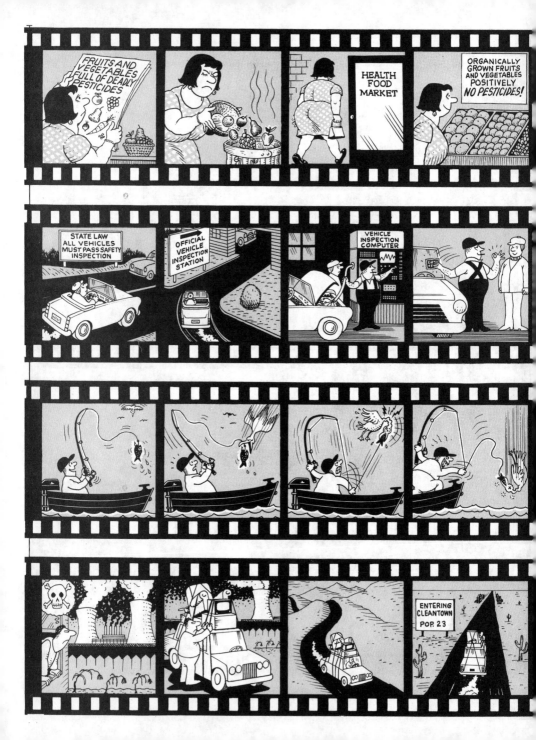

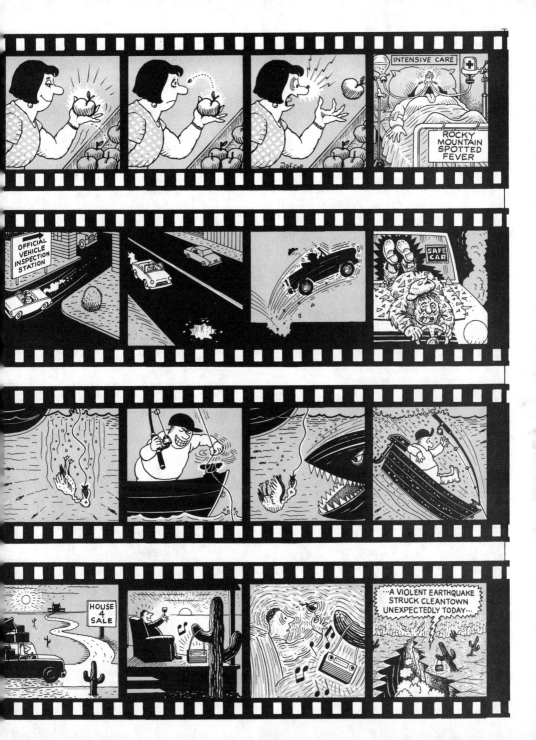

**Cassandra** was given the gift of prophecy because of her looks, but in an ironic twist, no one believed anything that came out of her mouth.

**Milli Vanilli** was given the gifts of record contracts and Grammys because of their looks, but in an ironic twist, no one will ever again believe anything that comes out of their mouths.

**PARALLEL BARBS DEPT.**

Thousands of years ago, the ancient Greeks and Romans worshipped a plethora of goddesses and gods which they believed to be all powerful and omnipotent. Of course, this was just mindless superstition. Modern civilization has taught us that only rock stars are all powerful and omnipotent! Still, from Mars to Martika, from Janus to Janet Jackson, these bigger than life figures have been revered and idolized for centuries. So, join us now, won't you? as MAD exposes...

# THE STARTLING ANCIENT MYTHC

ARTIST: RICK TULKA

**Hephaestus** was hailed for being the god of fire. Despite being short, unattractive and misshapen, he somehow managed to wed the most beautiful goddess in Olympia.

**Billy Joel** is hailed for "We Didn't Start the Fire." Despite being short, unattractive and misshapen, he somehow managed to wed Chrisy Brinkley, the most beautiful goddess in the swimsuit issue.

**The Phoenix** was a mysterious animal who hid in a secret location every 500 years, set itself on fire and reemerged from its ashes with a new appearance.

**Michael Jackson** is a mysterious animal who hides in secret locations and releases an album every five years. He's been known to set himself on fire, and he frequently reemerges with a new appearance.

# SIMILARITIES BETWEEN
# OGY & MODERN ROCK

WRITER: DESMOND DEVLIN

**Medusa** was a frightening monster in ancient Greece, with grotesque, slimy snakes instead of hair. No living thing could look directly at her face without being turned into stone.

**Prince** is a frightening monster at PMRC headquarters, with grotesque, slimy hair. No living thing can look directly at his face without being turned into a punching bag by his private goon squad.

**Midas,** a minor king, received a priceless gift—anything he touched turned into gold. He quickly became rich with his new talent, but as soon as he got his power, he lost it. His ears were changed into those of an ass, and although he tried to hide under his hat, his shame was obvious to everyone.

**2 Live Crew,** a minor rap group, received a priceless gift—prosecutors craving headlines. They quickly became rich, but as soon as they got their audience, they lost it. Fans with ears thought the group asses, and while they tried to hide behind the First Amendment, their lack of talent was obvious to everyone.

**The Sphinx** was a terrible creature, sent as a plague by Hera, who held Greek citizens hostage with its riddle no one could answer: "What has four legs in the morning, two legs in the afternoon and three in the evening?"

**New Kids on the Block** are a terrible group sent as a plague by Maurice Starr, and hold radio listeners hostage with their riddle no one can answer: "How did five total white-bread dweebs get up the nerve to call their incredibly lame debut album *Hangin' Tough?*"

**Orpheus** reacted to the tragic death of his wife by descending into the dark and slime of the realm of the dead. He convinced the ghouls of the underworld that it was important that she be restored to life.

"Biographer" **Albert Goldman** reacted to the tragic death of John Lennon by descending into the dark and slime of celebrity exposés. He convinced the ghoulish public that it was important that false and vicious rumors about Lennon be brought to life.

# ONE TUESDAY MORNING

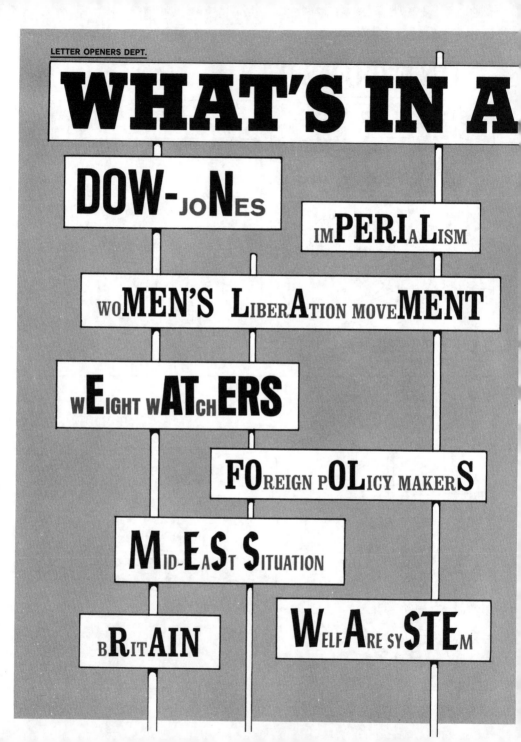

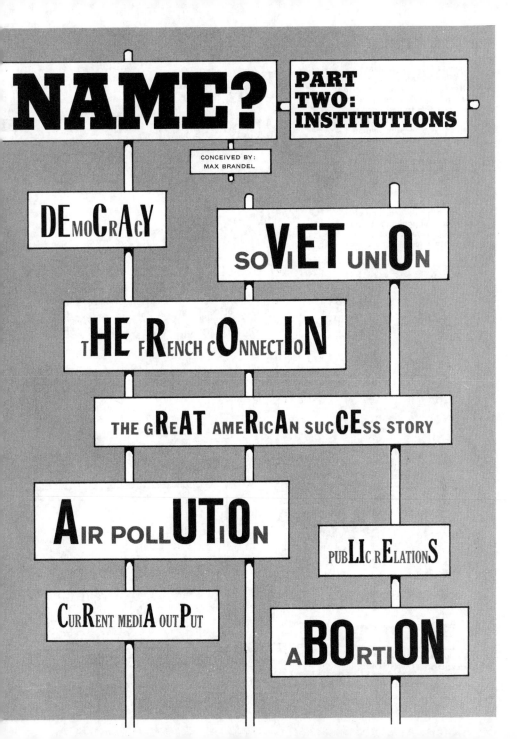

In June of 2000, President Bill Clinton called a press conference to divert attention from yet another scandal...oh yeah, and also to announce the success of The Human Genome Project — a 7-year, multi-billion dollar effort by thousands of scientists to "map" our DNA for the first time in history. According to medical researchers, results from the Genome Project will enable us to cure diseases, prevent birth defects and slow the effects of aging. Yeah, yeah... big whoop. What WE found that was more interesting were these really...

# AMAZING FACTS

## (AND SURPRISING DISCOVERIES) FROM THE HUMAN GENOME DNA PROJECT

Homo sapiens share 99% of their genetic makeup with chimpanzees...but only 43% with the WWF's Chyna!

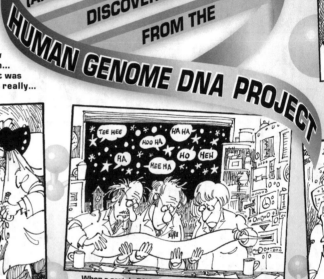

When a certain DNA string is played backwards on a gene-sequencing machine, it translates into "We can't believe you morons fell for that 'Paul is dead' gag we pulled back in '68! Signed, The Universe"!

Even with the success of the Human Genome Project, not a single American college student has been inspired to switch majors to Genetics from trendy, kick-back ones like Philosophy Of Women's Studies Through *Sex And The City* or Feng Shui For Your Minivan!

There is almost a 100% correlation between having the gene for alcoholism and the gene for mistakenly thinking the entire world wants to hear you sing Karaoke all friggin' night long!

ARTIST: PAUL COKER      WRITER: MIKE SNIDER

If the entire Genome code of 3 billion A's, C's, G's and T's is pronounced aloud, it sounds exactly like Gilbert Gottfried's standup act!

Incredibly, the genes for gullibility, judgementalism and joining the Republican Party are all right next to each other on the same chromosome!

The whole Human Genome can now be accessed on the Internet and, according to surveys, is more interesting than 57.8% of AOL chat rooms!

The long-accepted double-helix structure of DNA is actually only a single-helix; Watson & Crick were both drunk as hell from the lab Christmas party when they looked through the microscope!

The wealth of new scientific knowledge gained from the Genome Project virtually guarantees that, henceforth, every kid in America will flunk high school Biology the first time around and have to take it over again!

Congressmen and Senators are five times more likely to approve funding for Genetics research if the phrase "cloning Pamela Anderson" appears somewhere in the appropriations bill!

If the entire Human Genome were stretched out flat and laid end to end, it would be almost as long as the line of health insurers and drug companies looking to use that information to price-gouge and deny medical coverage!

# THE MAD D.

## CHAPTER ONE

See the DJ work!
Work! Work! Work!
First he gives the news!
Then he does a commercial!
After that the weather report!
Then he does another commercial!
Next he gives the sports update!
Followed by a station break and the correct time!
Question: Why is he called "disc jockey" when he hasn't
    played a disc in the past 47 minutes?

## CHAPTER THREE

Hear the studio technicians laughing!
Har! Har! Har!
They laugh at everything the DJ says!
"It's raining outside—lovely weather for ducks!"
Har! Har! Har!
Do they really think the DJ is funny and amusing?
Let's rephrase the question—Do they want to keep their jobs?
Har! Har! Har!

## CHAPTER FIVE

Hear the DJ speckle his banter with interesting information!
Like how the gang at Via Veneto Ristorante on West 54th Street
    listen in every day!
And how Irma at A-1 Dry Cleaners on East 23rd Street wears the
    station's sweat shirt!
And how Vinnie, the expert mechanic at Sassone Auto Repair,
    personally requested this next great golden oldie!
What a nice guy the DJ is for passing out this valuable
    information!
Ever wonder where the DJ eats, has his clothes laundered,
    and his car fixed—for free?

# J. PRIMER

ARTIST:
JACK DAVIS

WRITER:
LOU SILVERSTONE

## CHAPTER TWO

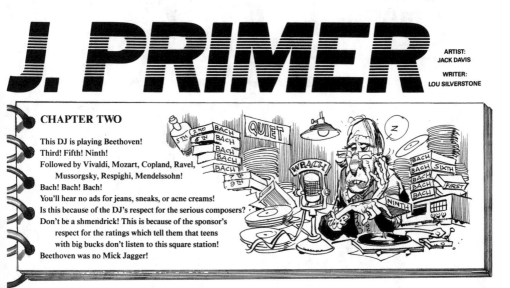

This DJ is playing Beethoven!
Third! Fifth! Ninth!
Followed by Vivaldi, Mozart, Copland, Ravel,
    Mussorgsky, Respighi, Mendelssohn!
Bach! Bach! Bach!
You'll hear no ads for jeans, sneaks, or acne creams!
Is this because of the DJ's respect for the serious composers?
Don't be a shmendrick! This is because of the sponsor's
    respect for the ratings which tell them that teens
    with big bucks don't listen to this square station!
Beethoven was no Mick Jagger!

## CHAPTER FOUR

See the DJ is interviewing his guest!
He plays his guest's recordings!
He tells his guest how great he is!
At the show's end, he invites his guest to come back anytime!
Does he really like the guest that much?
Does he really think the guest is as wonderful as
    he said all show?
Don't be a shmendrick! The DJ likes anyone who'll
    do his show free!

## CHAPTER SIX

See the angry man and lady!
They listen to this "zany" DJ every morning!
They listen to his vulgarity, obscenity, and blasts
    at the flag, mom, and apple pie!
Why do they listen to him?
So they can record all the vulgar and obscene things
    he says—and then write to the FCC demanding the
    DJ be taken off the air!

# A MAD LOOK AT... HUNT

# ING

ARTIST & WRITER: SERGIO ARAGONES

In a recent issue, you may recall, we gave a timely and puckish lesson in onomatopoeias! We cleared up the popular misconception that an onomatopoeia is a Rumanian fish delicacy! In the likely event that you missed it, an onomatopoeia is a word that *sounds* like the thing it denotes—like "squish," for example. Anyway, we've continued our exhaustive research into this matter and we're exhausted. But as luck would have it, we've managed to milk another article out of this esoteric pap! We've discovered that if you listen carefully, you'll find that some noises actually sound like famous people's names. Confused? You won't be after checking out these ...

Did you ever notice that a three-step ladder has a big label on it warning you not to use the top two steps? And that light fixture instructions tell you what wattage to use "to reduce risk of fire"? Why all this over-cautiousness?

# WARNING LABELS

## Designed to Head Off

ARTIST: BOB CLARKE    WRITER: DICK DEBARTOLO

### ROAD CHIEF SUPER BIKE

**WARNING:** Do not ride this bicycle on highways, streets, roads, sidewalks or any other surfaces not recommended by manufacturer.

Protective gloves, footgear, helmet, goggles and body padding **must be worn** by rider as well as anyone standing in the vicinity of this bicycle.

Attempting to balance yourself on two wheels can result in **physical injury.**

Manufacturer **assumes no responsibility** for consequences if bicycle is ridden at speeds in excess of one (1) mile per hour.

### STICKY STUFF GLUE®

DO NOT use Sticky Stuff Glue® on Plastic, Wood, Paper, Fabric or any other materials not expressly covered by our warranty.

Once tube is open, DO NOT inhale or exhale within a two-mile radius of this product.

Store unused portion at Room Temperature, but UNDER NO CIRCUMSTANCE should it be stored indoors.

Any and all leftover glue MUST BE DISPOSED OF using Federally Approved Guidelines for explosives and other hazardous toxic materials.

### HI-GENE—the sanitary straw
#### SAFETY GUIDELINES

1. Removal of paper wrapper will result in contamination of straw due to atmospheric bacteria, voiding any and all sanitary claims made by manufacturer.
2. Placement of straw in hot, cold or warm liquids will severely shorten the life expectancy of this product.
3. Do not place either end of straw in mouth or gagging may occur.
4. For maximum protection against germs and possible infection, manufacturer recommends discarding straw after each sip and using a new one.

**Simple! In an attempt to limit their liability from lawsuits, manufacturers are putting more and more warnings on their products. How far will this warning trend go? Probably to new heights of stupidity! You'll see as we now look at...**

# OF THE FUTURE

## Potential Lawsuits

### SNOWMAN
### Air Conditioner

FOR SAFE OPERATION OF YOUR SNOWMAN AIR CONDITIONER, FOLLOW THESE SAFETY RULES CAREFULLY!

a. Shut off main power source to your entire block before plugging unit into a properly-wired electrical outlet.

b. Do not place this unit on a window sill without first supporting sill with cast iron I-beams.

c. Under no circumstance should this unit be used in areas of high humidity or extreme heat.

d. Touching or adjusting knobs while unit is running is not recommended. To adjust Temperature Setting from low to medium or medium to high cool, shut off unit, adjust setting and wait six hours before restarting.

### THE BIG HIT HAMMER
#### READ BEFORE USING

DO NOT use your Big Hit Hammer to strike any object other than household nails appearing on our approved list of authorized household nails.

BE SURE to allow hammer to cool off between strikes.

FOR SAFEST RESULTS, use your Big Hit hammer only under the strict supervision of a Professionally Licensed Carpenter.

### LITTLE INDIAN TOY BOW & ARROW SET
#### WARNING! THIS TOY IS NOT A TOY! WARNING!

• Do not view or open this package unless in the presence of an adult American Indian.

• Keep arrows in a secure place, far away from bow.

• Keep bow in a secure place, far away from arrows.

• Under no circumstance should this bow be used to shoot arrows at any person, animal, object or target!

# DUCK EDWING HANGS
# THE

ARTIST AND WRIT

# OUT AT MALL

ER: DUCK EDWING

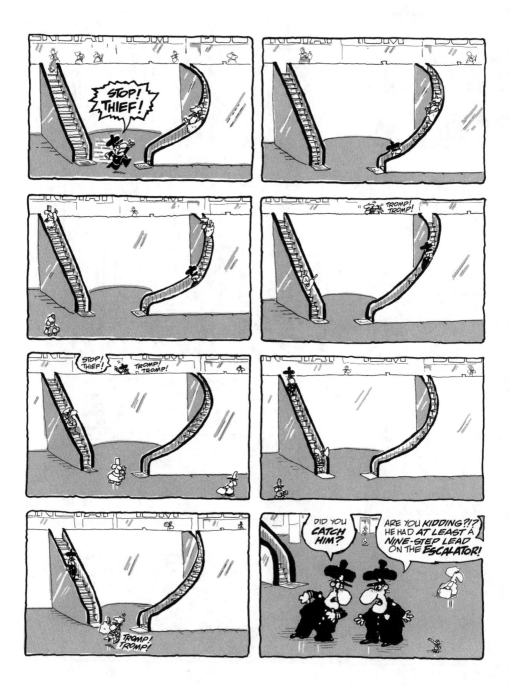

# YOUR MAD HOROSCOPE

TODAY'S BIRTHDAY:

Loved ones are grateful if you try not to spit while blowing out the candles on your cake.

## ARIES
### March 21—April 19
A strange shifting in the stars may cause you to experience some pleasure while viewing a rerun of Sheriff Lobo. Do not worry. This is only an illusion, and will pass, like a cheap meal. Do not treat lovemaking as a hobby or you could do permanent damage to yourself with wrongful applications of model airplane glue.

## TAURUS
### April 20—May 20
Your enthusiasm is contagious and so is your rash, so lay off the romantic entanglements. Complete one project before beginning a second. However, it is not necessary to complete one project if you're planning to move directly on to a third. Your grades can improve overnight, providing you write legibly on your arm.

## GEMINI
### May 21—June 21
After years of diligent brownnosing, you rise to the upper echelons of corporate power. Too bad your company is about to go under! This is typical of the way your luck has been running recently and will continue to run for some time. Do not fret! You still have a lot of drive left in you. Take a trip to Detroit!

## MOON CHILDREN
### June 22—July 22
The position of your stars is identical to those of Aquarius, Capricorn and Sagittarius. How this can be, we don't know. (But it does go a long way in explaining your lack of originality in life!) We suggest that from now on you read those three horoscopes and then pick out any advice you think looks good to you.

## LEO
### July 23—August 22
Your main stars have shifted in such a way that, when connected by straight lines, they strongly resemble either a profile of Alexander Haig or an aerial view of New Jersey. (This is open to artistic interpretation.) Such a configuration strongly suggests that you will soon be overtaken by a desire to invade Secaucus.

## VIRGO
### August 23—September 22
Give a hand at home. Get ahead at work. Give a passing stranger the eye, and a passing motorist the finger. Lose an arm and a leg at the track. Get something off your chest. Lend your ears to fellow countrymen. Stick your nose in other people's business. Get your ass in a sling. Put your foot in your mouth. Hang loose.

## LIBRA
### September 23—October 23
The position of Yank, the main star influencing your destiny, advises that now is an excellent time for a torrid romantic fling. However, the position of the Moral Majority condemns a torrid romantic fling as a no-no. The choice is yours. Either be bored out of your skull on earth, or burn for all eternity in hell!

## SCORPIO
### October 24—November 21
A good day! An annoying neighbor will cease to bother you as you are evicted in the AM. Improve your personal ties by throwing out the very wide ones with the polka dot prints. Nobody has been wearing them for years! Look for your mailbox to be flooded with letters as someone pours an entire can of alphabet soup in it.

## SAGITTARIUS
### November 22—December 21
A study of your stars has failed to uncover any information about your future. This could mean that you have no future. In fact, it's quite possible that you recently passed away, and your loved ones have been derelict in making the proper arrangements. Seek the advice of an expert, however, before having yourself cremated.

## CAPRICORN
### December 22—January 19
Take a chance on a new co-worker. They're only a dollar each and, who knows, you may just win her! The AM may seem horrible today, however, it will begin to look better and better once you see what the PM has in store for you. An unexpected raise and promotion at work enables you to pay for your emergency brain surgery.

## AQUARIUS
### January 20—February 18
Your Moon has very quietly moved from the House of Leo to the Condominium of Stanley. (Tax Purposes.) This signals a dramatic upheaval in your emotional state. Warm thoughts will singe your brain. Because Uranus and your piles are one, you could be in big danger! Beware of fools, envious of your many shortcomings.

## PISCES
### February 19—March 20
A sensational day! An unexpected romance blooms out of a chance encounter at a local vigilante meeting. Be frank with your boss. That way, when you screw up, he will fire Frank and not you! Put your priorities in alphabetical order and stop accepting second best. It's much too good for you!

**WRITER: JOHN FICARRA**

## RED-HOT PEPPER-FLAVORED TONGUE DEPRESSORS

No need to describe the hysterical reaction when you use one of these on your patients!

## PORNOGRAPHIC INK BLOTS

Dirty pictures cleverly hidden in Rorschach cards! Ask them what they see... and they'll be too ashamed to tell you! Lots of laughs!!

## ITCHING PLASTER CASTS

Mix our "Itching Powder" into the plaster before applying any type cast! Drives 'em crazy!

Attention, all you Doctors out there! It's time you exploded once and for all the myth that Doctors are serious people, intent on healing the sick, with no

# MAD'S PRAC CATALOGUE F

ARTIST: AL JAFFEE

## COWS' INTESTINES

Leave these lying around Post-Op, and watch their faces when they come to!

## FUNNY INSTRUMENT BAG

Contains 8" needles, rusty saws, bent pliers, One look and they pass out!

## BLURRY EYE CHARTS

Watch them squint, strain and rub their eyes while you howl with laughter!

time for foolishness and no sense of humor. (By the way, what are you doing, reading MAD?!) You can accomplish this impossible task by using the items in

# TICAL JOKE
# OR DOCTORS

WRITER: BEPPE SABATINI

## MANGLED I.D. BRACELETS

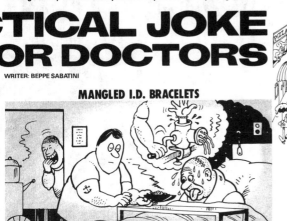

Slip one of these into a patient's plate of hash before the Orderly takes in his tray of hospital food. Yeow! Perfect for your stubborn overweights!

## "PLEASE DISROBE" SIGNS

A scream! Put them in your waiting room, your hallway, your lobby—everywhere! Then, switch 'em all on! Your office'll look like a Nudist Colony!

## RUBBER NOSES

Slip one of these onto your nose job patient before she comes out of the anesthetic! When she does, she'll take one look and go through the roof!

## FAKE PRESCRIPTIONS

Each one has pre-printed swear words in Latin! Watch 'em get punched out by their Pharmacist!

## ADULT-PROOF PILL BOTTLES

Watch as they struggle for hours because these special bottles cannot be opened! Perfect for hypochondriac (and other complaining) patients!

## DRIBBLING SPECIMEN BOTTLES

Wait'll they try carrying these into your Lab!

We've all sung about Old MacDonald and his cows and pigs and sheep. But farming has changed, and these days he's got more to contend with than the old "moo-moo here" and "oink-oink there." As you'll see in this updated version of ...

# OLD Mac

Old MacDonald farmed the land—E-I-E-I-O!
But failed to prosper as he'd planned—E-I-E-I-O!
With a wheat blight here and a corn blight there—
Here a blight, there a blight, ev'ry crop a sad sight;
Old MacDonald lost four grand—E-I-E-I-O!

Old MacDonald, smart guy he—E-I-E-I-O!
Sprayed all his crops with DDT—E-I-E-I-O!
With a cough, cough here and a hack, hack there—
Here a choke, there a choke, worse than cig-a-rette smoke;
A wheat blight here and a corn blight there—
Here a blight, there a blight, ev'ry crop a sad sight;
Old MacDonald groaned "Why me?"—E-I-E-I-O!

Old MacDonald prayed for rain—E-I-E-I-O!
To save his rotting fields of grain—E-I-E-I-O!
With a dry spell here and a dry spell there—
Here a drought, there a drought, ev'ry harvest wiped out;
A cough, cough here and a hack, hack there—
Here a choke, there a choke, worse than cig-a-rette smoke;
A wheat blight here and a corn blight there—
Here a blight, there a blight, ev'ry crop a sad sight;
Old MacDonald prayed in vain—E-I-E-I-O!

24

# DONALD

ARTIST: GERRY GERSTEN

IDEA: DAN LOZER    WRITER: FRANK JACOBS

Old MacDonald, sad to say—E-I-E-I-O!
Had cred-i-tors he could not pay—E-I-E-I-O!
With a seed bill here, a manure bill there—
Here a debt, there a debt, making ulcers worse yet;
A dry spell here and a dry spell there—
Here a drought, there a drought, ev'ry harvest wiped out;
A cough, cough here and a hack, hack there—
Here a choke, there a choke, worse than cig-a-rette smoke;
A wheat blight here and a corn blight there—
Here a blight, there a blight, ev'ry crop a sad sight;
Old MacDonald moaned "Oy vey!"—E-I-E-I-O!

Old MacDonald, sought relief—E-I-E-I-O!
He called D.C. and hailed the chief—E-I-E-I-O!
Got a con job here and a snow job there—
Here a stall, there a stall, up against a stone wall;
A seed bill here, a manure bill there—
Here a debt, there a debt, making ulcers worse yet;
A dry spell here and a dry spell there—
Here a drought, there a drought, ev'ry harvest wiped out;
A cough, cough here and a hack, hack there—
Here a choke, there a choke, worse than cig-a-rette smoke;
A wheat blight here and a corn blight there—
Here a blight, there a blight, ev'ry crop a sad sight;
Old MacDonald cried "Good Grief!"—E-I-E-I-O!

Old MacDonald got bad news—E-I-E-I-O!
His bank refused his IOUs—E-I-E-I-O!
With a "Screw you!" here and a "Screw you!" there—
Land they took, cows they took, wiping out the poor schnook;
Got a con job here, and snow job there—
Here a stall, there a stall, up against a stone wall;
A seed bill here, a manure bill there—
Here a debt, there a debt, making ulcers worse yet;
A dry spell here and a dry spell there—
Here a drought, there a drought, ev'ry harvest wiped out;
A cough, cough here and a hack, hack there—
Here a choke, there a choke, worse than cig-a-rette smoke;
A wheat blight here and a corn blight there—
Here a blight, there a blight, ev'ry crop a sad sight;
OLD MacDONALD NOW SELLS SHOES—E-I-E-I-O!

# ONE DAY ON THE HIGHWAY

It's another Election Year. Once again incumbent and upstart politicians are crawling out from the sewers and vying for various political offices around the country. Because there are so many candidates, the Primary System was devised as a way of winnowing the field... separating the wheat from the chaff...allowing the cream to rise to the top. This process used to work! But no more! You'll see what we mean as you rhyme along with the following...

# 10 LiTTLE CANDIDATES

**Ten** little candidates,
Their records in review;
One took some "contributions"
From an S&L or two;
Said he, "Somebody set me up;
The charges I deny;"
This brings our number down to nine;
Oh, sure, and horses fly.

ARTIST: PAUL COKER     WRITER: FRANK JACOBS

**Ten** little candidates,
Still in the race somehow;
There's one, we hear, who dodged the draft;
Said he, "Don't have a cow!"
I sweated bullets building my
Political career;"
You'd think by now there would be eight;
Get real! They're all still here.

**Ten** little candidates,
All upright gents, you'd think;
One bounced a hundred checks or so,
Which caused an awful stink;
Said he, "I've been the victim of
An underhanded plot;"
In case you wonder where we stand,
We're down to seven—NOT!

**Ten** little candidates,
All claiming that they care;
One lobbied for a logging firm
That stripped a forest bare;
He's got an offshore drilling plan
That scares us half to death;
We should be down to six by now;
Oh, yeah? Don't hold your breath.

**Ten** little candidates,
Still running, if you please;
Said one, "To save our country,
We must crush the Japanese!
The imports that they dump on us,"
He said, "must soon be gone,"
Then drove off in his Subaru;
We're down to five? Dream on!

**Ten** little candidates,
All getting in their licks;
One smeared his foe with TV ads,
Midst other dirty tricks;
Said he, "My staffers are to blame;
They planned it all themselves;"
Which brings our number down to four
If you believe in elves.

**Ten** little candidates,
Each hoping to prevail;
One came out with a budget plan
That's guaranteed to fail;
If he gets in, our lives will be
More screwed up than they are;
You say we should be down to three?
Nice try, but no cigar.

DEBT - 3,857,400,
000,000,000,000,
0,000,000,
000,000,000
= NO NEW TAXES
+ FREE LUNCH

1208

**Ten** little candidates,
Each pondering his fate;
One claimed he was "pro-family"
While cheating on his mate;
Said he, "Don't take some bimbo's word—
She's only spouting lies;"
Guess what? The number hasn't changed;
Surprise! Surprise! Surprise!

**Ten** little candidates,
Still with the urge to run;
One tickled crowds with racial jokes;
Said he, "'Twas all in fun;
The darkies know I'm on their side;
I've got one on my staff;"
What's that? You think we're down to one?
Ha-ha! It is to laugh.

**Ten** little candidates,
Who will not disappear,
And please don't ask us to explain
How come they're all still here;
We'll find out on Election Day
Which one the voters choose,
Although, by now, it should be clear
Whoever wins, we lose.

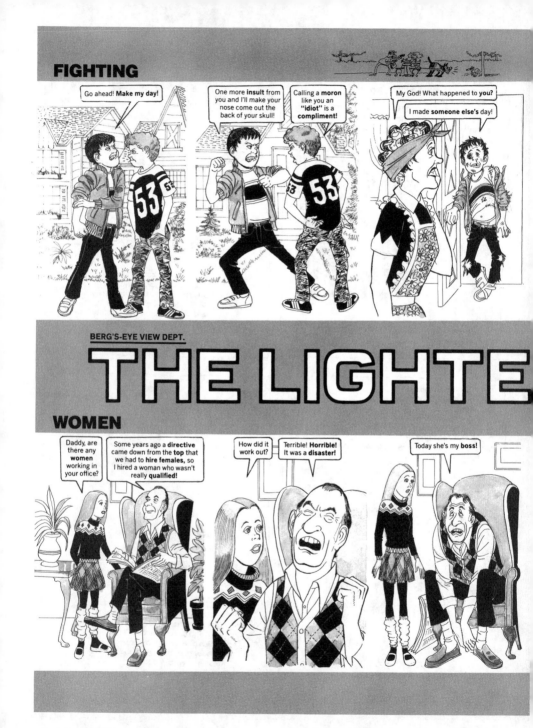

Many of us are familiar with the titles of famous books of the past—even if we never bothered to actually take the time to read any of them! Their authors gave them the titles they thought were most appropriate at the time. But if those same books were written today, their names would probably be somewhat different to reflect our modern times. To see what we mean, check out...

# MAD'S UPDATED BOOK TITLES
## FOR THE 90'S

MS. MINIVER

LADY CHATTERLEY'S LIVE-IN FRIEND

REBECCA of Sunnybrook High-rise

DAYS OF WINE COOLERS AND ROSES

Goodbye, Mr. Microchips

CRIME AND PLEA BARGAINING

UNCLE TOM'S CONDO

The RED BADGE of CHUTZPAH

WAR AND DETENTE

ARTIST: BOB CLARKE          WRITER: WILLIAM GARVIN

ATTENTION K. MARX SHOPPERS DEPT.

With the recent stunning collapse of many Communist regimes all over the world, it may just be a matter of time until we see ads for the...

WORLD COMI

EVERYTHING MUST GO!

Dros Vyutnya! I'm CRAZY GORBY, here with loads of used Glasnost bargains! Just look at our first item: **25,000 Plaster Busts of Lenin!** They can easily be converted into busts of your favorite Western heroes, including Shakespeare, Frank Zappa, Steven Spielberg and more!

ARTIST: JOHN POUND

You'll want several of these...The **Official Jock-strap of the Soviet "Women's" Olympic Weight Lifting Team!** The 1984 Olympics boycott left us with too many, but our loss is your gain!

Here we have some lovely **Wrist and Ankle "Jewelry" from Siberia!** They were formerly used to restrain inmates...uh, mental patients, who were all miraculously "cured" when I took over the government!

# ...MUNISM CLOSE-OUT SALE

Need paper to jot down phone messages and shopping lists? Try these **Pre-Marked Ballot Note Pads!** Before Glasnost, we printed up a 10-year supply of already-filled-out voter ballots! Luckily, they're as one-sided as the elections we planned to use them for!

We've got boxcars full of **Marxist-Version History Books**... Every one a comedy classic! Just listen to these titles: "Stalin: Prince of Peace," "1979: The Soviet Rescue of Afghanistan," "The Happy Days of Mao's Cultural Revolution" and hundreds more!

WRITER: MIKE SNIDER

We've recently removed all of our **Electronic Bugs** from the American Embassy in Moscow and they can be yours! Each listening device is KGB-guaranteed for one full year!

Men! Check out these **Custom Soviet Ill-Fitting Suits!** We've got racks and racks of 'em! For proper fit, be sure to specify a size OTHER than your own!

Here's a handyman's special: **127,345,000 Gallons of Drab Socialist Paint!** Available in gray, off-gray, brownish-gray and other depressing grays!

Hoo-boy! pick up a few of our **10,000 East German Border Dogs** and never fear intruders in your home again! These easy-to-care-for pups eat anything—or anyone!

Hey, Comrades! Forget the Berlin Wall! Give the souvenir that GLOWS in the DARK! **A Piece of Chernobyl!**

And look at this great **free T-shirt** you'll get with every $25 purchase! Order now! I don't know how much longer they—or I—will last!

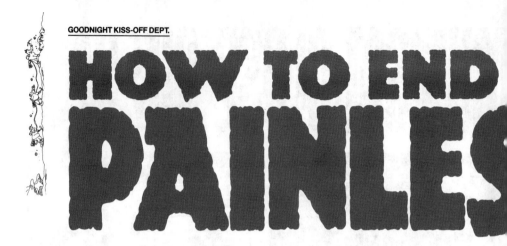

# HOW TO END
# PAINLES

I know holds that can paralyze a 200 pound linebacker!

Have you ever been to a baby lamb slaughter house? It's brutal!

I gotta get outta here! There's my truant officer and I'm supposed to be in my social studies class now!

Let's walk past the Post Office, I'd like to see if my picture is still hanging!

# A DATE
# SLY

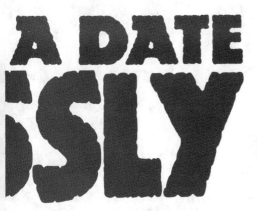

ARTIST AND WRITER: PAUL PETER PORGES

Oops! Nine-thirty! Time to call my parole officer!

It's a mysterious rash that has medical science baffled!

Why pay top dollar for tickets when we stand a good chance of sneaking into this concert free!

I ordered live snails for two!

Can you cash my unemployment check?

What's in a movie title? Maybe a hidden, true review! Here's...

# MAD'S INSTANT MOVIE

ARTIST: GERRY GERSTEN
WRITER: RUSS COOPER

TEXAS**VI**L**LE**

JACO**B**'S L**AD**DER

HA**RleM** NIGHT**S**

# LATE ONE NIGHT IN A WATERFRONT TAVERN

For years, motorists have been driving by road signs and reading them one at a time, even though it's far more telling to read them as a group! Yes, their true meanings are easily seen when...

**When ROADSIDE Signs overLAP**

ARTIST: GEORGE WOODBRIDGE    WRITER: HENRY CLARK

*is!! The next time your personal chatter is tuned-in to by unwanted ears, give 'em more than they bargained for with MAD's patented ...*

# ROPPER-EKERS

**WRITER: MIKE SNIDER**

## IN A CLASSROOM

Of **course** I can **smell it!** He's **sitting** right in **front of me!**

Well, if **I** had something **that gross on the** back of **my neck,** I'd sure **know about it!**

My **boyfriend** left town so I'm just going to **pick someone** out of this **class** and **swear** he's the **father** of my **child!**

## IN ADJOINING APARTMENTS

I **can't tell** if the **gas is on** or **not**—give me a **match!**

Spike's new girl **hates Heavy Metal,** so we'll be **rehearsing here from now on!**

Who **cares** where they all went! As long as the **Pest-Control** guy got 'em out of **our** kitchen!

## ON AN AIRPLANE

Well, as long as the **co-pilot's sober!**

Tell the **stewardess?** What the **hell** is **she** supposed to do, **climb out** and **fix it herself?**

It's called **Spontaneous Projectile Vomit.** I never know **when** it's going to **strike,** but when it does, **watch out!**

It is widely believed that a person experiences four psychological phases when grieving over death. They are: Denial—you refuse to believe the obvious; Anger—you get really pissed off at the circumstances; Depression—you become distressed at the realization; Acceptance—okay, you just deal with it. Here at MAD, we figured that there are some other situations in life when people experience these same grieving phases! So, we will now ask you to look at yourself and your emotions as you read up on...

## BEING FAT

DENIAL

ANGER

DEPRESSION

ACCEPTANCE

## AGING

DENIAL

ANGER

DEPRESSION

ACCEPTANCE

## BEING LOST

DENIAL

ANGER

DEPRESSION

ACCEPTANCE

# MAD STAGES OF...

ARTIST AND WRITER: RICK TULKA

## BALDNESS

DENIAL

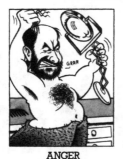
ANGER

DEPRESSION

ACCEPTANCE

## NAUSEA

DENIAL

ANGER

DEPRESSION

ACCEPTANCE

## STUPIDITY

DENIAL

ANGER

DEPRESSION

ACCEPTANCE

It's said "True love is a many splendor thing," and this being the case, every girl longs to meet her perfect match, her own Prince Charming, the proverbial Mr. "Right." Unfortunately, it's also said, "A good man is hard to find" and this makes finding Mr. "Right" more difficult than finding

# GUYS YOU'RE LIKELY TO MEET BEFO

ARTIST: ALYSE NEWMAN

MR. "RIGHT—'TIL YOU MENTION THE WORD 'MARRIAGE'"

MR. "RIGHT OUT OF THE 60'S"

MR. "RIGHT INTO THE BACK SEAT"

MR. "RIGHT AWAY, MOTHER!"

MR. "RIGHT AFTER THE POST-GAME SHOW"

MR. "RIGHT OFF THE ASSEMBLY LINE"

*an intelligent person in the audience of the Morton Downey, Jr. Show! We don't mean to discourage you ladies, but the sad truth is you'll probably get involved with an impressive bunch of losers before you finally find the fellow for you. So brace yourself for the worst, 'cause here are the...*

# RE MR. 'RIGHT'

**WRITER: MIKE SNIDER**

MR. "RIGHT GUARD CANDIDATE"

MR. "RIGHT ON, OLLIE NORTH!"

MR. "RIGHT DOWN THE MIDDLE"

MR. "RIGHT INTO INTENSIVE CARE GO YOUR PARENTS!"

MR. "RIGHT AFTER MY DIVORCE, BABE"

MR. "RIGHTSIDE-DOWN"

*Remember the time you played Red Rover with your friends and you got ready to run and break through their locked arms? Remember your surprise when instead your so-called "friends" held*

# RULES FOR GAMES THE W

## BATTLESHIP (for 2-year-olds)

1. Steal game from underneath your brother's bed.

2. Swallow all of the little plastic ships.

3. Go to the hospital to have your stomach pumped.

4. Add up points for each ship the doctor recovers from your stomach.

5. If you get 10 or more points, you win!

ARTIST: JACK DAVIS

## SCRABBLE (for 8 to 14-year-olds)

1. Make sure that all parents and adults are a safe distance away from the board.

2. Each player grabs a handful of letters.

3. All players take turns trying to spell the most obscene, profane and foul words they can think of.

4. Award extra points for dirty words with more than four letters and for medical terms.

*you down and ran off with your shorts? You fool! Games NEVER stick to regulation play! To pre-pare you for those unexpected developments (sorry, we can't retrieve your shorts), MAD presents...*

# AY THEY'RE <u>REALLY</u> PLAYED

## TRIVIAL PURSUIT (for 60–year–olds)

**1.** Play the game normally until a question comes up about MTV, Nintendo, or Madonna.

**2.** Stop the game and start talking about the good old days before there was any such thing as MTV, Nintendo or Madonna.

**3.** Eat a big bowl of fiber and go to bed early.

WRITER: MICHAEL GOODWIN

## FOOTBALL (for 7 to 10–year–olds)

**1.** Begin playing in a friendly manner.

**2.** Continue until one team outscores the other by 50 points.

**3.** If you are the losing team, begin to play dirty.

**4.** When a fight breaks out, erase the score.

**5.** The team with the least amount of players to run home crying wins!

# DODGEBALL (for 8 to 13-year-olds)

**1.** Have all the popular kids form a circle around all the unpopular kids.

**2.** Peg all the girls first to get them out of the way.

**3.** Use the inflatable rubber ball until there is only one boy left in the middle.

**4.** If he is too fast to be hit with the ball, see if he can dodge sticks and rocks.

**5.** When the boy quits, or is knocked unconscious, everyone in the circle wins!

# HIDE AND SEEK (for 40-year-olds playing with 3-year-olds)

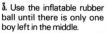

PHEW.

I'M GONNA GETCHA!

**1.** Explain the rules to your annoying, hyperactive 3-year-old nephew.

**2.** Tell him to go hide and not come out till you find him.

**3.** Go sit in your favorite easy chair and enjoy the silence.

**4.** Occasionally yell out, "I'm going to get you!" so the little brat stays hidden.

**5.** Continue using these rules until his mother finally comes to pick him up.

# ONE NIGHT IN A POLICE STATION

# A MAD LOOK AT FAST FOOD

ARTIST AND WRITER:

SERGIO ARAGONES

## THE OL' CELL GAME DEPT.

Today's streets are filled with people carrying radios, TVs, calculators, and computers. Soon they will also be filled with something else—Dead Batteries! With that in mind, here's

# NEW USES

## Chess Pieces

KING — 9 Volt Battery

QUEEN — D Battery

BISHOP — C Battery

KNIGHT — AA Battery

ROOK — AAA Battery

PAWN — Disc Battery

ARTIST & WRITER: AL JAFFEE

## Ear Plugs

## Cuckoo Clock Weights

# FOR OLD BATTERIES

## Hair Curlers

## Scale Weights

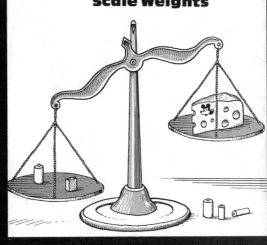

## Executive Desk Toy

KLIK KLIK KLIK KLIK

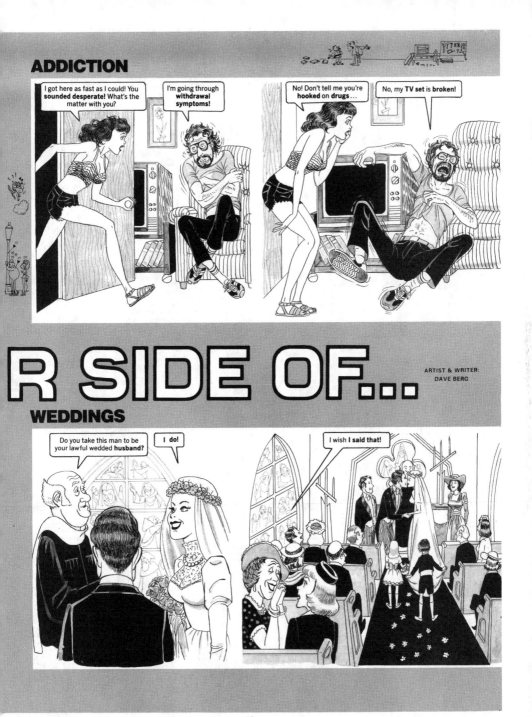

Thinking about what career to get into? Wondering whether or not you'll fit in? Well, here's the fourth in a series of tests designed to help you choose your future line of work. Mainly, discover your true abilities by taking...

# MAD'S APTITUDE TEST NUMBER FOUR
# WILL YOU MAKE A GOOD POLITICIAN?

1. Complete this sentence. Once elected, a politician pushes to create new jobs for his _____ .
   - A. Family
   - B. Cronies
   - C. Campaign contributors
   - D. All of the above.

2. When a candidate says he has an open mind about major issues, this usually means:
   - A. He can be bought by anyone.
   - B. Those reports that he's "wishy-washy" are true.
   - C. He's waiting to see the public opinion polls before he commits himself.
   - D. Any of the above.

3. As a politician, you attack your opponent with smears and innuendos. Is this a good practice?
   - A. Yes, if it's a close race and this is the only way you can get votes.
   - B. Yes, if you're trailing badly and want the perverse pleasure of destroying his character and reputation.
   - C. No, if you have an insurmountable lead and therefore can come off as a statesman.
   - D. Any of the above.

4. During a campaign, you hear your opponent advocate oil drilling on public land. How should you respond?
   - A. Call him an anti-environmentalist.
   - B. Say he's a tool of the big oil interests.
   - C. Label him a right-wing reactionary.
   - D. All of the above.

5. Your opponent changes his mind and now is *against* oil drilling on public land. How do you respond now?
   - A. Declare that he's keeping the U.S. dependent on foreign oil.
   - B. Say he's against creating thousands of new jobs.
   - C. Label him a bleeding-heart liberal.
   - D. All of the above.

6. When a Senator attacks "dishonesty in government," it's an indication that:
   - A. The other party is in and his is out.
   - B. His previous attack on "Creeping Socialism" didn't work.
   - C. It's a smoke screen to cover up what's being said about *him*.
   - D. Any of the above.

7. As a Congressman, you take a fearless, independent stand on a crucial bill. What does this mean?
   - A. You have a safe seat.
   - B. You're planning to retire, so what's the difference?
   - C. You meant to take the other side but, as usual, got confused.
   - D. Any of the above.

8. Like other politicians, this legislator prefers to speak on TV rather than make public appearances. Why?
   - A. The cue cards help him recall key facts, such as the name of his party.
   - B. The make-up prevents viewers from seeing he's over the hill.
   - C. He can edit in applause, cheers and appropriate fanfare.
   - D. All of the above.

9. As a politician, you support housing projects for the poor. What is your motive?
   - A. It packs them together in one place, preventing their spilling over into better neighborhoods—which goes over great with middle and high-income voters.
   - B. It shows you've got compassion, which goes over great with low-income voters.
   - C. It means big bucks to the building contractors who are contributing to your campaign.
   - D. All of the above.

10. Complete this sentence. When faced with a decision of conscience, a politician should do what's best for _____
    - A. His re-election.
    - B. The most influential lobbyists.
    - C. His pocketbook.
    - D. All of the above.

ARTIST: GEORGE WOODBRIDGE
WRITER: FRANK JACOBS

## SCORING

*If you answered "D." to all the questions, you have the ability to make a great Politician.*

It's been countless years of tortured, sleepless nights since we last played our ghoulish game! You might remember how it's played: we take a

# HORRI
# POLIT
# CLIC

ARTIST: PAUL COKER

Digging Up A SCANDAL

Twisting A FACT

Ducking A QUESTION

Reviving An OLD ISSUE

Hanging On To A SLIM LEAD

familiar phrase or expression, and interpret it
our own, twisted way to create a fiendish monster!
So, when better to play than election year? Here's

# FYING
# TICAL
# HES

*The Congressman who was defeated
by a hand puppet!* **NEXT DONAHUE!**

**WRITER: FRANK JACOBS**

**Exercising A VETO**

**Hammering Out A COMPROMISE**

**Toasting A VICTORY**

**Breaking A PLEDGE**

**Launching A CAMPAIGN**

Nowadays, Travel Agencies are packaging all kinds of tours for all kinds of people with all kinds of special interests, all designed to help them relax, leave their tensions behind and have a good time. But that doesn't make any sense. People work hard their whole lives developing their tensions, mainly in the form of their neuroses! Why should they want to give them up? The truth is...most people prefer to carry their neuroses with them! So why not design tours specifically for them? We'll show you what we mean with

# THE

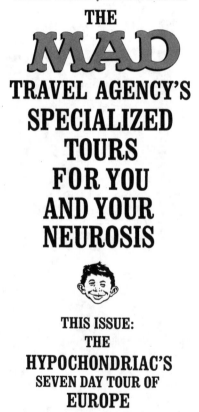

## MAD

# TRAVEL AGENCY'S
# SPECIALIZED
# TOURS
# FOR YOU
# AND YOUR
# NEUROSIS

## THIS ISSUE:
## THE
## HYPOCHONDRIAC'S
### SEVEN DAY TOUR OF
## EUROPE

ARTIST: HARRY NORTH, ESQ.    WRITER: STAN HART

### DAY 1

You leave Kennedy Airport, New York, at 8:00 P.M., just in time to be exposed to the unhealthy damp night air. You'll be seated next to two other tourists, and God only knows what germs they've been exposed to. While on board, you'll receive a head set for the movie, which might prevent you from hearing all the coughing and sneezing going on throughout the plane—but you'll know it's there. You'll be relieved to find that the utensils for your meals aloft are sealed in plastic bags, but the 6-hour flight will give you plenty of time to worry about whose filthy hands packed them inside the plastic bags.

### DAY 2

You arrive in London and are whisked to your hotel overlooking the historic Thames River, the scene of the terrible London Plague of 1348. You'll spend the rest of the day at leisure, wondering if it was a "628-year-Plague," and it's time for it to return. You'll notice that the drinking glasses in your bathroom are wrapped in cellophane and marked "Sanitized For Your Protection." A little bit of British drollery there, since you know the maid only wipes the glasses with a dirty rag and shoves them into the cellophane. You'll also notice that the paper band over the toilet seat assures you that it, too, is "Sanitized For Your Protection"—probably with the same dirty rag used to wipe the glasses.

## DAY 3 & 4

After a hearty breakfast of English sausage (which will give you gas and make you think you're having a heart attack), you'll be escorted to all the points of interest in London. You'll tour Buckingham Palace (but not get to see the Queen, since she's probably ill and they want to keep it a secret for political reasons). At the Tower of London and Westminster Abbey, you'll see where all the famous Englishmen are buried (which will be a wonderful reminder of how fleeting life really is, and that death is always lurking, even for the great). The changes in temperature going in and out of these wonderful landmarks will probably give you a chill, so you can spend the next day in bed, nursing a cold.

## DAY 5

You fly to Paris. The flight takes less than an hour, but it's a great opportunity to take your temperature and compare symptoms with fellow passengers. In Paris, you'll be escorted to the famous Eiffel Tower, where someone already at the top will probably spit, and the germ-laden spittle will undoubtedly land on your head. You will then visit Notre Dame Cathedral where you can pray you'll get out of this infested country alive. At night, you'll be taken to Pigalle, where you'll surely contract a venereal disease from sitting on a toilet seat in the Crazy Horse Saloon.

## DAY 6

You leave Paris (and not a moment too soon!) and arrive in Rome. First, you will visit the Colosseum, where the Christians were fed to the lions, and where you can sit and reflect upon how lucky they were to have died quickly instead of lingering on, like you're doing. Next, you'll visit St. Peter's and The Vatican, where you can arrange for a private audience with the Pope so you can pray together for God to restore your health. (Only the Pope doesn't look too well himself, so what's he going to do for a nobody like you? Besides, imagine what you're liable to get by kissing His Holiness's ring! Who knows who kissed it before you!) At night, you'll dine at the famous Alfredo's, where the highly-seasoned food will give you diarrhea, or constipation, or both.

## DAY 7

You are transported by bus to the fabulous French Riviera. The bus is especially designed so the windows don't close completely, exposing you to the dangerous 75 degree temperature and probably giving you pleurisy. In your hotel, instead of the usual Gideon Bible at your bedside, you'll find a volume of "Symptoms Of Incurable Diseases Of Europe" for introspective reading. You can visit one of the many lavish gambling casinos, where you can play roulette and wonder what kind of people handled the chips before you. From Nice, you'll fly home with enough time aloft (8 hours) to worry if the U.S. Health Service will allow you to re-enter the country with all the diseases you picked up on your fabulously exciting trip to Europe.

**NEXT ISSUE: THE PARANOIAC'S 7-DAY TOUR OF JAPAN**

# ONE NIGHT IN A LIVING ROOM

Not too long ago, we confirmed the deaths of Mr. Clean, Charlie the Starkist Tuna and several other merchandising characters. It seems, however, that our list wasn't complete, and for MAD this won't do at all! Here, therefore, are *more*

# OBITUARIES
## FOR MERCHANDISING CHARACTERS

ARTIST: BOB CLARKE      WRITER: FRANK JACOBS

## Noid Dies After Plot Fails to Pan Out

The Noid, longtime Domino's nemesis, died today after a failed attempt to sabotage the company's pizzas with tainted anchovies.

"It was clearly an act of revenge by a desperate creature," said a Domino's executive. "After we dropped him from our advertising campaigns, he vowed to get even. I guess he still wanted a slice of the pie."

It is believed that the Noid infiltrated an unheated oven, then was baked to death after it was turned on. He tried to escape, but was held fast by the melting cheese.

Funeral arrangements are being handled by Domino's, who promise to deliver him to his grave in less than 30 minutes.

## NBC Peacock Dies

The NBC Peacock, 47, died today of poor exposure after failing to fight off an epidemic of cable-TV programs and video-cassette releases.

He will be replaced by a turkey.

## Famed Party Animal Spuds MacKenzie Dies

Spuds MacKenzie, who electrified the nation with his beer drinking, carousing and gorgeous women, died today after being run over by a truck he was chasing. The Budweiser party animal had just turned six.

"He spotted a Miller Lite truck and went crazy," explained a Budweiser spokesman. "He was growling and snapping, determined to chase off the competition, but he got too close to the wheels. It's a great loss and we're as crushed as he is."

MacKenzie was hired by Budweiser as spokespooch in 1988, but not after some controversy. Several company executives feared he was giving the firm a black eye, and rumors persisted that he refused to be housebroken.

"Let's be fair to Spuds," the spokesman said. "Sure, he occasionally couldn't control himself at parties, but it's not easy holding all that beer."

MacKenzie will be buried on the company grounds, along with his leash, muzzle and diamond-studded collar. Pallbearers include Mighty Dog, Pluto, Snoopy, Marmaduke and McGruff, the Crime Dog.

## Suicide Claims Life Of Exxon Tiger, 27

**Suicide has claimed the life of the Exxon Tiger. He was 27.**

The great cat, who inspired the slo-gan, "Put a tiger in your tank," was found in his locked garage with his motor running, a victim of carbon monoxide poisoning.

"I guess you could say it was a case of putting the tank in the tiger," joked an Exxon official.

According to friends, the Tiger had been ex-tremely depressed ever since the Exxon oil spill in Alaska. As an endangered species, he was saddened by the loss of wildlife and felt ashamed of being the Exxon symbol.

"We'll probably stuff him and keep him as a trophy," said the Exxon execu-tive, "or maybe use his hide as a slip-cover."

The company has no plans to acquire another tiger. "Most likely, we'll come up with another animal as a symbol—like a snake or a vulture," the executive said. He is survived by a brother, Tony the Tiger.

## Energizer Rabbit Dies Of Digestive Disorder

**The Energizer Rabbit died today of a digestive ailment, brought on by eating the burritos while interrupting a Taco Bell commercial.**

"He couldn't resist the Mexican food," an Ener-gizer spokesman said. "Within hours he was going and going and going. It wasn't a pretty sight! We tried to rush him into a Kaopectate commercial, but by then it was too late. He was going, going, gone!"

## Mr. Peanut, 72, Dies In Mental Hospital

**Mr. Peanut, longtime Planters em-ployee, died yesterday at 72. He had been confined to a mental hospital, suf-fering from a severe iden-tity crisis.**

"He tried to put on rich, fancy airs with his top hat and monocle," said a company psychia-trist, "but deep down he knew he was only work-ing for peanuts. He be-came terribly depressed, and despite years of ther-apy, we couldn't get him out of his shell. In the end, he was a certifiable nut case."

As of today, company officials had not decided whether to give him a fu-neral or a posthumous roast.

## Mr. Zip Dies at 36

According to a press release post-marked March 25, 1987, but received only today, Mr. Zip is dead after col-lapsing beneath several tons of junk mail. He was 36.

## Smooth Character Dies After Missile Attack

Smooth Character, the humped symbol of Camel Cigarettes, has died of injuries suffered during a missile attack. He was 11.

According to a close friend, the Marlboro Man, the Smooth Character had been visiting relatives in Kuwait during Operation Desert Storm. He was struck by fragments of a Patriot Missile that had intercepted an incoming Scud.

"Actually his death is good for us," a Camel spokesman said today. "It proves beyond all doubt that smoking doesn't kill you, but missiles do."

## Bluebonnet Girl, 41, Dies

The Bluebonnet Girl, 41, died today of exhaustion. Company officials blamed her death on an ever-increasing workload.

"It was clear she was spreading herself too thin," said a spokesman.

In accordance with her will, she will be cremated with her ashes scattered over all 50 states. "After all," she said recently, "everything's better with Bluebonnet on it."

## Uncle Ben, 84, Dies In Racial Incident

Uncle Ben, 84, died today from injuries suffered in a racially motivated incident.

According to witnesses, he was stopped by Los Angeles police officers for no apparent reason. Though normally mild-mannered, Uncle Ben became stirred up and boiled over at the unlawful detainment, and a pressure-cooker situation quickly developed.

"We told him to put a lid on it," said one of the officers, "but he was in hot water from the start."

"No way," said Aunt Jemima, a neighbor. "Sure, he got steamed, but what they did to him goes against the grain."

Funeral arrangements are not complete, due to no one knowing Uncle Ben's religious preference. It is believed he was recently converted.

## California Raisins Die of Old Age

The California Raisins, who sang and danced their way to national acclaim, have died of old age, according to news heard through the grapevine.

"It's not all that surprising," said Sun Maid, a close friend. "They were all dried up and wrinkled and feeling boxed in with age."

The group made their show-business debut as youngsters, calling themselves The Grapettes. Though green newcomers, they soon displayed the seeds of greatness. "A most pleasing bunch," said a local critic, who lauded them for their good taste.

As the years passed, however, the group appeared to run out of juice, forcing a major career change. "When they hung us out to dry, we gave our routine a new wrinkle," said one of the raisins last year, "and the fruit of our efforts paid off."

# Stupid Pet O

of your pet trick schtick! We suggest you try MAD's...

# wner Tricks

**ARTIST AND WRITER: PAUL PETER PORGES**

# MAD MAGAZINE READER'S COMPETITION

ENTRIES JUDGED BY: JOE RAIOLA AND CHARLIE KADAU

**Results of Competition #1,** *in which we asked you to create an appropriately titled outgoing phone message, one that people could leave on their answering machines to replace the dreadfully boring "I'm not in now, leave your name and number after the beep and I'll get back to you" style message.*

## FIRST PRIZE OF A RARE COPY OF MAD #275 WITH THE MISSING CAPTION, REPORTED TO BE WORTH OVER $80,000 TO:

### THE "JUST PLAIN SILLY" PHONE MESSAGE

"Hi, this is *(your name)*. At the moment I'm peach buffalo in squirming tub visiting hollow beverage. Trombone pleasantry? Noodle lengthening putty service of rewinding magnitude. Scrumptious tongue mystery hat. Tomahawk, tomahawk. Aluminum monkeys festering. You'll have 30 seconds to leave a message after the beep. Please speak clearly. (BEEEEEEP)

*Submitted by: Doug Feeble, Gump, WI*

## SECOND PRIZE OF AN ALFRED E. NEUMAN TABLECLOTH KIT TO:

### THE "HIGH TECH" PHONE MESSAGE

*(To be spoken in a mechanical-sounding voice)*

"Hello, you've reached *(your phone #)*. To leave a message for *(your name)*, press 1 now. If you wish to be called back, press 2 now. If your message will be one minute or longer, press 3 and 5 now. If your message will be under one minute, press 4, 7 and 8 now. If your message is extremely important and you can't wait any longer to leave it, press 6 nine times and 9 six times now. If you've been stupid enough to press any buttons during this totally useless recording, leave your message now!" (BEEEEEEP)

*Submitted by: Louise Gummy, Pemberton Pines, VT*

## RUNNER-UP PRIZES OF A FIVE-MINUTE PHONE CALL FROM FRANK JACOBS TO:

### THE "WHEN YOU DON'T WANT TO RETURN ANYONE'S CALL" PHONE MESSAGE

"Hi, this is *(your name)* and I'm not home now. After the beep, please leave your name, today's date, the time of your call, the phone number you can be reached at, the best times to call you, the temperature at the time of your call, your Social Security number, your feelings on the current trade deficit, your inseam measurement, your favorite film directed by Alan Parker, and your message. People failing to leave all of this information will not have their calls returned. You have 30 seconds." (BEEEEEEP)

*Submitted by: Frederick Battering Ram-Simpson, Provo, UT*

### THE "EVERYBODY WANTS TO BE A MOVIE STAR" PHONE MESSAGE

"Hello, you've reached the *(your name)* Multiplex Theatre. Now showing in cinema one, "The Phone Message," an offbeat and disturbing adventure starring *(your name again)* as The Person Who's Never Home, with Sally Struthers as The Answering Machine, Joe Piscopo as The Dial Tone and introducing YOU as The Irate Phone Caller!" (BEEEEEEP)

*Submitted by: Lee Cheechee Lee, Jr., Skankville, NY*

*And as in all our competitions, everyone who entered before the Nov. 15th, 1990 deadline receives a free one-year subscription to MAD.* **Be sure to enter next time!**

At one time or another, you've probably seen a horse wearing blinders. Blinders are a good thing, because they keep the horse in a straight line and out of trouble, since it's unaware of what's going on around it. Sometimes, people are so unaware of what's going on around them, it seems like they're wearing blinders, too! It boggles the mind to consider how many lives could be changed for the better if someone would pull the blinders off these misguided souls and shout in their face...

# "HEY-LO BE

ARTIST: AL JAFFEE

# A MAD LOOK AT

# EDDINGS

ARTIST & WRITER: SERGIO ARAGONES

Ever wonder about the correlation between seemingly unrelated events—
between say, the number of crimes per 1000 households and the number of

# CAUSE OR CO

**POLITICIANS RE-ELECTED TO CONGRESS**

**VOTER S.A.T. SCORES**

**CAR CHASES ON T.V.**

**SELF-PROCLAIMED EVANGELISTS**

**HOTEL RESERVATIONS UNDER THE NAME "JOHN SMITH"**

**CLEVELANDERS LEAVING CLEVELAND FOREVER**

**CIGAR SALES**

**WOMEN WHO OWN GUNS**

**MISSING PERSONS**

homes that display plastic snowmen? Is there a connection?? *Ummm*…no.
But other statistical pairs *do* suggest definite links. You decide! Are they…

# INCIDENCE??

ARTIST: GEORGE WOODBRIDGE    WRITER: DAN BIRTCHER

**CAR INSURANCE PREMIUMS**

**GLOBAL WARMING**

**SALES OF X-RATED VIDEOCASSETTES**

**CLEVELANDERS WHO REALIZE
THEY'RE IN CLEVELAND**

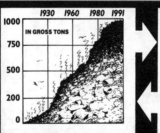

**LANDFILL INCREASE**

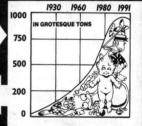

**IMPORTS OF CRAPPY LITTLE
CARNIVAL PRIZES**

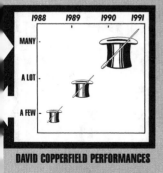

**DAVID COPPERFIELD PERFORMANCES**

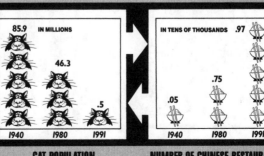

**CAT POPULATION**

**NUMBER OF CHINESE RESTAURANTS**

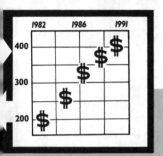

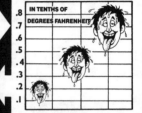

These days, lots of people on the verge of taking the long dirt nap are opting for video wills. Why? We have no idea. Some say it's a more personal and touching way to bid farewell to their loved ones. But it's also dreadfully BORING watching the soon-to-be-very-dead person droning on about who gets their Kmart wristwatch and who gets their World's Fair coffee mug. They forget that video wills are *TV shows*! They need production values! Gimmicks! Flash! It is with this in mind that we present…

# HOW TO SPICE UP YOUR VIDEO WILL

ARTIST: TOM BUNK     WRITER: JEFF KRUSE

Provide a fun theme for your loved ones to enjoy.

Arrrgh, mateys! Welcome aboard me **Last Will** and **Testament**, where I'll divvy up me **booty**! Heh heh!

Hire a young, sexy stand-in.

I, Debra Danley, being of **sound mind** and **body** in this, my **87th year**…

Do the whole thing in gangsta rap.

And to **my ho**, that bitch who's **always wack**, I leave my **crib**, and my **nine** for **you** ta **pack**!

Speak in your own made-up language (except for a few names of family and friends) to keep them guessing as to who was left what.

Glootah narsh neenie, borfata atafrob, **Uncle Phil**. Opthvoo, mi yi fe **Cousin Jeremy** neenie nasrh glootah. Poko.

# ONE DAY WITH A WISHBONE

# CREDITS

## *The MAD Bathroom Companion*

**Introduction** by Trey Parker

**"One Fairly Nice Day Downtown"** written and illustrated by Don Martin (*MAD* #150)

**"Spy vs. Spy"** written and illustrated by Antonio Prohias (*MAD* #261)

**"*MAD*'s 14 Rules of Good Behavior"** by Frank Jacobs, illustrated by Paul Coker, Jr. (*MAD* #261)

**"Zonk Me Out at the Ball Game"** idea by John Ambrosio, written by Frank Jacobs, illustrated by Al Jaffee (*MAD* #261)

**"Drama on Page 15"** written and illustrated by John Caldwell (*MAD* #262)

**"Announcements of the Day"** by John Prete, illustrated by George Woodbridge (*MAD* #262)

**"*MAD*'s Dual Purpose Clothing Accessories"** by Mark A. Dressler, illustrated by Al Jaffee (*MAD* #262)

**"A *MAD* Look at Pro Wrestling"** written and illustrated by Sergio Aragonés (*MAD* #262)

**"In the Operating Room with Don Martin"** written and illustrated by Don Martin (*MAD* #151)

**"The Lighter Side of..."** written and illustrated by Dave Berg (*MAD* #263)

**"Violent Mother Goose"** by Frank Jacobs, illustrated by Jack Davis (*MAD* #263)

**"Spy vs. Spy"** written and illustrated by Antonio Prohias (*MAD* #262)

**"*MAD* Dots"** by Mat Jacobs (*MAD* #263)

**"A *MAD* Look at Water Sports"** written and illustrated by Sergio Aragonés (*MAD* #264)

**"At the Bedside, Part 1"** by Charlie Kadau, illustrated by Harry North, Esq. (*MAD* #265)

**"Are You a Good Driver?"** by John Prete, illustrated by Paul Coker, Jr. (*MAD* #265)

**"How to Pick Up Guys"** by Arnie Kogen, illustrated by Will Elder & Harvey Kurtzman (*MAD* #265)

**"Spy vs. Spy"** written and illustrated by Antonio Prohias (*MAD* #263)

**"If Super-Heroes Needed Extra Money"** by Bob Supina, illustrated by Angelo Torres (*MAD* #265)

**"The Lighter Side of..."** written and illustrated by Dave Berg (*MAD* #264)

**"Horrifying Crime Cliches..."** by Frank Jacobs, illustrated by Paul Coker, Jr. (*MAD* #267)

**"The Three Mile Island Children's Zoo"** written and illustrated by Tom Hachtman (*MAD* #267)

**"Those Ridiculous Little Things TV Commercials Say!"** by Tom Koch, illustrated by George Woodbridge (*MAD* #267)

**"Head Trip"** written and illustrated by Sergio Aragonés (*MAD* #267)

**"Spy vs. Spy"** written and illustrated by Antonio Prohias (*MAD* #264)

**"New Clothing Care Symbols That Tell It Like It Is"** by Charlie Kadau, illustrated by Bob Clarke (*MAD* #268)

**"If Society's Unwritten Rules of Behavior Were Actually Written Down"** by Mike Snider, illustrated by George Woodbridge (*MAD* #268)

**"A *MAD* Look at Going to the Movies"** written and illustrated by Sergio Aragonés (*MAD* #269)

**"*MAD*'s Modern-Day Puzzlers"** by David Ames, illustrated by Harvey Kurtzman (*MAD* #271)

**"Summer Has Arrived When..."** by Tom Koch, illustrated by Paul Coker, Jr. (*MAD* #273)

**"Living on the Edge"** by Duck Edwing, illustrated by Duck Edwing & Harry North, Esq. (*MAD* #271)

**"A *MAD* Look at Dating"** written and illustrated by Sergio Aragonés (*MAD* #271)

**"Spy vs. Spy"** written and illustrated by Antonio Prohias (*MAD* #265)

**"Clever Ways to Get Out of Embarrassing Situations"** written and illustrated by Paul Peter Porges (*MAD* #274)

**"Back in the Operating Room with Don Martin"** written and illustrated by Don Martin (*MAD* #151)

**"New and Improved Store Kiddie Rides"** by Dan Birtcher, illustrated by Al Jaffee (*MAD* #304)

**"The Lighter Side of..."** written and illustrated by Dave Berg (*MAD* #265)

**"Abra-Cadaver"** by Duck Edwing, illustrated by Harry North, Esq. (*MAD* #274)

**"A *MAD* Look at Baseball"** written and illustrated by Sergio Aragonés (*MAD* #273)

**"Every Super Bowl Week You're Sure of Seeing . . ."** by Mike Snider, illustrated by Paul Coker, Jr. (*MAD* #277)

**"Why Owning a VCR Is Better than Going to the Movies"** by Tom Koch, illustrated by Harvey Kurtzman (*MAD* #274)

**"Drama on Page 98"** written and illustrated by John Caldwell (*MAD* #275)

**"Spy vs. Spy"** written and illustrated by Antonio Prohias (*MAD* #266)

**"The Colossal Courtroom Confrontation"** written and illustrated by Duck Edwing (*MAD* #277)

**"*MAD* Opens a Typical Magazine Sweepstakes Package"** by Charlie Kadau & Joe Raiola, illustrated by Bob Clarke (*MAD* #279)

# The MAD Bathroom Companion — Number Two

## The MAD Bathroom Companion — Turd in a Series

**"You Know You're in a Second Marriage When…,"** written and illustrated by Lloyd Gola (*MAD* #244)

**"Interpreting the News,"** by Gary Alexander (*MAD* #163)

**"Making Baseball Card Collections Complete,"** by Desmond Devlin, illustrated by John Pound (*MAD* #296)

**"A *MAD* Look at Palm Reading,"** written and illustrated by Sergio Aragonés (*MAD* #145)

**"Things You Can Do For Your Dog On His Birthday,"** written and illustrated by Paul Peter Porges (*MAD* #255)

**"A *MAD* Look at Tarzan,"** by Duck Edwing, illustrated by Jack Davis (*MAD* #161)

**"TV Emmy Awards We'd Like to See,"** by Mike Snider, illustrated by Michael Montgomery (*MAD* #266)

**"Snappy Answers to Stupid Bumper Stickers,"** by Larry Siegel, illustrated by Bob Clarke (*MAD* #252)

**"The *MAD* Practical Driving Test,"** by Tom Koch, illustrated by Paul Coker, Jr. (*MAD* #256)

**"While Clamming in New Jersey,"** written and illustrated by Don Martin (*MAD* #130)

**"Fortune Cookies That Are Relevant,"** by Dick DeBartolo and Don Epstein (*MAD* #162)

**"The Lighter Side of…,"** written and illustrated by Dave Berg (*MAD* #238)

**"One Day on a Hike,"** written and illustrated by Don Martin (*MAD* #131)

**"The Name Game of the Rich and Famous,"** by J. Prete, illustrated by Mort Drucker (*MAD* #286)

**"A *MAD* Look at Some Widely Held Misconceptions,"** by Mike Snider, illustrated by Harvey Kurtzman (*MAD* #273)

**"Spy vs. Spy,"** by Duck Edwing, illustrated by Bob Clarke (*MAD* #272)

**"Odes to Appliances, Gadgets and Other Modern Conveniences,"** idea by Marilyn Atkins, written by Frank Jacobs, illustrated by George Woodbridge (*MAD* #269)

**"Duck Edwing Looks at Funerals,"** written and illustrated by Duck Edwing (*MAD* #253)

**"When 'Doublespeak' Takes Over Completely,"** by Frank Jacobs, illustrated by Sergio Aragonés (*MAD* #295)

**"Patterns of Speech,"** idea by Max Brandel, illustrated by Bob Clarke (*MAD* #158)

**"Specialized Nautilus Machines For Practical Everyday Activities,"** by Larry Siegel, illustrated by Al Jaffee (*MAD* #287)

**"One Day in a Garage,"** written and illustrated by Don Martin (*MAD* #136)

**"What It Will Be Like When Every Device 'Talks,'"** by Dick DeBartolo, illustrated by Paul Coker, Jr. (*MAD* #251)

**"*MAD*'s Alibis For All Occasions,"** by Tom Koch, illustrated by Jack Davis (*MAD* #272)

**"More Ads We Never Got to See,"** by Dick DeBartolo, illustrated by Harry North, Esq. (*MAD* #248)

**"One Night in the Acme Ritz Central Arms Waldorf Plaza Statler Hilton Grand Hotel,"** written and illustrated by Don Martin (*MAD* #142)

**"If Computers Are So Brilliant…"** by Tom Koch, illustrated by George Woodbridge (*MAD* #258)

**"A *MAD* Look at Amusement Parks,"** written and illustrated by Sergio Aragonés (*MAD* #146)

**"Pastimes for Nerds,"** written and illustrated by Paul Peter Porges (*MAD* #256)

**"Spy vs. Spy,"** by Duck Edwing, illustrated by Bob Clarke (*MAD* #274)

**"The *MAD* People Watcher's Guide to an Airport,"** by Mike Snider, illustrated by Tom Bunk (*MAD* #299)

**"Truth in Road Signs,"** by Dick DeBartolo, illustrated by Bob Clarke (*MAD* #260)

**"The Lighter Side of…,"** written and illustrated by Dave Berg (*MAD* #253)

**"*MAD*'s Aptitude Test Number One: Will You Make a Good Doctor?"** by Frank Jacobs, illustrated by George Woodbridge (*MAD* #243)

**"All You Need to Know You Learned in Nursery School,"** by Tom Koch, illustrated by Paul Coker, Jr. (*MAD* #296)

**"If Famous Movies Were Made Into Comic Strips,"** written and illustrated by Russ Cooper (*MAD* #295)

**"A *MAD* Guide to Social Behavior,"** by Chris Hart, illustrated by Bob Jones (*MAD* #289)

**"One Day During a Cavalry Attack,"** written and illustrated by Don Martin (*MAD* #154)

**"Laundromat Bingo,"** by Rurik Tyler, illustrated by Bob Clarke (*MAD* #260)

**"*MAD* Mini-Movies Featuring the Fickle Finger of Fate,"** written and illustrated by Al Jaffee (*MAD* #269)

**"The Startling Similarities Between Ancient Mythology & Modern Rock,"** by Desmond Devlin, illustrated by Rick Tulka (*MAD* #306)